The
Pre-Raphaelite
SISTERHOOD

The
Pre-Raphaelite
SISTERHOOD

Jan Marsh

St. Martin's Press
New York

Library of Congress Cataloging in Publication Data

Marsh, Jan.
  The Pre-Raphaelite sisterhood.

1. Pre-Raphaelites—Relations with women.   2. Women artists—Great Britain—Biography.   3. Artists—Great Britain—Biography.   I. Title.
N6767.5.P7M37   1985   759.2 [B]   85-11813

ISBN 0-312-63738-1

First published in Great Britain by Quartet Books Ltd.

First U.S. Edition

10 9 8 7 6 5 4 3 2 1

Contents

A section of photographs follows page 184.

Acknowledgements

Any work on the Pre-Raphaelite circle is indebted to the vast amount of previous work in biographies, editions, articles etc., which are too numerous to cite. The author would, however, like to thank all those who answered inquiries, offered assistance and located material. Particular thanks are due to Diana Holman-Hunt and Lance Thirkell for their generous assistance in conversation and regarding material in their possession. Grateful acknowledgement is also made to Hilary Morgan, Sharon Buckley, Nell Penny and Pat Thane for their support and contributions to the making of this book. In addition, thanks are also due to: Ashmolean Museum; Birmingham Museum and Art Gallery; British Library MSS Department; Judith Bronkhurst; Laura Hamilton, Carlisle City Art Gallery; Rare Books Department, Cornell University; Fitzwilliam Museum MSS Department; Dr I. Gordon; A.R. Dufty, Kelmscott Manor; Paddy Kitchen; London Library; Jeremy Maas; Lady Mander, Wightwick Manor; Lynda Nead; Oxford Local History Library; Princeton University Library; Dr I. Robinson; Southwark Local Studies Library; Mrs Virginia Surtees; Tate Gallery; William Morris Gallery, Walthamstow; and the William Morris Society.

The pictures are from the following sources: City Museum and Art Gallery, Birmingham (17, 21); Carlisle Museum and Art Gallery (7, 22); National Gallery of Ireland, Dublin (31); Fitzwilliam Museum, Cambridge (30); Johannesburg City Art Gallery (14); Manchester City Art Gallery (37); National Portrait Gallery, London (40, 44); Mrs V. Surtees, London (42); Tate Gallery, London (4, 5, 12, 13, 15, 19, 20, 23, 24, 25, 26, 27, 33, 35, 43); Mr

L. Thirkell, London (47); Victoria and Albert Museum, London (34, 38, 48, 49); William Morris Gallery, Walthamstow (36); Witt Library, Courtauld Institute of Art, London (1, 2, 6, 10, 46).

Prelude

If there is one image that conveys the idea of Pre-Raphaelite art it is that of a woman's face, set with large, lustrous eyes and surrounded by a mass of loose hair, looking soulfully out of the canvas. Neither sad nor cheerful, but somehow charged with an intense, internal passion, this face has a brooding, haunting quality that engages attention but remains distant, remote, impersonal.

At another level, Pre-Raphaelitism evokes vivid, memorable anecdotes about the private lives of the painters – how the girl who posed for Millais' drowned Ophelia caught pneumonia, how Rossetti married his model and after her death dug up her coffin to retrieve his poems, how Holman Hunt fell for a ravishing slum girl and left her being educated while he went off to paint in the Holy Land. These are the stories everyone knows, even if they know nothing else.

From both an artistic and a biographical perspective, women are important in the Pre-Raphaelite movement. But while their faces are seen everywhere – in oil paintings, watercolours, drawings – their voices are never heard. As depicted, they are silent, enigmatic, passive figures, not individuals engaged in activity but objects to be gazed upon by painter and spectator. True, they often stare back, but it is hard to tell what they are thinking, and frequently they look away or have their eyes closed in what seems to be unfulfilled yearning. They are alluring but they almost never smile. In real life, it is believed, they were equally beautiful and silent. If they spoke, nothing of significance has been recorded.

This book sets out to reconstruct the lives of the women who moved in the Pre-Raphaelite circle. This is not because they have, like the majority of women in history, been hitherto forgotten or ignored. On the contrary, most of the many books on Pre-Raphaelitism, from the scholarly to the sensational, pay the women a good deal of attention – as the models, mistresses and wives of the painters. Naturally, however, they have been viewed exclusively in relation to the men, and described only in such terms. Their personal characteristics and even their behaviour have been 'read off' their appearance in the paintings. Even with portraits this is a risky procedure and would hardly be admissible evidence in other fields but here it has generally formed the public view of what 'Pre-Raphaelite women' were like. And I confess that when I began I shared many of these generally received ideas – ideas about the women's surpassing beauty, for example, or their tragic lives and sexual permissiveness. But, as feminists frequently point out, the male or patriarchal view does not constitute the whole of history. And so this is a modest attempt, begun out of simple curiosity, to reverse the mirror and look directly at the women's own experiences, viewed in the context of the historical class and gender relations of their time. It establishes a chronological narrative and discusses issues that extend beyond this framework and serve to inform it. It is not an exhaustive record of all known facts nor is it a work of art history. Rather it is an interpretative account of the lives of a group of women in the mid-nineteenth century.

The women concerned are Emma Madox Brown, Elizabeth Siddall, Annie Miller, Fanny Cornforth, Janey Morris and Georgiana Burne-Jones. The demands of space and coherence made it impossible to include full accounts of all the other women known to have moved in the Pre-Raphaelite circle. In particular, Christina Rossetti has been excluded from this account, partly because she did not belong to the group under discussion, but chiefly because her life and work deserve attention in their own right; she should not be defined simply as one of the 'Pre-Raphaelite women'.

Inevitably, one result of looking at their lives directly, rather than through the mediation of the art and artists, has been to demythologize the Pre-Raphaelite women. A lot of the 'facts' turn out to be legends. But while accuracy is properly the chief concern in a study such as this, debunking is not my main aim; there are other varieties of truth. It is anyway pointless to try to suppress myth on the grounds of factual error: like other stories, the

Pre-Raphaelite legend, which is still strong and vigorous today, serves other purposes and will perhaps one day be studied in its own right. Here I would say only that the romance of the Pre-Raphaelite women tends both to glorify them, raising them like Hollywood film stars above the level of ordinary mortals into a mythic realm of tragic heroines and fatal sirens, and paradoxically to diminish them, reducing their real, complex, contradictory personalities and lives to flat figures in a fantasy landscape and taking away from them all sense of active life. They should not be so unproblematically defined.

Before introducing them, however, it is necessary to say something, at least briefly, about the artistic and social world they joined when they entered the Pre-Raphaelite circle. Since so much has been written about the painting and the major figures involved, I shall outline only the main features here; readers unfamiliar with the subject should consult one or more of the many existing works on Pre-Raphaelite art and artists.

The movement began in 1848–9, when a group of young artists in London initiated a new style of painting. The three most important members of the group, which briefly styled itself the Pre-Raphaelite Brotherhood, were John Everett Millais, Dante Gabriel Rossetti and William Holman Hunt. An important and slightly older associate was Ford Madox Brown. They all belonged to the professional rather than propertied middle class and had to make their own way in the world. They were eager and idealistic, influenced by evangelical religion and inspired by literary, historical and biblical subjects which they drew and painted with directness, clarity and a new presentation of colour and composition. Ten years after it began, Pre-Raphaelitism was reinvigorated by the enthusiasm and ideas of a younger generation, in particular by Edward Burne-Jones and William Morris; by 1870 it had, as a movement, largely exhausted its original energies.

In personal terms, the painters shared the cultural beliefs of their class and gender, which included, in the 1840s and 1850s, emergent Victorian attitudes towards women, attitudes whose residual effects may still be traced today although in most respects they have altered out of all recognition. Many of these attitudes were very clearly expressed in contemporary art, and in order to position the women in context I shall first explore some pertinent examples in both painting and poetry. This, it must be stressed, is not to interpret the art in personal terms (although that can be done) but to floodlight, as it were, the background against which art and life may be viewed.

Courtship is the theme of several early Pre-Raphaelite paintings. This reflected both the personal situation of several of the young painters and a wider contemporary concern selected by them, albeit unconsciously, for representation. By this date the choice of marriage partner was a process in transition; previously it had been determined largely by consideration of family factors, now it was increasingly thought of in terms of romantic love. This transition is part of the theme explored by one of the most popular of Romantic poems, Keats' 'The Eve of St Agnes'. The love of Porphyro for Madeline is opposed by her family and triumphs only through the clandestine 'escape' of the lovers from the jurisdiction of the family.

More significantly, Madeline is a sheltered, characterless girl whose only mentioned activity is dreaming of her prospective lover, like an early Mills & Boon reader, rejecting the pleasures of a social gathering for those of curling up alone with the perfect fantasy; for on St Agnes' Eve 'young virgins might have visions of delight/And soft adorings from their loves receive', if they observe a ritual which, it may be noted, is dependent on complete passivity and receptivity:

> As, supperless to bed they must retire,
> And couch supine their beauties, lily white;
> Nor look behind, nor sideways, but require
> Of heaven with upward eyes for all that they desire.

The hero, by contrast, is an active figure, who risks the wrath of Madeline's barbaric brothers and outwits them by a daring approach to her old nurse, who agrees to conceal him in his beloved's bedroom. Hidden while she prepares for bed, he also has his vision of delight, expressed in the language of religious adoration:

> Rose-bloom fell on her hands, together prest
> And on her silver cross soft amethyst,
> And on her hair a glory, like a saint:

> She seemed a splendid angel, newly drest,
> Save wings, for Heaven – Porphyro grew faint:
> She knelt, so pure a thing, so free from mortal taint.

At the same time, the sexual nature of the quest and the encounter
is made clear in the verse. Porphyro watches Madeline undress; as
she takes down her hair, 'Unclasps her warmed jewels one by one'
and 'loosens her fragrant boddice' he lays out various exotic treats
and presents for her in an exact replica of the romantic courtship
behaviour required of young men in search of a wife.

   The climax of the poem is presented as their mutual realization
of love and is written in the language of erotic excitement and
coition, from a male point of view:

> At these voluptuous accents, he arose,
> Ethereal, flush'd, and like a throbbing star
> Seen 'mid the sapphire heaven's deep repose;
> Into her dream he melted . . .

Immediately afterwards, Porphyro tells her plainly what has
happened: 'This is no dream, my bride, my Madeline!' This
consummation sequence is followed by some discussion that reads
rather oddly in a romance. Madeline pleads that he will not
abandon her, as 'a deceived thing – A dove forlorn and lost' while
Porphyro stoutly promises marriage with descriptions that hold
more than an anachronistic hint of the Victorian middle-class
dream of home as haven:

> Ah, silver shrine! here will I take my rest
> After so many hours of toil and quest

Needless to say, the future of this marriage is not spelt out in any
detail: the lovers steal away into the night and out of the poem,
foreshadowing a million fictional romances. It is, after all, a tale
for the young; and on such terms it attracted the painters. In 1848
Holman Hunt used it for one of his earliest works, which depicts
the end of the story, as the lovers creep past the drunken porters.
The happy ending was also shown in Arthur Hughes' ambitious
triptych of 1856, where the central panel is a picture of Madeline's
chamber as Porphyro plays his lute to waken her. The left panel

shows him approaching her home and the right panel portrays the couple's escape into the night. In 1862 Millais produced the most famous version, showing Madeline (for whom the model was his wife Effie) standing in the centre of a large room disrobing, as her 'rich attire creeps rustling to her knees'.

Tennyson wrote another version of 'St Agnes' Eve'. This is a shorter poem, spoken through the mouth of a young girl, also a virgin, who is contemplating a vision of becoming not a wife but a nun. Ostensibly, it is a negation of the courtship theme, for the narrator renounces marriage in favour of holy service. There are rich levels of meaning here, for in contemporary terms the alternative to marriage, for 'pure' young women, was indeed celibacy and barrenness, if not precisely the convent. But the language suggests that the spiritual consummation envisaged is itself a metaphor for sexual courtship and physical congress, much as in Keats' version:

> He lifts me to the golden doors;
>   The flashes come and go;
> All heaven bursts her starry floors
>   And strows her lights below,
> And deepens on and up: the gates
>   Roll back, and far within
> For me the Heavenly Bridegroom waits
>   To make me pure of sin.
> The sabbaths of eternity,
>   One sabbath deep and wide –
> A light upon the shining sea –
>   The Bridegroom with his bride!

At least three Pre-Raphaelite picture versions of this text exist, all dating from the 1850s. One is in ink and wash by Millais, showing a young nun in front of an altar, looking out of a window on to the snowy night. It has been described as 'an image of the artist's own yearning . . . for his future wife, Effie Ruskin – and equally of hers for him'; it is related to a portrait of Effie and formed one of the gifts that passed between them during their 'courtship' period.[1] Three years later Millais produced another version of the same subject for an illustrated edition of Tennyson's poems. A third version is by Elizabeth Siddall and shows a female figure with a halo stretching out her arms on a high window sill; it is more an image of imprisonment than fulfilment.[2]

None of these pictures, whether inspired by Keats or Tennyson, treats its subject with explicit sensuousness or urgency; the sexual message is latent, so as to be almost unreadable. In any case, several of the pictures are too dark – part of the purpose being to paint a nocturnal, moonlit scene – for the viewer to be quite sure what is meant to be going on. The artists were attracted by the romance and fantasy of the theme rather than its erotic content, selecting the spiritual and 'holy' aspects of the texts and rendering them in a spirit of idealism that rose almost to worship. This reflected contemporary attitudes towards young women and sexual emotion. Like Porphyro and Madeline, Victorian lovers who might hardly know each other were impelled together by a mixture of idealism and desire and woke to find themselves married.

Another poem by Tennyson that caught the Pre-Raphaelite imagination was 'The Lady of Shalott'. The very familiarity of this text obscures its relevant layer of interpretation in relation to the position of women. The Lady, as we all know, is imprisoned in a tower, forbidden to look directly on the world and condemned to an activity which reproduces images of that world: embroidering scenes seen in the mirror. She is banned from participation. Despite its simple form, the poem may be, indeed should be read in several ways; one of the meanings is that the woman is waiting in limbo, under a strong injunction to do nothing else, good yet unsatisfied. Her first murmur of rebellion comes with her glimpse of two lovers 'lately wed' which causes her to exclaim, 'I am half sick of shadows!' Then she sees Lancelot, whose arrival brings a heavy sexual charge to the verses. Not only does he have a 'mighty silver bugle' hanging from his 'blazon'd baldric', but the colours are suddenly bright and the rhythm strong:

> The sun came dazzling thro' the leaves
> And flamed upon the brazen greaves
> Of bold Sir Lancelot.

> His broad clear brow in sunlight glow'd;
> On burnish'd hoofs his war horse trode;

> From underneath his helmet flow'd
> His coal-black curls as on he rode . . .

This vision of delight causes the Lady to take the fatal step:

> She left the web, she left the loom,
> She made three paces through the room;

and the curse is upon her. Even the weather is changed by her transgression and it rains as, dying, she floats downriver to Camelot where

> Out upon the wharfs they came,
> Knight and burger, lord and dame;
> And round the prow they read her name
> 'The Lady of Shalott'.

The missing but half-heard rhyme 'shame' hints at the mysterious nature of the Lady's crime. As I read it, she is punished for taking action, for engaging directly with the world, for initiating a sexual encounter. For such unwomanly behaviour the penalty is death. Middle-class girls, we may note, were prohibited from proposing marriage. At one level, therefore, Tennyson's poem functions as a warning to women against breaking the mirror of their imposed role and shattering the rules on which middle-class courtship relations were based.

Holman Hunt was the earliest to tackle the Shalott motif and returned to it throughout his life, always depicting the moment when the curse falls on the Lady – in a drawing of 1850, an illustration of 1857 and two much later oil paintings. From the background details, it is clear that the artist made a symbolic connection between the Lady's action and the Fall, as a moment of moral disobedience. His figure is penned inside a strange loom of no known derivation, held in by strands of silk that she seems powerless to break. Elizabeth Siddall's drawing of 1853, showing the Lady seated at her loom turning to look out of the window, places more emphasis on the moment of action. In Millais' drawing of 1854 the Lady floats downriver and in Rossetti's illustration of 1857 Lancelot is at the centre of attention, gazing into the face of the Lady whose death he has unwittingly caused.

However it is interpreted, the story held a powerful fascination for the painters, whose obsession with the theme suggests a powerful urge to maintain the Lady's curse and retain masculine control, in art as it could not always be secured in life.

A corollary of the passive role defined for women was the grief and shame of the deserted or rejected girl, whose distress, in Romantic terms, is likely to be followed by despair and death. The 'old maid' had only a comic place in Victorian culture. This is the essence of the Pre-Raphaelites' favourite Shakespearian heroine, Ophelia, and we can see how the visual artists' reworkings of the *Hamlet* text reflect nineteenth-century attitudes towards women. Ophelia's story is that of an innocent girl who loses her father and is rejected by her lover. She goes mad and drowns. The passage that most frequently inspired the painters is well known:

> There is a willow grows aslant a brook
> That shows his hoar leaves in the glassy stream;
> There with fantastic garlands did she come . . .

In her madness, she falls in the water and, singing, floats downstream, borne up by her clothes:

> but long it could not be
> Till that her garments heavy with their drink,
> Pull'd the poor wretch from her melodious lay
> To muddy death.

Millais' celebrated version of this, painted in 1851–2, showing Ophelia floating surrounded by flowers, and Arthur Hughes' contemporaneous version which depicts a younger girl dressed in a shift, strewing reeds into a slimy pool, are both faithful to the text. Millais tends to glamourize; Hughes conveys more spookiness, more sense of mental imbalance. Both play down Ophelia's sexuality or marriageability, Millais by submerging the figure and Hughes by infantilizing it. This is not to argue that Ophelia ought to be shown in a sexy manner, but to underline the fact, in the artistic handling of their theme, that Ophelia's rejection and subsequent insanity have removed her from the social world. In lunacy, as in death, there can be no matchmaking, no romantic fulfilment.

Rossetti chose a different passage in 1858 for his intricate drawing *Hamlet and Ophelia*, which emphasized the breaking of the engagement. Ophelia comes to return her betrothal gifts and Hamlet feigns madness:

HAMLET I did love thee once.

OPHELIA Indeed, my lord, you made me believe so.

HAMLET You should not have believed me; for virtue cannot so inoculate our old stock but we shall relish of it: I loved you not.

OPHELIA I was the more deceived.

HAMLET Get thee to a nunnery, why wouldst thou be a breeder of sinners? I am myself indifferent honest, but yet I could accuse me of such things . . .

This particular choice of subject has, as I shall show, a good deal of direct biographical relevance in respect of Rossetti's rejection of Elizabeth Siddall, but the point here is not a personal one. Ophelia's popularity as a Pre-Raphaelite subject reflects contemporary belief in Romantic love and concern for the sad plight of unmarried women, who had no future to look forward to.

These are, of course, not the only meanings to be found in the paintings. It is, however, worth noting that such displacement – or the presentation of contemporary themes in archaic or literary guise – often functions as a way of handling, if not confronting, subjects that are in some degree disturbing. A certain cultural respectability is carried over from the aesthetic sources. And the fact that women form such a large, even dominant, component of Pre-Raphaelite subject matter suggests that the painters' most compelling concerns lay precisely in this area.

One reason for this may be that attitudes to women and the attitudes of women themselves were undergoing significant changes in mid-nineteenth-century Britain. Traditional beliefs were being replaced by those we now describe as Victorian but, almost as soon as they were formed, these were themselves challenged and defied. Social behaviour is, of course, rarely homogeneous and certainly was not so in Victorian London, which was experiencing acute and rapid changes as the first phase of urban, industrial and metropolitan expansion gave way to the period of high Victorian entrepreneurial consolidation. This very interaction between assumed social attitudes and the changing, emergent needs of women shaped the lives of what I have termed the 'sisterhood' behind the Pre-Raphaelite Brotherhood.

The central concern is with the personal lives of individual women and here I have chosen to use their first names and even their diminutives. It is possible, when writing historically about women, to use their surnames in the same way as is habitually adopted for male subjects. But it has its awkwardnesses (for example, when women change their names on marriage) and also seems somewhat solemn and unsisterly when writing, as here, about their daily lives and personal concerns. I have therefore chosen to use first names in order to reclaim and indeed raise those names by which women are customarily diminished in biographical writing. In general the names are those used by the women themselves. In order not to give a false sense of greater importance, it also seemed a good idea to refer to the men by their first names. But there were problems with this, for there are too many Williams, and in many cases men were known by surname even to their closest friends, and are simply not recognized under their baptismal names. The guiding principles of equality and intelligibility were thus often impossible to combine; the end result therefore is one of compromise and inconsistency. However, the reader should assume that whatever looks like undue familiarity is intentional. The Notes follow the conventional practice of identifying people by their initials: a list is given at the head of the References.

PART ONE

Youth

I

Lizzie Siddall first entered the Pre-Raphaelite circle around the end
of 1849. But – and it is important to establish this in view of her
later reputation – she was not then renowned for her beauty.
Rather the reverse, because it was for her plainness that she was
originally picked as a model. Later opinions, even from those who
had known her from the beginning, were so influenced by her
position as Pre-Raphaelite beauty and tragic heroine that this fact
was successfully obscured; it is as if the notion of the correspondence between Love and Beauty in the shape of the artist's ideal
beloved was so strong that it retrospectively altered earlier,
everyday judgements.

The story of how Lizzie was 'discovered in a bonnet shop' is a
familiar one, and marks the start of the legend. To recount it
again, in its various versions, is to examine what it tells us about
her, and why the myth arose. Behind the myth, she was a real
person.

In 1849 Walter Deverell, a fellow pupil of Gabriel Rossetti and
Holman Hunt at the Royal Academy schools, was teaching
part-time at the School of Design, which gave technical lessons to
artisans, and also working on a large oil painting. This was based
on a scene from *Twelfth Night*, and showed Orsino, Feste and
Viola dressed as Cesario. In keeping with Pre-Raphaelite ideas
about artistic 'truth to nature' he took his figures from life rather
than from antique or idealized forms, and was therefore looking
for models who fulfilled his conception of Shakespeare's characters. He used his own attractively epicene appearance for Orsino,
and Gabriel Rossetti for Feste; all that remained was to find a girl
who could be dressed up to look like a boy, preferably one with

red hair. At the time, this was a distinctly unfashionable feminine
look. An unattractive girl in *Mary Barton* (1848) was described as
'plain, red-headed, freckled . . . never likely to become a
heroine'.[1] Furthermore, red hair was traditionally ascribed to
Judas Iscariot and had connotations of baseness and betrayal.

One day, so ran the story told by William Michael Rossetti, the
Pre-Raphaelites' chronicler, Walter accompanied his mother to a
milliner's shop in Cranborne Alley off Leicester Square, where he
spotted red-haired Lizzie working in a back room; thinking her
face suitable for Viola–Cesario, he asked his mother to ask the
milliner 'for permission for her assistant to sit to him'. There was
apparently no need to ask the assistant herself. Permission being
granted, the tall, good-looking girl, 'with a stately throat and fine
carriage', was successfully launched on a new career.[2]

Reading this account, Holman Hunt, who was always jealous
regarding the origins of Pre-Raphaelitism, penned his own
version of Lizzie's discovery and in his autobiography offered
histrionically to 'invite the reader into my studio when first
Gabriel Dante Rossetti heard the name of Eleanor Siddall', as
Walter called to announce his find, allegedly with the dramatic
words: 'What a stupendously beautiful creature I have found, by
Jove! She's like a queen, magnificently tall, with a lovely figure, a
stately neck, and a face full of the most delicate and finished
modelling . . .' and so on.[3] In this version, Gabriel immediately
rushed off to inspect the paragon, but Hunt himself was too busy
to go. He displayed his inside knowledge, however, by referring
to the stunning model by her unfamiliar middle name, Eleanor.

Both storytellers, after stressing Lizzie's unrivalled beauty,
went on to emphasize her good manners and refinement. William
Michael insisted that she was 'ladylike' and 'committed no faults
of speech',[4] while Holman Hunt attributed to Walter the
observation that 'while her friends, of course, are quite humble,
she behaves like a real lady . . . and without any affectation,
knowing perfectly how to keep people at a respectful distance'.[5]
The message, clearly, was that Lizzie was both good-looking and
(although from the lower classes) refined and modest – the
Victorian feminine ideal. She was very young and virginal and not
over-educated. William Michael said she was about sixteen years
old. As she was in fact over twenty we may begin to doubt his
infallibility, but the age naturally enhanced his general picture of

'maidenly and feminine purity'. The truth is that retroactive camouflage was being applied: Walter was not looking for a demure beauty, nor did he find one.

Another version of the tale says that the first to find Lizzie was not a painter at all but William Allingham, Irish-born poet of fairyland who, when in London, paid court to actresses and shopgirls when he was not buttering up literary lions. Allingham was said to have flirted with several Cranborne Alley milliners, including one named Ellen Britten who lodged in the Waterloo Road and worked in the same shop as Lizzie. When Walter was searching for a red-haired model, Allingham took him along to have a look at Ellen's friend. A direct approach would have constituted a sexual proposition; as Lizzie was respectable, Walter was obliged to induce his mother to visit the shop and speak to the milliner on his behalf. This account is plausible: it removes, for one thing, the unlikelihood of Walter going to choose hats with his mother – he was a busy young man and she had two daughters to take shopping. But unfortunately the story did not come directly from Allingham, who died in 1889, but from his much younger wife Helen, who retold it to Violet Hunt, who used it in her book on Lizzie published in 1932 – an unreliable chain of hearsay.[6] Its point, however, is that Allingham, with an eye for pretty girls, did not think Lizzie worth pursuing. After her death but before her posthumous fame, he wrote: 'Her pale face, abundant red hair and long thin limbs were strange and affecting – never beautiful in my eyes.'[7]

Mrs Deverell, according to this version, asked if Lizzie would pose for her son, using her position as a lady to guarantee his good faith; Lizzie replied that she would have to obtain her mother's permission, and so Mrs Deverell obligingly went all the way to the Old Kent Road, in order to persuade a tradesman's wife that her daughter would run no moral risk in sitting to this young artist. This is not in itself unconvincing: other models like Alexa Wilding and Jane Burden had similar scruples and a few weeks after Lizzie began to pose, a servant girl found by Fred Stephens resolutely refused to pose at all. It is a pity that no corroboration exists, for such an errand would have been remarkable and strong evidence of the Siddall sense of propriety. Mrs Deverell was unable to give her own account of events, for she died within a year of Lizzie's discovery, and the account written fifty years later by Walter's sister-in-law, who had known neither him nor Lizzie, is not informative.[8] It is likely, however, that Lizzie did need her family's consent, for she was not yet of age and still living at home under her father's charge. It may not have been projected that she abandon her profession as milliner at this stage, for Viola–Cesario required only a few days' sitting, and if the work took place in the New Year of 1850, as seems likely, then it fell into the period between Christmas and the Easter season when milliners were normally laid off.[9]

How did Lizzie come to be working as a milliner's assistant? Although 'humble', in Hunt's words, her background was not as low as has sometimes been assumed and the gap between her social position and that of the young painters was not so very large. The Siddall family had some pretensions to past grandeur not dissimilar to those of the Durbeyfields in Hardy's novel *Tess of the D'Urbevilles*. 'I have always understood,' wrote Lizzie's niece many years later, 'that Hope Hall, Sheffield, should have been inherited by my grandfather', adding that Lydia Siddall, Lizzie's sister, 'was always intensely proud of her family'. A tradition asserted that the Siddalls were entitled to a coat of arms and other attributes of the landed gentry.[10]

As Lizzie's grandfather was apprenticed to a scissormaker in 1783, it is more probable that she came from a long line of craftsmen in South Yorkshire, where the name Siddall was a frequent one. Such delusions of lost glory were far from uncommon: Holman Hunt's family also claimed to have come down in the world, and the Rossettis built up their father's reputation and aristocratic connections, especially when the family was sinking economically. It was probably Gabriel who persuaded Lizzie to call herself Siddal, a less common spelling.

Whatever his ancestry, her father Charles Siddall was born in Sheffield around 1800 and trained as a cutler, that is a time-served craftsman who made, repaired and dealt in cutlery. It was a skilled occupation, one of the many 'small trades' in metal-working in the early industrial period that required specialist handtools and a workshop; the goods produced were normally sold direct to the public, sometimes from the front part of the 'shop'. In the first half of the nineteenth century independent artisans of this type were perhaps the majority, but with mechanization, mass production, heavy industry and factory employment, skilled workers were steadily drawn into wage labour. A parallel trend saw the separation of manufacturing and retailing, and the emergence of a new class of shopkeepers, dealers and wholesalers. By mid-century, this process was affecting even the Sheffield craftsmen, who cherished their independence and were widely renowned for the quality of their cutlery.

Long before this, however, Charles Siddall had left Yorkshire for London. On 13 December 1824 he married Elizabeth Eleanor Evans at Hornsey parish church in Middlesex, where bride and groom were both resident. Hornsey was then a rural district five or six miles from the city. It is not known how Elizabeth Evans came to be living there: she was born in Shoreditch and was a year or two younger than her husband.[11] Although Mrs Siddall lived to a good age, dying in 1892, unfortunately none of those who published books about her famous son-in-law in the decade after his death sought out the old lady, nor did they record any family information from her. Her granddaughter dismissed suggestions that she had been a housemaid, saying, 'from my remembrance of her she did not know the first thing about housework'. Her sister Lucy married a man called William Day and kept a grocer's shop in Barnsbury, North London. Mrs Siddall was recalled as possessing 'a wealth of beautiful hair that fell to her knees like a cloak'.[12]

Pregnancy may have precipitated her wedding, for it looks as if the Siddalls' eldest child, Ann, was born in the first half of 1825. Some time after their marriage, the couple moved to Sheffield, where their second child, Charles, was born around 1827.[13] The family soon returned to London, perhaps in search of better prospects, and were living in Charles Street, off Hatton Garden in Holborn, when their second daughter was born on 25 July 1829, and christened Elizabeth Eleanor after her mother. Her baptism at St Andrew's parish church took place when she was a year old. Although tradition suggests that the Siddalls were dissenters, attending a non-conformist chapel, at this date the established local church was the only place where official baptisms, marriages and burials could take place. Lizzie's father was described as an ironmonger.[14]

Holborn was a centre of small trades and shops, of which jewellery and watchmaking longest survived the office takeover in central London, and retail trade was an expanding commercial

field owing to London's increasing population. Small businesses
grew into large ones, and a shop could be the first step on the
upward ladder to wealth and status. Charles Siddall made efforts
to expand his business. By 1832 he was listed in street directories
as a retail ironmonger running a 'Sheffield warehouse' at both 7
Charles Street and 13 Cecil Street, Strand. Lizzie had a younger
sister named Lydia, two years her junior. The family then moved
south of the Thames and the births of her younger siblings record
other moves within a small radius: Mary and Clara in 1833 and
1836 in Southwark, James in Bermondsey in 1838 and Henry in
Blackfriars in 1842.[15] With this last move, the Siddalls were
established in Upper Ground, on the south side of Blackfriars
Bridge.

In the 1840s this was part of a thriving working-class
community, socially mixed and mobile. It was close to the famous
New Cut market with its shops and stalls and street-sellers as
described by Henry Mayhew:

> There are hundreds of stalls and every stall has its one or two
> lights . . . One man shows off his yellow haddock with a candle
> stuck in a bundle of firewood; his neighbour makes a
> candlestick of a huge turnip . . . One man stands with his
> red-edged mats hanging over his back and chest, like a herald's
> coat; and the girl with the basket of walnuts lifts her
> brown-stained fingers to her mouth as she screams, 'Fine
> warnuts! sixteen a penny, fine war-r-nuts!' . . . The pavement
> and the road are crowded with purchasers. The housewife in her
> thick shawl, with the market basket on her arm, walks slowly
> on, stopping now to look at the stall of caps, and now to
> cheapen a bunch of greens.[16]

With so many children, and the ironmongery counter and
workshop on the ground floor, the Siddall household must have
been short of space, but such overcrowding was by no means
unusual.[17] Mrs Siddall, it may be noted, had eight babies in
eighteen years; the youngest, Harry, was mentally retarded. In
1842 Charles Siddall took another shop in the Old Kent Road,
then a relatively prosperous and new working-class area rather
than the poor slum district into which it later declined. As the
population of London doubled between 1821 and 1851, the

built-up area expanded to relieve pressure on the crowded and insanitary inner districts (even new dwellings were not obliged to be connected to main sewage or water services until 1848) and it was from older urban areas like Blackfriars that residents moved south and east, filling the small fields and market gardens that flanked the Kent Road out of London with new buildings – industrial, commercial, residential. By 1849 the Siddall family was living at 8 Kent Place, south of the Bricklayers Arms and just opposite the Deaf and Dumb Asylum. Behind the terrace lay a glue factory and tan yard where soon the South East Railway Company was to build its freight terminus. The house itself fronted the street, in a good location for a shop, and seems to have been built around 1820; it had a long narrow garden behind. There were eleven shops in the row, selling beer, groceries, cheese, fish, butchers' meat and greengrocery. The wares would have been set out in front; the shopkeepers' families lived on the premises, as was the usual practice.[18]

This was hardly a background to be ashamed of, but as class attitudes stiffened during the century the social gulf between those 'in trade' and those in business and the professions widened, and it seems that neither Lizzie nor the Rossetti family wished to draw attention to her precise origins. William Michael always described her father as a Sheffield cutler, giving the impression of a horny-handed artisan rather than a shopkeeper. Without labouring Lizzie's class position, it is important to recognize its insecurity. This was caused both by its location on the lower edge of the bourgeoisie, which was characterized by an acute sense of social gradations, and by economic factors. The age was one of dramatic and sometimes frightening mobility, when the fluctuations of the British economy meant that a small business might equally prosper or founder. A retailer whose shop failed would be forced into wage employment and dependency, a condition many feared. It was an uncertain world whose features are well evoked in the novels of Dickens' middle period, with their host of shabby-genteel, hopeful characters. Despite his moves from place to place, however, Charles Siddall does not seem to have prospered, although the business evidently held its own, and the family dream of past gentility may have been a form of compensation for present failure.

Perhaps his mistake was to cater for working-class rather than

middle-class custom, for the Old Kent Road, although respectable, was not a high-class area. One of Lizzie's earliest childhood
memories was of being acquainted with the notorious murderer
James Greenacre, hanged in 1837 for killing the woman he had
promised to marry on discovering she had no money; the body
was dismembered and distributed around various parts of
London, exciting the public in successive grisly finds. At the time
of the murder Greenacre was actually living in Camberwell, but in
1832 he had lived at 2 Kent Place, trading as a grocer, and it is
possible that he patronized the Siddall ironmongery shop although
not, according to newspaper reports, for the murder weapons.[19]
Later in life Lizzie displayed a taste for the sensational and macabre
and it seems this tale grew in the telling; she was clearly close
enough to the popular culture of the streets to relish it.

There is no record of where or how Lizzie was educated.
Several of her later acquaintances remarked on her good manners
and her love of art and poetry – both items that featured largely in
the education of young ladies – although it was said that her
fondness for verse had been awakened by finding a poem of
Tennyson's printed on a sheet of paper used to wrap butter. Her
own work indicates that she was far from culturally savage, as has
sometimes been implied. Her brother James recalled their father
reading verse and fiction to the family, and Lydia grew up able to
'reel off pages from memory' from the books of Dickens.[20] Mr
Siddall was also said to have sung in a chapel choir. 'I never
perceived her to have any religion,' William Michael wrote of
Lizzie, but her own poems and drawings show a sentimental
attachment to the imagery if nothing else of conventional
worship. It seems likely that the Siddall children were brought up
as chapel- or churchgoers; a friend later said she looked like a good
little girl who always said her prayers. As was true of much
organized evangelism in the 1830s, this was as much a social as a
religious aspect to life, devotional practices being an index of
respectability. Some of Lizzie's refinement may well have been
due to class aspirations of this kind.

The family was not wealthy enough to employ living-in
servants, which was a key mark of status at a time when society
could almost be divided into those who employed and those who
worked as domestic servants. Although daily washerwomen and
charwomen may have been used, the several daughters must have

done a good deal of housework and housekeeping themselves. Like women in nearly all other social classes, they were expected to sew and repair their own clothes and household linen and, while the boys followed their father's trade, the girls looked to millinery and dressmaking for a living. Clearly, the shop was not sufficiently successful to keep them in idleness. But neither were they pushed straight into wage labour.

Millinery was part of the fashion business. It involved the trimming of ladies' bonnets with ribbons and bows according to season and taste. For occupational purposes it was regarded as an offshoot of dressmaking; in 1841 a total of 70,000 women were employed in the garment trades, of whom about a quarter were apprentices and assistants. London was the largest market, with some 20,000 employees, and roughly ten per cent of the capital's female workforce were seamstresses, dressmakers and milliners.[21] Millinery lay in the upper strata of the trade and attracted the genteel and the ambitious. The Misses Barker in *Cranford*, for example, were daughters of the lowly parish clerk but built up their millinery business by careful cultivation of an aristocratic connection and thus rose to entertain true ladies on terms of virtual equality. In another of her books, Mrs Gaskell gave Mary Barton the choice of factory work, domestic service or dressmaking and millinery; as a weaver's daughter she was almost excluded from the last by her inability to pay a premium. The daughters of poor gentlemen such as clergy or half-pay officers also went into millinery, as it was regarded as clean and genteel.

Girls were apprenticed to working milliners at around thirteen years of age and spent five years learning, first as a beginner, then an 'improver'. Premiums of about fifty pounds were paid by living-in apprentices, who received bed, sometimes shared, and board; outdoor apprentices lived at home and paid lesser or no premiums. Improvers might earn a small wage. Despite the overcrowding of the profession, prospects were good, for a trained milliner could set up in business herself and take on apprentices, using their premiums as capital and their work as cheap labour. But fashion was fickle, and a good deal depended on talent and luck.

Conditions, as revealed by a commission of inquiry into

children's employment in 1843, were often poor and work was
seasonal, concentrated in two periods from Easter through to July
(the summer Season) and from October to Christmas. The hours
could be long, but the evidence suggests that a greater problem
was irregular demand and long slack periods. It was a sought-after
occupation, however, with definite status among working girls. It
demanded dexterity and an eye for colour and style. A newly
trimmed bonnet was a mark of being up-to-date with the latest
fashions, most of which came from Paris at the start of each
Season. Milliners thus mediated between the upper classes who set
styles and the middle and lower classes who strove to follow
them.

Among men, milliners had a reputation for 'immorality' that
derived from the belief that young women were essentially vain
and flirtatious and the fact that milliners enjoyed a degree of
independence from masculine control not allowed to most wives,
daughters or servants. It is hard to tell how far this reputation was
justified; certainly Arthur Munby, a creditably clear-sighted
observer of London working women in mid-century, recorded his
impression 'that the morality of the milliner class is lower than
that of any other: they have all the temptations and none of the
safeguards of the classes above and below them'. A milliner he
knew complained that the other girls gossiped chiefly of 'their
gentlemen friends, who give them presents and take them to
casinos'.[22] But, as he also remarked, modesty was 'an affair of
class as well as of sex'[23] and middle-class standards of correct
behaviour were not appropriate to working girls.

It seems that Lizzie did not belong to the flirtatious type of
milliner – that anyway was the message strongly conveyed by
those who insisted on her 'maidenly' demeanour and reserve,
obviously anxious lest prejudice against millinery lead to wrong
assumptions about her character – but like Munby's young friend
Louisa she must have led a relatively unsheltered life. Milliners
were required to dress well in the shop, and were observed and
accosted by young 'swells' as they went to and from work; as a
result, Munby noted, 'Louisa herself, although a virtuous respectable girl has not – nor can any such a girl have – that *ignorance* of
vice which one desires in a lady.'[24] By 1850, when Lizzie was
twenty, working daily in central London, she could not have been
the innocent, unaware, passive figure of popular legend. As a

milliner's assistant she was earning a small wage. For a model payment was negotiable but could be as high as one shilling an hour, while the hours worked were limited; it represented, in effect, a relatively well-paid part-time job and one which Lizzie evidently preferred to the bonnet shop in Cranborne Alley.

For *Twelfth Night* she sat sideways on a bench, leaning forward with her hands clasped and face in profile. Her auburn hair was pulled back off her forehead, and her expression, anxious rather than adoring, may have been caused by the awkward costume the artist had chosen for Cesario to wear. In his initial studies for the subject, Deverell dressed his model in a knee-length tunic with voluminous sleeves, a striped under-tunic and long hose[25] but the finished oil painting had Cesario in a short red tunic with long flaps instead of sleeves, one white and one pink stocking and ridiculously pointed 'medieval' slippers. This was in keeping with current ideas about historic dress but must have caused a non-professional model like Lizzie considerable embarrassment. Young women did not show their legs, even in private. Something of this was expressed by William Michael in his review of the picture, where he remarked primly: 'The costume of the figure is too flimsily theatrical and we think the impolicy as well as the immodesty of her very short dress must have been overlooked by the painter.'[26] He also commented, incidentally, that the figure's head was 'not physically beautiful enough' for Viola.

By all accounts, Walter Deverell was a charming young man and it has been argued, and not unconvincingly, that Lizzie fell in love with him during her sittings.[27] His poems and paintings however suggest that by contrast with other members of the Pre-Raphaelite circle he was not yet very interested in women as romantic objects; he painted sisterly portraits of his sisters and their friends, for example, and none of his verse was about love. Emotionally and practically, he had other worries in this period, which saw the death of his mother followed by that of his father, before Walter's own decline and death in 1854, and it cannot be deduced that he felt any especial affection for Lizzie. Her feelings are not documented and her later poems referring to an earlier lost love may be interpreted in other ways. Her sittings for Cesario–Viola did not last beyond February 1850 and she was soon working at her next job, for Holman Hunt.

Hunt, who was busy with a large oil showing *A Converted*

British Family Rescuing a Christian Missionary from the Persecution of the Druids,[28] had been having what William Michael described as 'his apparently indispensable bothers with models'[29] and when Lizzie became available he adapted his design so that the woman bathing the missionary's face became younger.[30] This figure, for which she posed holding a bowl and sponge, has a plain anxious face, with straight red hair looped back behind her neck. She is clothed in a rough shapeless skirt topped by a cape that seems to be made out of sacking or some hessian fabric; one arm is bare to the shoulder. Altogether, not a flattering appearance, especially to one familiar with the current fashions in dress. It may be noted, too, that the entire British family in the picture was intended to have a 'savage' aspect appropriate to the Dark Ages in which the subject was set.

Lizzie was evidently a good model, who came when appointed and sustained her poses well; she was not uncouth and undertook her role more responsibly than young ladies from the artist's own social circle. But she was definitely not regarded as a beauty, nor, in the early months of 1850, was she paid any particular attention by Gabriel Rossetti. Indeed, in March the Pre-Raphaelite Brotherhood *Journal* recorded that he was searching for a red-head from whom to paint the hair of the Virgin in his new picture *Ecce Ancilla Domini*. The suitable servant girl found by Fred Stephens flatly refused to sit and Gabriel desperately looked for another model.[31] Significantly he did not think of using Lizzie. It is probable that she was known only as a 'plain' model. With red hair, she had prominent eyelids, pale eyes fringed with gingery lashes and a long top lip that may have covered protruding teeth. It is not intended to endorse this description as ugly, since I believe such judgements to be part of the continuing oppression of women, but there is no doubt that in the Victorian period, women's looks were important, and by the criteria of the time Lizzie's appearance would not have been highly rated. Later, when her 'beauty' was an established fact, Holman Hunt apologized for her appearance in his *British Family*, blaming his haste to finish the picture and his desire to give the girl 'a rough character'; the result, he claimed, was that the head bore no resemblance to the sitter 'in grace or refinement'.[32] But she had not been selected for those qualities and it is more likely that the painting gives us a good, unglamourized likeness.

The same problem recurred with his next picture, for which she was a principal model. The subject, chosen in the summer of 1850, was taken from the final scene of *Two Gentlemen of Verona*, in which Valentine rescues Sylvia from being ravished by Proteus, while Julia looks helplessly on. His decision to depict this moment in which morality overpowers sexuality reflects Holman's concern with virginity which is also found in other works of this period, but more interesting is the choice of Lizzie to pose for Sylvia, a Duke's daughter. Her status as a model was rising. It appears that the drawings for the picture were done in August, for she was then at Holman's studio – a fact that emerged from a letter written at the end of the month by Gabriel in which he told his brother in a short paragraph that 'Hunt and Stephens have been playing a disgraceful hoax on poor Jack Tupper, by passing Miss Siddal upon him as Hunt's wife'.[33] Gabriel was angry on Tupper's behalf and insisted that Hunt write to apologize to his friend, who had been placed in an awkward position.

This curious incident almost defies interpretation. Did Lizzie take part in the so-called joke? Did she join Holman and Stephens in their hoax, or was she ignorant of the whole high-spirited affair? Practical jokes were popular and too much should not be read into the incident except in so far as it relates to Lizzie. Convention decreed different behaviour to married and single ladies and attentions to a gentleman's wife were not appropriate to a hired model, who was normally ignored, like a servant. For an unmarried employee to pose as a wife, even in jest, was rather shocking. If the hoax was perpetrated without Lizzie's consent, modesty might have prevented her from sitting to Holman again; as she did so, she must either have taken an active part in the deception or not minded the misrepresentation. This implies a degree of youthful friendship between painter and model, suggesting that their relationship was not merely formal. Was there some attraction between them which revealed itself obliquely in the shape of a make-believe marriage? Could Holman's choice of Lizzie to model for Sylvia have had personal significance? At the end of his life Hunt told a friend that Lizzie had been 'on the point of marrying someone else' when she was courted by Rossetti.[34] Could he have meant himself? Such an explanation, even if exaggerated, would account for his use of the name 'Eleanor Siddall' and the evident friendship between them at this date. For more than a year, Lizzie modelled mainly if not exclusively for Holman Hunt.

During the autumn of 1850 she was at home, while the rest of *Valentine Rescuing Sylvia* was being painted. According to William Michael, she sat to Gabriel for his watercolour of a girl later titled *Rossovestita*[35] around this date, but without his identification this would be hard to prove, for the figure's face is conventionally rendered and bears more resemblance to earlier drawings that reproduce a demure girl's face, typical of the period without much degree of portraiture.[36] William Michael later claimed that Gabriel fell in love with Lizzie 'before 1850 was far advanced'[37] although elsewhere he dated their relationship from '1851 or thereabouts'.[38] It is my belief that he did not know when his brother first met or fell for Lizzie. Hunt, who was in a position to know, said that after her entry into the artists' circle, Gabriel 'did not for a full year or two profess any strong personal feeling for her'.[39] If she did sit for *Rossovestita* it seems most likely to have been in the early weeks of 1851, when for a short period Gabriel and Walter shared a studio in Red Lion Square. In any event, there is no strong personal feeling in the painting.

Holman, having completed the background and other figures, wrote early in 1851 to ask her to come and complete Sylvia's pose; and 'one morning in the spring the young lady appeared'.[40] Her new costume was an advance on that of the British peasant – a finely embroidered satin gown. She wore her hair up, with a gold fillet and an elaborate little headdress. The kneeling pose was awkward and it is clear that its original angle, shown in the preliminary design,[41] was modified in practice. In the painting[42] Sylvia is kneeling upright instead of leaning backwards in horror and relief; much of the sense of arrested movement has been lost thereby but it looks an impossible position for a model to maintain. More puzzlingly, in the painting, Sylvia does not look much like Lizzie, while the face on the design has been erased completely. As originally painted and exhibited at the Royal Academy in 1851, however, Sylvia did have Lizzie's features. In the course of criticism designed to defend Pre-Raphaelite painting against its detractors, John Ruskin commented unfavourably on the 'commonness of feature' displayed in many of Hunt's figures, a defect that was particularly visible in the face of 'the unfortunate type chosen for the face of Sylvia'.[43] Hunt, whose hallmark as a painter was painstaking verisimilitude and who had chosen his model carefully, nevertheless agreed with the critic and repainted the face.[44] He blamed himself in retrospect for not having done his model justice but we may take it that the likeness was in fact too good and had to be modified to fit the idealizing concept of figure painting that still held sway. Lizzie's face was taken out of the picture because she did not look like a Duke's daughter.

When she was not modelling, Lizzie was at home in Kent Place. The Census taken in April 1851, shortly after she posed for Sylvia, showed her at the age of twenty-one living in her parents' house. Lizzie gave no occupation, which was not unusual since women and girls, like men above a certain social level, were not expected to work at a specific job, but it is negative evidence that she had given up millinery. Her new career was not regarded as a full-time occupation; in the whole of the 1851 Census only two women were classified as artists' models.[45] It was rather an irregular means of earning: Lizzie's next job came in the autumn and was for Gabriel, who was now working in Ford Madox Brown's studio in Newman Street; he was planning a picture based on an incident taken from the poems of Tibullus, showing him returning unexpectedly to his wife Delia. The first study for Delia, dated November 1851, was drawn from Emma Hill, Brown's young model, posing in a household chair in her ordinary clothes. Her eyes are closed and she is chewing a strand of necklace from which hangs a heart-shaped locket. Emma, whose baby daughter Catherine was one year old, was the right age to portray a young wife but on this occasion she sat somewhat stiffly, and the remaining studies for Delia were all drawn from Lizzie, who seems to have been able to give the exact expressiveness to the role; certainly Gabriel made a large number of successful drawings. She posed in a variety of costume gowns, with a strand of her loose hair between her teeth; her eyes were closed in a gesture of yearning. A watercolour version in which Delia looks both wistful and passionate was completed before the end of 1851.[46]

Hindsight indicates that the drawings for Delia marked an emotional as well as an artistic event and may be seen as the start of Lizzie's transformation into a Pre-Raphaelite star. Under Gabriel's hand she was made to look not plain but romantically appealing; his vision was not as literal as that of Hunt, who incidentally had no high opinion of his friend's talent for portraiture. 'Rossetti's tendency in sketching a face,' he wrote, 'was to convert the features of his sitter to his favourite ideal type and if he finished on these lines, the drawing was extremely charming, but you had to make believe a good deal to see the likeness.'[47] In the Delia studies, Gabriel was perhaps not so much 'converting' Lizzie's looks as discovering in her face qualities of pathos and expression that other observers might not see. It is impossible to distinguish what she, as a model, brought to the subject: conventional art criticism acknowledges only the artist's expression of skill and feeling. The Delia drawings are a good example of Gabriel's ability and imagination, for he selected the pose and the loose hair that give the subject its tenderness and intimacy: Victorian ladies kept their hair neatly dressed at all times except when going to bed. However, I would suggest that Lizzie entered into the spirit of this pose so well as materially to assist the artist in his work, and that in this way Gabriel's feelings for his model were first awakened. The Delia drawings are certainly full of affection. In common with other members of the Pre-Raphaelite Brotherhood, Gabriel was ready to fall in love, and the handling of the Delia–Tibullus scene expresses the urgent idealized passion characteristic of young romance.

William Michael wrote that Gabriel and Lizzie 'probably' became engaged before the end of 1851 and although this was not strictly true, it does help to date the start of their emotional involvement. Further evidence was contained in Gabriel's *doppelgänger* drawing entitled *How They Met Themselves*, which was done at the time of their wedding and bears the dates '1851 1860', representing the span of time between the two pairs of lovers who meet in a forest.[48] The first date thus marks the start of their fateful relationship. It was not an engagement in the usual sense, with a formal announcement, family introductions and the like. Lizzie did not meet the Rossettis nor is there any record of Gabriel being presented at Kent Place. It is doubtful whether they had much opportunity to be together, for apart from Brown's studio, there was nowhere they could meet privately (both were still living at home) and 'spooning' in public was indulged in only by the lower classes. There was no gossip linking their names romantically and altogether very little evidence of any sort of engagement, official or unofficial. In view of later events, of course, it was necessary for one to be invented. But if Gabriel and Lizzie were emotionally attracted at this date, the fact seems not to have been openly acknowledged.

Lizzie continued to sit to other painters. In December 1851 when she had only just finished posing for Delia she agreed to work for John Millais as the model for his drowned Ophelia. It seems possible that Millais saw the Delia drawings and recognized in them a sad, pathetic quality that suited his conception of the heroine driven to madness by her lover's rejection. As it happened, work did not get under way as planned, for Lizzie's brother Charles was gravely ill and early in January 1852 he died. The cause of death on the certificate was given as scrofula (a disease of the lymph glands) and diarrhoea.

The existence of Lizzie's elder brother was not much remarked in the Pre-Raphaelite circle and indeed William Michael dated Charles's death to 'shortly before her acquaintance' with Gabriel. She was said to have spent the weeks before his death 'in lengthened and very exhausting attendance on the sick-bed' of her much-loved brother.[49] As well as grief the family suffered an economic blow in losing Charles. The next oldest boy was James, then only thirteen years old and, although destined to follow his father as a cutler, not yet a breadwinner. These circumstances perhaps put Lizzie under greater pressure to earn: Millais wrote to tell Hunt that he had received 'a letter from Miss Siddall by which (owing to the death of her brother) she cannot sit to anyone for a fortnight'.[50] Mourning was evidently not allowed to last long.

The sittings for *Ophelia* began with the head; both the drawings and paintings of this were completed by 6 March. Then they proceeded to the figure, the story of which is one of the best-known of all Pre-Raphaelite tales. Millais found an 'old and dirty' antique dress, 'all flowered over in silver embroidery' which Lizzie wore while lying in a tin bath full of water kept warm by an arrangement of oil lamps burning underneath. Then 'just as the picture was nearly finished, the lamps went out unnoticed by the artist, who was so intently absorbed in his work that he thought of nothing else, and the poor lady kept floating in the cold water till she was quite benumbed. She herself never complained of this . . . but the result was she contracted a severe cold.' As a result her father wrote threatening to sue Millais for fifty pounds for doctor's bills and loss of Lizzie's earnings. 'The matter was satisfactorily compromised,' wrote Millais' son, by a suitable, but lower payment – and Lizzie was soon back at work.[51] This seems to confirm that in 1852 Lizzie was a working model rather than Gabriel's ideal beloved or betrothed.

At about this time she worked for Holman again, sitting for Christ's hair in *The Light of the World*. Christina Rossetti, Gabriel's sister, also modelled for the head, intended as an ideal rendering, and the differences between her experience and Lizzie's are interesting to note. As a lady and an acquaintance, Christina was chaperoned by her mother when she went to pose and received no money; Lizzie was not accompanied, and was paid by the hour.[52] That she also interested herself in the work in progress is shown by Hunt's recollection of how, on one occasion, she went all the way to his studio in Chelsea on her own initiative, to tell him that she had seen in a religious bookshop a print that exactly resembled his picture. Originality of composition was a great concern of professional painters but, happily for Hunt, his own visit to the bookshop revealed only slight similarities between print and painting. He believed that Lizzie's imagination had transposed his lantern and crown accessories on to a conventional image of the Saviour. However it is clear from the anecdote that she took a personal interest in his work.

Modelling was an occupation of dubious repute, about which it is hard to discover many facts.[53] Owing to the nudity involved, female models were popularly associated with prostitution and indeed in the early history of the Royal Academy life classes, appear to have been recruited from brothels. Artists were generally believed to share the loose morals of their models, a view well illustrated by the landlord of the Red Lion Square studio when he told Deverell and Rossetti to keep their models 'under some gentlemanly restraint' since some painters sacrificed 'the dignity of art to the baseness of passion'.[54] Generally, the idealistic young men of the Pre-Raphaelite Brotherhood did not wish to seduce their models and preferred to distance themselves from the allegations of licentiousness levelled against certain Academicians; for this and other reasons they rarely painted nudes although for the purposes of figure painting they were necessarily obliged to study from nude models. Because of contemporary notions of ideal form, models were normally selected for their good looks and good figures and there is some evidence that this was regarded as a favourable way for a pretty working-class girl to improve her position in life. Both male and female models were employed in the studios of individual artists and in subscription clubs such as the Clipstone Street Artists' Society where life classes, either nude or costume, were held weekly. Here Mrs May and Miss Guyson were regulars in 1851, and early in 1852 a new model by the name of Anne Ryan appeared who was considered 'a little beauty'.[55] She was subsequently employed by John Millais for some of his most famous early pictures and his portrait of her shows a dark-haired, cherry-lipped charmer.[56] 'Alas for Miss Ryan,' wrote Millais' son. 'Her beauty proved a fatal gift: she married an ostler and her later history is a sad one. My father was always reluctant to speak of it, feeling perhaps that the publicity he had given to her beauty might in some small measure have helped (as the saying is) to turn her head.'[57]

There were also models who sat only in costume or for heads and hands, and most of the 'amateur' models recruited by the Pre-Raphaelite painters fell into this category. There is no indication, for example, that Lizzie ever posed in the nude. Even so, modelling was not regarded as a respectable occupation since it involved being alone with one or more men. As Munby might have observed, this was a matter of class as well as sex; it was indecent only when a young *lady* went unchaperoned; girls of a lower class did not count. The social divide between women who worked for money and those who did not is a key feature of the nineteenth century and the very fact that Lizzie had a job marked her as no lady. The fact that she evidently preferred modelling to millinery suggests that she was sufficiently independent not to be troubled by associations of immorality.

It is unclear at what date she first became aware of being in love with Gabriel. His own work indicates that his feelings for her grew slowly and imperceptibly, and were not at once openly expressed. His poem 'A Last Confession' describes a young man who falls in love with a girl who is not at first aware of his emotion and who, incidentally, is given several of Lizzie's characteristic features, such as a 'high neck' and a lower lip 'sucked in as if it strove to kiss itself'. When the narrator eventually expresses his feelings, the girl rejects him and he kills her.[58] The theme of the indifferent woman recurred in Gabriel's watercolour *Beatrice Denying Dante Her Salutation*[59] which had been planned for some time but was realized in the summer of 1852, when Lizzie posed for the figure of Beatrice in a tiny cottage-studio on Highgate West Hill where Gabriel was temporarily living and working.

Gabriel needed to leave home – he was twenty-four years old – but could not afford to do so, and his casual studio habits did not suit the laborious, methodical Brown, so it was fortunate when another friend offered the use of the cottage, in the garden of a house named the Hermitage. It happened that the main house was being repaired and for a few weeks Gabriel was virtually alone at the Nest, as the cottage was called. He recalled the time there as 'one of the jolliest of my life'.[60] It was a tiny place with just two rooms, the one above being reached by an outside staircase and rustic gallery; the roof was thatched and the walls were buried 'in an exuberant growth of ancient ivy'. Inside, there were further 'gimcrack attempts at rusticity' in the shape of stained glass and grotto-work – altogether a fine Gothic setting for an artist who adored late-medieval art and poetry.[61]

Here Lizzie and Gabriel could be alone together for the first time. One day Gabriel's friend William Bell Scott, on a visit to London from his home in Newcastle, was directed up the steps by a servant and found himself 'in the romantic dusk of the apartment face to face with Rossetti and a lady whom I did not recognize, and could scarcely see. He did not introduce her; she rose to go. I made a little bow, which she did not acknowledge; and she left. This was Miss Siddall.'[62] The ambiguous nature of the situation rings true.

A month later Gabriel left the Nest, new tenants having taken the Hermitage, and for the first time publicly acknowledged his feelings for Lizzie, writing to tell Christina that he had in his possession 'a lock of hair shorn from the beloved head of that dear . . . radiant as the tresses of Aurora'. His language was exaggerated and larded with Latin allusions, as if to warn his sister against taking his words too seriously, but he was clearly enrapt. Lizzie, he wrote, had recently made herself two dresses, one grey and one black, 'the first bringing out her characteristics as a "meek unconscious dove" while the second enhances her qualification as a "rara avis in terra" by rendering her "nigro simillima cygno" '.[63]

In the same letter, however, he also used the artists' familiar term for Lizzie – the Sid. Derived from the usual custom of calling models by their surnames only, this term was affectionate, but also slightly derogatory. More significant, perhaps, was the fact that he commended her drawing, at which, he told Christina, she showed real promise.

For Lizzie was not content to remain a model. It is impossible to tell whether she had earlier aspirations of her own or whether they were stimulated by being in artists' company, but by 1852 she was ambitious enough to try her hand at drawing. Because the Pre-Raphaelite women are normally viewed merely as satellites of the men, Lizzie's drawing and painting are usually dismissed as wholly derivative and uninteresting. This judgement will be discussed later; what is remarkable is that she asserted her claim to a creative role from which her gender, class and occupation all tended to exclude her. Gabriel's encouragement was crucial, of course, but the initiative may well have been hers. At some stage, it seems, she complained of being treated as nothing more than a model, as a sort of clothes-horse with interesting hair, and lamented that 'no one cared about her soul'. This stirred Gabriel's sympathy, and love and instruction went hand in hand. In August, she went to Hastings for what may have been her first seaside holiday; the resort was a favourite with the Rossetti family and Gabriel must have made the arrangements. He joined her there, and on their return to London he began to look seriously for a place of his own or rather one to share with his brother who, as a civil service clerk, could be relied on for rent. In October, after some househunting, he found a small villa in Crouch End, Hornsey and sent his mother a list of furniture he would require. But the house was never taken. Instead, the following month Gabriel was installed in an apartment named Chatham Place on the north bank of the Thames near Blackfriars Bridge, with William Michael as co-tenant. This was significantly closer than Hornsey to the Old Kent Road, and from the beginning, part of the motive was that Lizzie could visit. The week he moved in, Gabriel told his brother not to invite Hunt on Saturday 'as I have Lizzie coming, and do not of course wish for anyone else'.[64] William Michael regarded Chatham Place as suitable for convivial male gatherings of the sort not possible at home, and on several evenings in November and December 'the fellows' were invited for conversation, coffee and smoking. However, it was soon understood that Lizzie was frequently to be found in the apartment and consequently William Michael made less use of it himself than he had planned. This was, he admitted, an unconventional state of affairs, but he stoutly resisted any imputation of immorality or even ambiguity, and it is plain that in the eyes of the world Lizzie was still a model, whose visits to Chatham Place were for professional purposes. During the autumn *Beatrice Denying Dante Her Salutation* was finished and *Dante Drawing an Angel on the Anniversary of Beatrice's Death* begun, with Lizzie posing for the visiting Lady.[65] From this date she sat to no one except Gabriel, but this fact was not immediately publicized and in November Charles Collins wrote to ask if she would sit for 'the principal head' in his new picture. He was answered, according to Millais, 'in the most freezing manner, stating that she had other occupation' and Collins had to look elsewhere.[66]

This other occupation was her own drawing. In January 1853 Gabriel wrote to tell Brown that he was taking his 'pupil' to a photographic exhibition. The formality was rather undermined in the next sentence which referred enthusiastically to 'dear G's drawings'; her illustration of Wordsworth's pathetic poem 'We are Seven' was almost complete.[67] 'G' stood for 'Guggums', Gabriel's curious pet name for Lizzie and hers for him, an exchange that can only be indicative of considerable closeness.

It is my belief that, of Gabriel's friends, only Brown knew of Lizzie and Gabriel's secret relationship at this date. And it is time to look more closely at Brown's domestic situation, for in the spring of 1853, he and Emma Hill, whose daughter was now two years old, were married. The ceremony was kept from all except a few of Brown's acquaintance, who included Gabriel and Lizzie. Soon Lizzie and Emma were close friends and a Pre-Raphaelite sisterhood was in the making.

2

Something of a mystery surrounds Emma Matilda Hill's origins. She herself said she was born in Gloucestershire, and gave her date of birth as 1834,[1] but there is evidence that, like Lizzie, she was a few years older than was generally believed. In 1841 she appears to have been living with her father, Thomas Hill, a bricklayer, aged sixty, and her mother Catherine, aged forty-nine, in Essex Street, St Pancras; she was entered in the Census under her middle name Matilda and her age given as twelve.[2] If correct, this means she was born in 1829. Her birthday was on 16 May, so she was a few weeks older than Lizzie. She had an older sister Eliza, at whose wedding in 1846 Emma Matilda was a witness, and over the years she acquired a number of nephews and nieces.

To the end of her life, Emma preserved the memory of a rural upbringing. Her granddaughter recalled how the scent from Emma's shawl was 'like that of herbs and flowers growing in the country'[3] while her grandson recorded, in his memoir of Ford Madox Brown's life and work, that Emma was 'the daughter of a Herefordshire farmer' who left his widow 'with little more means of subsistence than a chancery suit'.[4] This lawsuit was, however, as fictional as that in *Bleak House* and but for Emma's own Census declaration of Gloucestershire as her birthplace this account of her rustic origins might be dismissed as wholly fanciful. But it seems possible that she was born in the corner of Gloucestershire that borders Herefordshire and that Thomas Hill was a small farmer who migrated to London during the agricultural depression of the 1830s, where there was a demand for labour owing to the residential building boom and subsequent railway construction. The only surviving tale of Emma's infancy fits well with a rural background, for it was claimed that the ghost of a huntsman had lifted her from the cradle, 'looked at her sadly, and put her down again'.[5]

Emma was 'without educational advantage'[6] and had 'few accomplishments and very little *savoir-faire*' owing to her 'early days in a farmhouse atmosphere',[7] a description that could be interpreted as indicating that she was ignorant and graceless. But she was not illiterate, and although her charms were chiefly physical, she was sweet-natured and easy to please. A soft dumpling of a girl, she had a round regular face, pink complexion and 'a fine abundance of beautiful yellow hair the tint of harvest corn'.[8]

She first met and modelled for Ford Madox Brown, the older friend and associate of the Pre-Raphaelites, in 1848, the year the Brotherhood was formed by the younger painters. Brown, whose first wife had died tragically young in 1846, leaving him with a young daughter Lucy, was smitten with Emma's looks and in 1848–9 used her repeatedly as a model, for Cordelia in *King Lear*,[9] for Juliet, for Philippa Roet and for the Fair Maid of Kent in *Chaucer at the Court of Edward III*.[10] A pencil study of her head, done, and dated 'Xmas 48',[11] may mark the beginning of her relationship with Brown, who at this period was employing various models.[12] Her next recorded appearance was on 10 February 1849, when Brown wrote in his diary – kept as an account of his painting not his personal affairs – that he had that day started to paint Cordelia's veil but had 'only laid in a part of it when a girl as loves me came and disturbed me'.[13]

During the rest of that month Cordelia's head was painted and repainted, and it was again reworked at the end of March shortly before the picture was sent in for exhibition. By July, Emma was seeing a good deal of Brown, who as well as painting took her to the theatre and for walks 'in the fields by Highgate'.[14] In September, after he went to Margate for a fortnight's holiday with his daughter Lucy, who normally lived at Gravesend with her aunt, he and Emma spent a week together near Ramsgate, an occasion that was later described as their honeymoon.[15] By this date, if not before, their relationship was a sexual one. A few months later Emma became pregnant; significantly, Brown's careful diary-keeping came to an end in March 1850, soon after her condition would have been confirmed.

It is doubtful that Brown proposed marriage. He was fond of Emma, but aware of his first obligation to Lucy and conscious of his lack of success as an artist and his lack of money – he depended chiefly on a tiny income from the ownership of some property, supplemented by occasional sales. In addition, Emma was neither socially fitted to be the wife of a gentleman-painter nor step-mother to his daughter; her moral position as artist's model and 'fallen' girl was a further difficulty. At the same time, Brown recognized his moral responsibility and duty as seducer. The solution, for the time being, was concealment. Emma's descendants did their best to obscure her origins, presumably in order to disguise her daughter's illegitimacy, and in a misleading if not deliberately falsified account stated that Emma met Brown while he was visiting Stratford-upon-Avon for his picture of Shakespeare; subsequently, owing to her mother's opposition to the match, she ran away and married him.[16]

It is more likely that Emma's mother was angry with the gentleman who had 'ruined' her daughter without promising marriage. Whatever the facts, Brown assumed his responsibilities and supported Emma through her pregnancy and confinement; her baby daughter was born on 11 November 1850. Catherine's birth, incidentally, does not seem to have been registered.[17] By the following spring mother and baby were installed in a little house at Stockwell, in South London where Brown, who spent half the week with them and half at his studio in town, painted them standing outdoors for *The Pretty Baa Lambs*.[18] This marked his unmistakable adoption of Pre-Raphaelite painting principles and Emma's first experience of open-air modelling. 'My painting room being on a level with the garden,' Brown wrote later, 'Emma sat for the lady and Kate for the child. The lambs and sheep used to be brought every morning form Clappam [*sic*] common in a truck.' One of the sheep ate all the flowers in the garden 'where they used to behave very ill'.[19]

The picture, unlike other Pre-Raphaelite paintings containing sheep such as Hunt's *The Hireling Shepherd*,[20] has no allegorical, social or religious message; its intention was simply to portray a hot summer's day with a young mother pointing out the animals to her infant. The use of 'baby-talk' in the title exactly conveys what is happening and although on the canvas Emma looks pink and uncomfortable in the hot sunlight, and little Kate, Katty or

Cathy, as she was variously called, is perched like a china doll
rather than a real child on her mother's arm, the picture was meant
as a simple celebration of the artist's pleasure in seeing mother and
daughter together. For some reason, Emma posed in an
eighteenth-century costume gown of pale-blue satin, quilted and
embroidered and seemingly inappropriate to the alfresco occasion;
in real life, the sober practical dress of the servant girl shown
kneeling in the background was probably what Emma would
have worn.

She also posed for other figures in 1851, including 'two sittings
of two hours each' just before moving to Stockwell, for the
Princess of Wales in the large *Chaucer* painting[21] and for the head
in the picture later known as *Take Your Son, Sir!*'[22] The history of
this unfinished picture is complicated and its interpretation
problematic, owing I think to the fact that it contained ambiguities
and also because it altered in conception over the years. It depicts a
young woman holding out her naked baby to its father, who is
seen in the mirror behind the mother's head, his hands stretched
out in a gesture that may be read as welcoming or apologetic. The
poses are awkward, not reassuring, and it is tempting to interpret
the subject as that of an unmarried mother presenting her bastard
to its father. At the same time, the mother's madonna position and
the mirror haloing her head make it plain that the baby's birth is
being celebrated. It is therefore possible to read the work simply as
'a celebration of marriage and parenthood' with a young bride
offering their first-born to her husband.[23] The ambiguities,
however, are undeniable: the mother's expression, apparently
taken from a study of Emma 'with her head back laughing'[24] is not
one of unalloyed maternal joy, and her wedding-ring finger is
carefully left invisible. The words of the title may be spoken with
aggressive intent or loving pride and the work has a disturbing
quality that is very different from Brown's other rendering of this
theme, *Oure Ladye of Good Children*.[25] All in all, it is my view that
Take Your Son, Sir! reflects the contradictory situation the painter
found himself in at the time of its conception. He and Emma were
a loving couple of proud parents, whose love and pride were also a
cause of shame and concealment. It is possible that this emotional
background was too raw to be satisfactorily mediated in paint, so
that the picture remained half-finished for some years; the baby
belongs to 1856–7 and is in fact the Browns' son Arthur, born in

September 1856. By this time the painter's domestic life had stabilized and his celebration of motherhood could be more straightforward. With Arthur's death in 1857 the picture again became too painful, despite an attempt to complete it in 1860 and another in 1892, after Emma's death. It remained unfinished. However interpreted, the emotional content is high.

Little Catherine was baptized on 18 April 1852, at the same time as the child of Emma's married sister, and the register reveals that her parents gave their names as Ford and Matilda Hill; 'since they were not yet married a degree of secrecy and mystification were essential'.[26] She was named Catherine Emily Brown Hill.[27] The 'false' surname was only partly a lie: it was Catherine's legal name, and her baptism was therefore not bogus but genuine. But quite what her parents hoped to achieve by this step remains obscure.

They had left Stockwell when the year's lease expired, and by September Brown was lodging in Hampstead and appears, over the winter of 1851–2, to have suffered from acute depression and possibly some form of breakdown. He described his condition as 'intensely miserable, very hard up and a little mad'[28] and in a letter to Emma from Hampstead he wrote: 'I feel certainly better in tone and spirits and hope shortly to be again a help to you in your troubles sweet love but at present I think I had better carry out Marshall's advice to the letter.'[29] John Marshall, who also attended Rossetti, was physician, friend, occasional model and associate, lecturing on anatomy at the School of Design to which Brown was attached. Emma's troubles were the fact that Katty had measles and her mother was in need of money; Brown offered her some from two sovereigns he had in hand. Finances were not good and over the winter Emma went as a living-in servant to the household of a young farmer at Hendon, which was within reach of Hampstead. Her existence was still kept a secret from all but Brown's close friends; in any case at this period he was reclusive and unsocial, seeing few people.

His letter, however, was addressed to his 'Dearest Wife', and thanked her for 'such loving words from such a sweet young wife . . . the only enjoyment I have left me so pray do not be sparing of it', which tells us not only that marriage was now contemplated but also that, whatever her educational deficiencies, Emma could read and write. The letter may indeed have been written in the early weeks of 1853 when she was living on North Hill, Highgate

and apparently attending a local ladies' seminary.[30] Several of the
Pre-Raphaelite women attended such establishments, which
offered a range of tuition from handwriting, spelling and simple
arithmetic through history and geography to music, deportment
and social accomplishments. In many respects, the information
imparted was superficial and the main purpose was to instruct
girls in 'ladylike' behaviour. This was the kind of conduct Emma
needed to learn before she could take her place in society as
Brown's wife. Manners, accent and how to stand, sit and walk
were all subjects of study, together with correct behaviour as
hostess and guest and a smattering of French to suggest even
greater refinement. In the absence of more serious study for girls,
such schools flourished, patronized both by the middle classes and
by those who aspired to join them. Emma was not a pupil for very
long and while at Highgate she also went over regularly to
Hampstead 'in the most inhuman weather' to pose as the young
emigrant's wife in the picture *The Last of England*.[31] For the sake of
dull, cold light, this was painted 'chiefly out of doors when the
snow was lying on the ground'.[32]

'About this time,' Brown's painting diary continued, 'I lost
many days through interruptions of a domestic nature'[33] – an
oblique way of referring to the fact that he and Emma had at last
got married. The ceremony took place on 5 April 1853 in St
Dunstan's-in-the-West, and was witnessed by Brown's friends
Tom Seddon and Gabriel Rossetti, who, it will be recalled, had
shared his studio during 1851–2 when Emma sat for the first Delia
drawing. Gabriel was the first guest Emma formally invited; he
addressed his reply politely to 'My dear Mrs Brown'[34] and on the
evening of 1 May he drew a tender little ink portrait of her, which
may have been a wedding gift. It remained in Brown's possession
for the rest of his life.[35] The wedding was not publicly announced,
presumably so that when eventually known the date would not
clash so noticeably with Cathy's age, and few people knew of it.
At the end of the year, however, Gabriel included it in his
summary of the year's news sent to Thomas Woolner, an original
Pre-Raphaelite Brother whose departure to Australia is thought to
have inspired *The Last of England*. The painting perhaps owed as
much to Brown's despondency during the previous twelve
months, his sense of failure and 'blighted hopes' together with his
feeling of responsibility towards his dependants. The wife's face,

and her hand clasped round that of the unseen infant within her cloak, express a tender trustfulness that probably mirrored the sitter's own. The young husband, brooding darkly and somewhat ill-temperedly, was painted from the artist himself.

Soon after their secret marriage, Brown and Emma were living in Hendon but moved on 1 September to the neighbouring parish of Finchley where they rented 1 Grove Villas, Church End, on the main road into London from Barnet. Here, with her daughter now nearly three years old, Emma's first sustained experience of housekeeping began. She was amiable and easy-going and without being especially silly seems to have borne some resemblance to Dora Copperfield in the matter of household management. She probably had little experience of handling money and was easily tempted into 'extravagances'. Brown, whose earnings were sporadic and who therefore had to budget carefully, took charge of the household accounts and in the early years of their marriage seems often to have treated her as a helpless youngster, to be occasionally rewarded with a day out or a new bonnet. However, I suspect that he relied a good deal on her gentle nature and placidity to assuage his moodiness and irascibility and that he was always grateful to her for living through the years of poverty without the complaints or anxiety that another woman, especially from a 'superior' class, might have expressed. Her stepson–in–law William Michael Rossetti later wrote of the 'domestic vexations' Emma caused (of which we shall hear more) but insisted on the firm and fond attachment of her husband, who never ceased to love her.[36] Other members of her family remembered her with great affection too. She is not a figure who plays a large part in this book, but her presence in the artists' circle and her experiences form constant motifs.

The irregularity of Emma's position made the unconventionality of Lizzie's at the Hermitage or Chatham Place pale by comparison but may have strengthened their friendship alongside that between their men.[37] Certainly the two couples were close. A plausible explanation of the name 'Guggums' in mutual use by Lizzie and Gabriel from 1853 onwards may be that it derived from little Cathy's early attempts at 'Gabriel', adopted by him and Lizzie as lovers' mock baby-talk. Brown himself was the only other contemporary to use it and on one occasion himself referred to his friend as 'Gaggy'.[38]

As yet, however, Lizzie's position was defined publicly as that of Gabriel's pupil, not his beloved. This undoubtedly enabled them to be together in a way that mere affection would not have justified, but as it has sometimes been assumed that Lizzie's 'studies' were simply a cover or euphemism for something much less proper, it is important to emphasize that both she and Gabriel took her work seriously, and that she placed as much importance on her painting as her affections. Her earliest known work *We are Seven* does not seem to have survived[39] but her dual role, as 1853 progressed, was illustrated extensively in Gabriel's drawings. Here, in repeated portrait sketches, she was both model and artist, shown concentrating at her own easel. These are among the least prettified drawings of Lizzie and testify to her seriousness. In an ink sketch dated 'Sept 1853' she was drawn leaning forward earnestly, her board propped against the back of a chair. She is intent on catching the likeness of her sitter, who is Gabriel himself, perched on two upright chairs, staring back firmly with his hands in his pockets.[40] Interestingly, the man is stiff and uncomfortable in the unaccustomed role of model. Lizzie's two activities were sometimes shown separately: as artist's model in *Giorgione Painting*[41] and as artist in *Love's Mirror*[42] where a girl paints her own portrait, assisted by a young man. This had direct biographical reference, for in the summer of 1853, having sold one of his first paintings, Gabriel went on holiday, leaving Lizzie working alone at Chatham Place on a self-portrait in oils. He advised her to keep the door locked and warned William Michael that she would sometimes sleep there.[43]

The portrait is interesting and competent for an artist without formal training or previous experience of oils. It belongs to the honest rather than 'improved' school of self-portraiture and is far removed from the chocolate-box feminine image of the time which women were accustomed to seeing. It is straightforward, uncompromising and surprisingly strong, emphasizing the large-lidded eyes, distinctive mouth and long neck. The head and shoulders are unadorned except for a small white collar; the hair is ginger against a green background and the face looks out from the circular canvas with a frank and slightly vulnerable expression but no touch of self-indulgence. There is stiffness in the handling and the work is not naturalistic, but the effect is successful and may be favourably compared with the similar portrait that Gabriel painted a few months later, also on a green ground in an oval frame, which presents a much more glamourized view of Lizzie.[44]

Her work is often dismissed as slight and derivative, of little intrinsic interest and less merit than much of the art produced in the Victorian age by women amateurs with a talent for accomplished sketching and neat watercolours. Feminist art historians have disputed this view and their revaluation of her work is long overdue.[45] There were many obstacles between Lizzie and art. She did not grow up in a world where young ladies drew and painted as part of their education and her artistic talents perhaps first found expression in millinery as part of fashion design. It was generally assumed that women could not be serious painters and thus in terms both of class and gender Lizzie was at a disadvantage; her readiness to challenge accepted views distinguished her from the usual forms of female passivity and imitativeness – although these characteristics were frequently ascribed to her. The content and quality of her work will be dealt with later; here, without qualifying the foregoing remarks, I want to stress that in her career she was undoubtedly assisted by Gabriel who, whatever his faults, was unselfish in encouraging others and did much to help and sustain Lizzie. If anything he was too encouraging, too lavish in his praise, too ready to persuade her to paint before she had learnt to draw, for example. Presumably owing to lack of life studies, she never seems to have mastered figures, and most of the people in her pictures have no legs. But if Gabriel's support was invaluable it was also reciprocated, for she helped him to produce some of his finest work, as Ruskin (if few others) recognized. So, it may be surmised, there was partnership as well as passion between them, based on shared activity, which was unusual in Victorian England, when male and female spheres were generally kept separate.

Lizzie's early ambitions were modest but professional, being illustrations to poems by Tennyson. The first was for 'St Agnes' Eve', with the virgin novice yearning for her vows. Her composition resembled Millais' on the same subject, which was completed at the beginning of the year and given to Effie Ruskin, apparently as some token of what then seemed impossible longing, but there is no evidence that

Lizzie saw or could have seen this work.[46]

Her next work was *The Lady of Shalott*,[47] which was inscribed
'E.E. Siddal Dec 15/53'. Again, this was a favourite theme with
the male painters of the Pre-Raphaelite circle, which underlines
her willingness to join them on their own ground. Her treatment
of the theme reinforced the conventional view of relations
between the sexes, working over 'contemporary distinctions
between the private indoor world of women and the public
outdoor world of men',[48] while offering at the same time an
'alternative' view based on what may be called intuitive feeling,
less obviously controlled by ideological pressure. Small and stiff as
it is, the drawing shows the Lady as a calm, composed figure, not
an agonized, fateful victim. Her appearance is familiar, even
prosaic, set in a domestic work room that is also a place of prayer,
as indicated by the crucifix on a low chest before the window. A
songbird (a favourite pet among women in the early Victorian
period)[49] is perched on top of the loom. Neither bird nor crucifix
features in the poem, but have been added by the artist as emblems
of her interpretation of the Lady. This, it may be noted, runs
counter to the image of a wicked, tragic transgressor so
powerfully suggested by the poem. But, as we have seen, it is a
text with many meanings.

Over the winter of 1853–4, as she continued to paint and draw
at Chatham Place, Lizzie's relationship with Gabriel became more
companionable, at least so it seems in his sketches of her reading
or sitting in an armchair. There is no indication, however, that she
took on a more domestic role. It was not one that appealed to her
and in any case Chatham Place was not equipped for wives. There
seems to have been no kitchen; meals were either eaten out or sent
up, and household chores were performed by the housekeeper,
Mrs Birrell, and her menials. Lizzie spent a good deal of her time
there, but she was not living at Chatham Place. Her existence was
barely mentioned by Gabriel to his family, then temporarily in
Somerset, or to his friends, who sometimes gathered for convivial
male evenings to which Lizzie was not invited. At the end of the
winter, Gabriel's long letter to Woolner in Australia contained
much news, but no mention of Lizzie.[50]

Only William Michael and 'old Brown' were in his confidence
regarding Guggums. To the latter Gabriel wrote in January 1854,
saying 'Lizzie sits by me at work on her design, which is now

coming really admirable. She has also finished the "Lady of Shalott" sketch and made quite another thing of it. She has followed your suggestion about her portrait, and done several things, which improve it greatly.'[51] In February, when Walter Deverell died of kidney failure, Gabriel wrote many sad letters, both to Walter's brothers and to his own friends, which bear witness to his deep sense of grief and loss; in none was Lizzie mentioned or associated with his feeling.

The following month, the decision seems to have been taken to introduce her to the Rossetti family on their return to London. 'Tell Christina,' Gabriel wrote to his brother, 'that if she will come here on Thursday, Lizzie will be here, and she can also see Gug's emanations [i.e. drawings]. I shall be glad if she will come, as I have told Lizzie she mentioned her wish to do so.'[52] Although there was no warmth between the two women, the meeting appears to have gone well and it was suggested that Lizzie should illustrate the collection of poems Christina was preparing; it was like Gabriel to have promoted such collaboration. The same week saw Lizzie's first appearance as hostess, with Gabriel writing to the Browns: 'Lizzie and I would be very glad if you could both fix an evening to come here.'[53]

She was also taken to meet the Howitts, who had moved into the Hermitage. Mrs Howitt, whose husband was then in Australia, was a writer and her daughter Anna Mary a painter who had studied professionally in Germany and who introduced Lizzie to a number of other women artists. Somewhat strangely, but perhaps as a result of the strain involved, these social events coincided with the first reports of Lizzie being 'very unwell', a reputation she was never henceforth to lose. Gabriel himself was rather surprised by the Howitts' diagnosis and their insistence that Lizzie be seen by the eminent Swedenborgian and homeopathic doctor, Garth Wilkinson. The Howitt women believed in alternative medicine, spiritualism and the like. Wilkinson diagnosed 'curvature of the spine' – for which there was no clinical evidence either then or later – and advised that she stop painting.

This was a typical instance of the way male medical practice worked to prevent unsanctioned female activity and it is good to record that it was rejected. Of course Lizzie must continue to paint, Gabriel told Brown. She was even now 'sitting by me working at the most poetical of all possible designs, and sends her

love to both Emma and you'.[54] She was also planning to illustrate
a collection of ballads which William Allingham, now resident in
London, was preparing for Routledge, and it is possible that she
was already busy with these. A stay in hospital was suggested, but
instead she went again to Hastings under the protection of two
new friends made through Anna Mary. Both were emancipated,
independent young women who figure in the history of
nineteenth-century feminism. Bessie Parkes was staying in Hastings and helped Lizzie find and settle into lodgings in the High
Street, while Barbara Leigh Smith was not far away on her
family's estate near Robertsbridge. Anna Mary was with Barbara
at Scalands – both were painters, while Bessie was a poet – and
together the three women took over the management of Lizzie's
illness, sending bulletins to Gabriel, who was detained in London
by his father's death. One report spoke of a decline in her
condition and immediately after the funeral he set off anxiously to
Hastings where he was relieved to find Lizzie 'rather better than
otherwise'. Politely, he disputed Bessie's alarmist account, saying
he had known Lizzie for several years 'and always in a state hardly
less variable than now, and I can understand that those who have
not had so long a knowledge of her would naturally be more liable
to sudden alarm on her account than I am'.[55] It is hard to judge
what Lizzie's condition may have actually been: weakness and
anaemia were common among Victorian women and perhaps
taken more for granted by Lizzie and Gabriel than by the robust
and energetic Bessie and Barbara; certainly Gabriel wrote to
Allingham cheerfully: 'Barbara and Anna Mary came over
yesterday, and walked some time with us; and Lizzie did not seem
over fatigued. Several ladies here are very attentive to her, and
seem quite fond of her. Her spirits are much better, and some of
her worst symptoms have abated.'[56]

She cannot have been gravely ill if she was going out for walks
and receiving visits. The whole question of Lizzie's health is not,
as is sometimes assumed, an objective issue of deciding which
organic diseases she suffered from, but rather a matter of the
ailments ascribed to her and of general and personal attitudes
towards her as a woman, an artist and a lady. Responses to illness
are complex and contradictory and it is not possible here to do
more than outline some of the main currents in the views of the
Victorians and their practice. As with modesty, it was a matter of

class as well as of gender. Working-class women were assumed to be robust and strong enough to shovel coal, push wagons, carry yoked pails, work in the fields and undertake many other tasks. Arthur Munby's curious admiration for the coarse strength and stamina of his servant-wife Hannah is a good illustration of this notion, which was of course a gross distortion of reality. As might be expected, the lower classes had higher rates of disease and ill-health than those above them in rank; their apparent robustness was simply taken from the fact that they were seen at strenuous manual work. Working men and women also tended to ignore ill-health; it could not often be cured, and sickness meant loss of income.

By contrast, the middle classes tended to overreact to health matters, fearful lest coughs and colds develop into fatal tuberculosis or pneumonia. In addition, weakness and debility were regarded as attributes of social refinement and higher class. This characterization went together with the pseudo-scientific categorization of physical types into 'higher' persons with fine features and domed heads, and 'lower' ones with low foreheads, heavy jaws and thick necks.[57] This characterization seems to have served partly to legitimize the general exploitation of the working class and colonial peoples (including the Irish, who were commonly portrayed as virtually negroid in appearance) and the specific exploitation, in relation to women, of female servants by bourgeois ladies, who claimed to be too delicate to scrub floors and scour pots. In the context of this configuration of views illness could be an index of status.

It functioned also as a means of suppressing women's activity and creativity, and the rise of the Victorian invalid accompanied the contraction of the role of the middle-class woman as a result of economic changes and the decline of the household business. As is known, female dissatisfaction with the limited sphere allotted to women was frequently defined as disease. At the same time, however, sickness had its benefits. Invalids received great attention and care and were relieved of onerous tasks. Unpleasant obligations could be avoided by a breakdown in health. At the age of fifteen Christina Rossetti was faced with the prospect of becoming a governess in order to contribute to the family finances; hitherto reasonably sturdy, she became weak and delicate with ailments no physician could diagnose and henceforth she lived as a semi-invalid who was often 'unwell' and could not be relied on. Some years later she acknowledged the purpose of her condition, telling William Michael, 'I am rejoiced to feel that my health does really unfit me for miscellaneous governessing.'[58]

Finally, as an example of the contradictory messages received from society by women, poor health was viewed as a barrier to wedlock, for both sexes. Much concern was expressed as to the physical condition of each spouse and a sudden breakdown in health was held to release the other partner from an engagement.

In this context, the promotion of Lizzie's ill-health in 1854 is easier to understand. Her new women friends seem to have made a determined effort to persuade Gabriel to marry her, perhaps because they responded to the romance of the poor, talented girl discovered by the young artist. Barbara told Bessie that Lizzie's gifts had been found 'by a strange accident such as rarely befalls woman', and that if she lived she would be a great artist, but her life had been hard and her fate was in doubt. She was Gabriel's 'love and pupil' and 'I do not doubt if circumstances were favourable, he would marry her. She is of course under a ban having been a model.'[59]

Both Barbara and Bessie could afford to ignore such social considerations, for each had inherited income. They had progressive views too and did not relish the subjection to a husband that marriage commonly entailed, but were realistic enough to perceive that in the absence of income, marriage was Lizzie's best way of fulfilling her promise and hope. It is possible that they felt that ill-health would both increase her 'ladylike' qualities, helping to erase the fact that her father was a shopkeeper, and also strengthen Gabriel's desire to rescue and raise her, as an expression of his love. If this was so, their intervention had an ironic quality, for Lizzie's ill-health, without specific symptoms, became a metaphorical albatross. However, the first weeks at Hastings were very pleasant: Gabriel's anxious attentiveness was especially noticeable. After a few days staying at an inn, he moved into the same lodgings as Lizzie, reassuring his mother that 'no one thinks it at all odd my going into the Gug's room to sit there'. It was of course regarded with suspicion, and Barbara had to intervene before the landlady would provide Lizzie's sitting room with a fire.[60] They spent their days idly, taking short excursions and 'rambling about the hills', amusing themselves by carving their initials on ruins and rocks.[61] This, a traditional lovers' occupation, was in some sense a public declaration, a substitute for the still missing engagement. There is a tradition that, on a day trip to Scalands in May, when Lizzie and Gabriel carved their initials on a window panel, he proposed to her in a bluebell wood and their feelings for each other were at last made explicit.[62] Some writers take the occasion to have been a sexual one. Both indeed later wrote poems that appear to commemorate some important event in a wood. Gabriel's was called 'The Portrait' and revolves round the image of a dead love 'mid mystic trees' (an apparent reference to the picture *How They Met Themselves*) standing

> As in the wood that day:
>
> That day we met there, I and she
>   One with the other all alone;
> And we were blithe . . .

He recalls drinking from a spring with his beloved, and a sudden storm interrupting some kind of declaration:

> But when that hour my soul won strength
>   For words whose silence wastes and kills
> Dull raindrops smote us, and at length
>   Thundered the heat within the hills.
> That eve I spoke those words again
> Beside the pelted window pane;
>   And there she hearkened what I said . . .

Lizzie's own poem was called 'The Silent Wood'[63] and contained similar themes in different mood:

> O silent wood, I enter thee
> With a heart so full of misery
> For all the voices from the trees
> And the ferns that cling about my knees.
>
> In thy darkest shadow let me sit

When the grey owls about thee flit;
There will I ask of thee a boon,
That I may not faint or die or swoon.

Gazing through the gloom like one
Whose life and hopes are also done
Frozen like a thing of stone
I sit in thy shadow – but not alone.

Can God bring back the day when we two stood
Beneath the clinging trees in that dark wood?

Only the transferred epithet 'clinging' indicates what may have happened on that original day in Scalands wood.[64]

Lizzie posed with flowers in her hair for the other three to draw, and back in the Hastings lodgings Gabriel made several studies of her that are unsurpassed for tender draughtsmanship, showing her standing by the window or sitting in a reclining chair, usually wearing a dress with deep pleated cuffs and a bodice gathered from shoulder to waist. She too was drawing. When he arrived in Hastings Gabriel found her working on an illustration to the ballad 'Clerk Saunders', one of those to be included in Allingham's collection, and she had sketched out some ideas for 'The Maid of Lochroyan' and 'The Gay Gosshawk';[65] he told Brown excitedly that Lizzie's 'fecundity of invention and facility are quite wonderful, much greater than mine'. She also completed a drawing to illustrate Gabriel's own ballad-style poem 'Sister Helen', with its macabre tale of a melting wax effigy of the faithless lover; and she did some sketching from life. On one of their walks, Gabriel recalled, they met 'a dark gipsy-looking girl of about thirteen' who was in charge of 'a very fine baby sister' and whom Lizzie brought home to draw. This I believe is the identity of the girl holding an infant shown in several sketches pasted into the photographic album of Lizzie's work Gabriel compiled after her death.[66] Gabriel thought the girl 'the image of savage active health', but on talking to her Lizzie discovered that she spent the winter months in bed, unable to go out owing to undernourishment and recurrent fever.[67]

Her own health showed no change. Barbara continued to suggest hospital care – first at the Sussex Infirmary and then at the new Harley Street sanatorium for governesses and 'ladies of small means' run by Florence Nightingale, then on the eve of her Crimean adventure. Lizzie rejected both and went to see a local doctor, who recommended merely that she move to new lodgings nearer the sea in order to avoid the summer heat. But Gabriel was getting bored. Hastings was 'slow', he complained to friends, and he missed the London gossip – the opening of the Royal Academy Summer Show and the annulment of the Ruskins' marriage, the scandal of the season. Earlier in the year Gabriel had met Ruskin for the first time and marked him down as a potential patron. Effie Ruskin had fallen in love with John Millais, and applied for her marriage to be dissolved on the grounds of non-consummation through her husband's impotence. Everyone in the artistic world was talking about it – except Gabriel. After Anna Mary and Barbara returned to town he felt very isolated.[68] Despite the fact that Lizzie was 'a sweet companion', as he told Allingham, he was anxious to return to London. He left Hastings in June, but by herself Lizzie was bored and lonely and Gabriel went to fetch her on 26 June. She was keen to continue painting and had prepared a design that was, Gabriel explained, 'practicable for her to paint quietly at my rooms'. The sight of death and disease all around her in a hospital would only affect her adversely and would obstruct her desire to become an artist. 'She wishes,' he wrote sympathetically, 'that something should be done by her to make a beginning, and set her mind a little more at ease about her pursuit of art.' This, 'more than anything else would be likely to have a good effect on her health'.[69] Such determination belies the legend of Lizzie as a frail, delicate flower and lifelong invalid. It also illustrates how the legend came into being at the very moment that she attempted to assert her identity in a male world.

And so, despite all the well-meant advice, in the summer of 1854, which was a bad season for cholera, Lizzie returned to London and went to work alongside Gabriel at Chatham Place, ignoring the hot weather and foul river. Her new picture was *The Nativity*,[70] a small watercolour containing a blue-robed Madonna holding a red-haired Christ child. The figures may be based on the sisters Lizzie drew at Hastings, for the child is an infant rather than a baby, but the picture itself is sketchy and does not seem to have been painted from life. The design, according to Gabriel, was 'lovely and original', but somewhat inept, as the Virgin appears to be perched halfway up the wall of a stairwell, with a window opening beside her and a door below; such a vertical composition was characteristic of much of Lizzie's work. The subject was of course wholly traditional but nevertheless ambitious: many of the great painters have painted the Nativity. It seems to belong to a series that includes Lizzie's *Holy Family*,[71] showing the Virgin and Joseph in the stable with a well-swaddled and shapeless baby, and Gabriel's *Annunciation*[72] and *Preparation of the Passover in the Holy Family*.[73] If this is so, it is worth noting that Lizzie's pictures antedate Gabriel's and may therefore be less derivative than is thought. He at least was always anxious to give her full credit for the originality of her ideas.

During the months that had passed since he had first introduced her to his friends, Gabriel's attitude to Lizzie had been undergoing some changes. It is not easy to determine exactly what these were, but a sense of how he was feeling emerges in a letter written to William Allingham on 23 July. She had seen Dr Wilkinson again and he thought her better, but she was still poorly. He wrote:

> It seems hard to me when I look at her sometimes, working or too ill to work, and think how many without one tithe of her genius or greatness of spirit have granted them abundant health and opportunity to labour through the little they can do or will do, while perhaps her soul is never to bloom nor her bright hair to fade, but after hardly escaping from degradation and corruption, all she might have been must sink out again unprofitably in that dark house where she was born. How truly she may say, 'No man cared for my soul.' I do not mean to make myself an exception, for how long I have known her, and not thought of this till so late – perhaps too late. But it is no use writing more about this subject; and I fear, too, my writing at all about it must prevent your easily believing it to be, as it is, by far the nearest thing to my own heart.[74]

Far from being the libertine of popular repute, Gabriel was at this date a sentimental and idealistic young man who painted pious and romantic subjects. In this letter we can see one of the most familiar attitudes of the Pre-Raphaelite men towards their women. Lizzie was to be rescued from her lower-class origins and elevated into a superior world, through art and love. She was to be idealized.

3

By this time Holman Hunt was planning a similar future for his model, Annie Miller.

A good deal could be written about Hunt's curious psychology of self-justification, although it is clear that large numbers of Victorian males were equally enthralled by the subjects of prostitution and illicit sex while maintaining a hatred of debauchery. The increasing moral rigour of the age was partly due to the growth of the bourgeoisie and its consolidation of economic power and ethical leadership in opposition to the aristocratic ruling class, whose lewdness was legendary; certainly Hunt's own history provides an illustration of this. The son of a City warehouse manager, he was placed as a clerk at a young age and seems to have nurtured ambitions to be a gentleman and an artist with some resentment against his family, who were unable or unwilling to finance his studies at the Royal Academy. His early friendship with Millais and Rossetti within the Pre-Raphaelite Brotherhood contained strong elements of rivalry and, as is also common among groups of young men, a lively interest in girls. Early Pre-Raphaelite Brotherhood correspondence frequently refers in teasing manner to the attractions of young women and, as I have indicated, young love and awakening sexuality were some of the first themes they chose to depict in art.

There is no evidence, however, that they indulged in sexual activity in these early days. They were not in a position to marry, and the piety they inherited from their families inhibited youthful experiments with servants and whores; indeed the problem for the three young painters who cruised the Tottenham Court Road looking for models was that as well as possibly offending

respectable girls, they risked picking up prostitutes, whom they
had been taught to abhor. As art students they were aware of
particular temptations with regard to nude models in the life class
and studio, and Hunt himself wrote disapprovingly of painters as
'a class of men who till this time have been thought excused for
some licentiousness'.[1] The Pre-Raphaelite Brotherhood, by contrast, were pure in word and deed.

But their natural human interest in sex was not to be buried and
expressed itself in art, often accompanied by a kind of moral
camouflage that did not always disguise its urgency. With the rest
of the nation in 1849–50, the Pre-Raphaelite Brotherhood followed Little Em'ly's flight and fall in *David Copperfield* as it
unfolded week by week in the manner of a television serial today.
Faust's seduction of Margaret or Gretchen was a favourite theme
with artists and illustrators.[2] In 1850 the three Pre-Raphaelite
Brothers were all working on similar subjects. Millais chose to
illustrate 'The Woodman's Daughter', a poem by Coventry
Patmore that describes the seduction of a country lass by a squire's
son, the birth and drowning of her illegitimate child and her own
eventual insanity; the picture aroused the same objection as
Valentine Rescuing Sylvia, with the face of the female figure, a child
of eight or nine, being likened to that of a 'vulgar little slut'. It was
later repainted to make it more acceptable.[3] Rossetti, staying with
Hunt near Sevenoaks ostensibly to paint outdoor backgrounds,
began a drawing based on a song from a play about women who
were 'neither wife nor maid' leading 'a jolly life/Between the
sunshine and the shade'; and he also started a picture suggested by
the desire of the lame Richard III 'to caper nimbly in a lady's
chamber/To the lascivious pleasing of a lute'.[4] Hunt's own
Sevenoaks background was for his *Valentine Rescuing Sylvia*, with
its theme of threatened rape, and in another Shakespearian subject
begun in 1850 he chose a comparable theme from *Measure for
Measure*, where Claudio asks Isabella to save his life by yielding up
her chastity.[5] Clearly sex, seen in this rather narrow biographical
manner, does not comprise the whole meaning or significance of
these works, although it is arguable that in general sex loomed
large in a great deal of nineteenth-century art and that only a
male-dominated form of cultural reverence prevents us from
seeing it as high-class pornography, based on the visual and sexual
exploitation of women by producers and consumers. The personal

relevance of the subjects lies in the fact that despite the archaic, literary settings, the themes clearly reflect contemporary power relations and concerns between men and women. Sexual initiation outside marriage meant dishonour for women, but not for men. Some of the tension evident in the paintings expresses, I believe, the Pre-Raphaelite artists' anxiety over this crude form of 'morality'.

In his next picture Holman pulled back from this rather dangerous theme – only rendered respectable by its Shakespearian sources – and chose a religious subject, showing Christ with a lantern, *The Light of the World*. But the sexual theme would not go away and in 1851, while the Christ was on his easel, Hunt was thinking of a 'material counterpart' based on Peggoty's rescue of Little Em'ly, 'when she had become an outcast'. The search for the right setting took him, in his own words, around and about 'to different haunts of fallen women'.[6] No doubt the prostitutes he encountered on this mission were accustomed to gentlemen who prowled but did not pay and indeed after broadcasting the idea to his friends, Holman seems to have become conscious of its prurient angle, for he did not proceed. It may, however, have been on one of these excursions that he first saw Annie Miller. She was then aged fifteen and living with her sister at the home of her uncle and aunt in a yard by Justice Walk, Chelsea, a cramped and probably insanitary slum just behind the large houses of Cheyne Walk, where, at 5 Prospect Place, Hunt had his studio.

Her mother had died in 1835 shortly after Annie's birth, and for about ten years she and her sister Harriet lived with their father, an ex-soldier who drove a builder's cart in the Kings Road. Both girls were said by a neighbour whose children they helped to mind to be 'dirty and covered with vermin'; Annie's hair was particularly wild and filthy. When his fitness deteriorated, Mr Miller was admitted as a pensioner of the Royal Hospital and his daughters went to live with their uncle and aunt, a cobbler and a washerwoman, who themselves lived on the margins of poverty, their first child having been born in the workhouse. They now lived in Cross Keys Court, behind the public house.[7]

If Hunt spotted her in the neighbourhood some time around 1851, however, there is no evidence that he approached her and indeed he appears then to have been preoccupied with the affairs of another working-class girl, whom he had discovered in Surrey (where he and Millais went in the summer to paint more backgrounds) and whom he had engaged to pose for his new picture, *The Hireling Shepherd*. Emma Watkins was a buxom, red-faced country girl, and the provocative sexuality of the shepherdess for whom she sat left no doubt as to Hunt's message, even if the painting is also an elaborate allegory on the spiritual condition of the contemporary church.[8] Emma lived at Kingston with her mother and brother, who was a groundsel-seller or street hawker, gathering weeds from waste land to sell in halfpenny bunches to the owners of cagebirds. This suggests that the Watkins family was very poor. In the winter of 1851 Emma travelled up to Chelsea to sit for the shepherdess, accompanied on the first two occasions by a young sailor whom she introduced as her fiancé. Perhaps reassured by Holman's correct manners, she soon came alone and eventually moved in, temporarily, to the same Prospect Place lodgings run by Mrs Bradshaw. This no doubt perfectly proper proceeding aroused a comic, teasing spirit among Hunt's Pre-Raphaelite friends, who called at the studio in order to view Emma sitting, or rather reclining. They nicknamed her 'the Coptic' in a now unfathomable allusion, and they attempted to play practical jokes by pretending to be her jealous suitor, hammering on the door with the aim of punching the painter for pinching his girl.[9] They at any rate felt the sexual implications of the situation – as did the author of a story published in *Household Words* several years later, much to the embarrassment of the Hunt family. By the time the tale appeared, moreover, Holman was renowned for his entanglement with another pretty working-class girl.

After finishing *The Hireling Shepherd*[10] he completed *The Awakening Conscience*. For this he had a new story, and a new model from whom to work.

Having watched Annie Miller growing up in the streets around Cross Keys Yard, he may have judged that her looks and her poverty made her a likely candidate to follow in little Em'ly's footsteps. Or perhaps he chose the subject of his new picture, showing a kept woman in a *maison de convenance* 'breaking away from her gilded cage with a startled holy resolve while her shallow companion still sings on'[11] and then began his search for a suitable model, finding Annie on his doorstep, as it were. In either event, he brought life and art together in such a way that they were ever afterwards confused, for the depiction of a woman renouncing her sinful way of life was accompanied by a 'real-life' plan to rescue Annie from a similar career. Hunt also, it later emerged, dreamed of raising her to be his lovely and loving wife. One wonders whether this was due in any degree to the news that Gabriel Rossetti had discovered that Lizzie Siddall was an artist, whom he was going to rescue from 'degradation and corruption'. Hunt was keenly conscious of competing both professionally and personally against his friends and fellow artists in their pursuit of fame, fortune, love, honour and success. Something comparable was to happen to his other Pre-Raphaelite Brother John Millais, who spent the summer and autumn of 1853 falling in love with Effie Ruskin, then imprisoned in a loveless, sexless marriage. Knight errantry, it may be remarked, was a favourite artistic theme.

Just as Hunt's painting strove for painstaking accuracy at the expense of feeling, so it was like Hunt to emulate others' actions without understanding their essence. Saving a young woman from an unhappy fate was typical of the ideals they shared, and Hunt's handling was characteristically crude. Lizzie's origins were humble, but Annie's were worse. Effie's position might be scandalous, but Annie's was potentially even more so. At this distance in time it is impossible to assess whether, when she met Holman, Annie was the forward, flirtatious, sexy figure of later legend. Like several of the women in this account, her views on life, love and Pre-Raphaelite men were rarely recorded and even the events of her life have to be reconstructed by inference from accounts by Hunt and his friends; in some ways her character and career have been so deeply confused with those attributed to the woman of *The Awakening Conscience* that they cannot now be disentangled.

Whatever the reality, her reputation today is that of a sexy, wanton girl, prodigal of her favours. This may be a mistake. The earliest known portrait of her, made at the beginning of 1854 by George Boyce,[12] who had a taste for pretty girls, especially models, shows Annie as a quiet-looking girl – she was about nineteen years old – with her head modestly bent and her hair pinned up in the nape of her neck. Holman, however, seems to have believed (or wanted to believe) that she was well on the road to ruin. Later, he was to describe Annie at the time of his rescue mission as 'without even the habits of cleanliness, living in the foulest of courts . . . allowed to prowl about the streets using the coarsest and filthiest language . . . in a state of the most absolute neglect and degradation'. He wrote to her father about his desire to employ Annie as a model and received no reply, from which he deduced that if he did not act she would fall victim to the first man who approached her.[13] It was ironic that his efforts to help seemed to stimulate exactly those effects he feared.

Ostensibly, Annie was chosen only to model for his new picture; at the same time he would arrange for her to receive some education, with a view to social improvement. Manners, cleanliness and literacy seem to have been the main lessons. There was no mention of marriage. But, as Holman's friends and patrons Mr and Mrs Combe at Oxford knew, he was looking for a wife, and objected strongly to the snobbish and mercenary aspects of the middle-class marriage market, with its assessment of young men and women on the size of their fortunes. At the same time, his immediate ambition was to travel to the Holy Land to paint authentic biblical scenes. The plan to rescue Annie may thus be seen as fitting a half-formed hope in his mind, whereby having indirectly shown (through the subject of his picture) the dangers her physical attractiveness posed, Holman would return to claim a beautiful and obedient wife.

Annie certainly came to believe that his interest in her went beyond the merely charitable. He believed she was in love with him and indeed it is more than likely that she did respond to the attentions of this courteous, rather intense young artist with his high moral principles. Annie seems to have been bright, attractive and intelligent, with an independent mind, ready to seize opportunities: she was streetwise, as we might say. Moreover, the attentions of a gentleman were not to be rejected by an uneducated, unskilled working-class girl in the 1850s, for whom the usual career openings where those of skivvy and scullerymaid. For his part, Hunt found her lively and stunningly good-looking and far more appealing than the prim, costive middle-class girls he was introduced to in Oxford.

Annie sat for the picture of the conscience-stricken woman in the autumn of 1853, wearing what appears to be a flannel nightgown with a broderie anglaise hem and a paisley shawl wrapped around her hips, with her hair loose down her back. In such déshabille, at noon, the woman is amusing her lover, sitting on his knee as he plays the piano, but the words of the song strike a chord of remorse in her soul. For the sake of authenticity, Hunt rented the room, in Woodbine Villa, St John's Wood, where all the furnishings were bright and new and vulgar and reinforced the message of *The Awakening Conscience*. It is not known whether Annie posed 'on site' or in the studio, and no detailed preparatory drawings have survived.[14]

The purpose of the picture was and remains plain and straightforward, although in my view the message is not lucid and without prior knowledge it is difficult to tell what is being represented. The woman's posture and expression suggest the sudden realization of burnt cooking in the oven rather than remorse for lost purity, and the static, waxwork quality of the painting does little for the sense of dramatic moment. There is a mass of critical comment on the contents, treatment and reception of the picture; my only additional remark is to suggest that just as the artist reproduced the current notions of morality by showing the fallen woman to be in need of redemption rather than her seducer (who is shown as shallow and base but not in the same acute state of sin as the woman), so he effectively presented his own unconscious role in respect of Annie Miller. He was the agent of her temptation who was not himself to be blamed. This is not to suggest that Hunt was a would-be seducer; as Millais later noted, when discoursing to Brown on the 'disgustingness of stale virginities', Hunt was able 'to be so long virtuous' because 'before doing anything whatever he always held a sort of little council with himself in accordance with which he acted'.[15] Rather, he failed to perceive that the implications of his offer to educate Annie were identical to those of an immoralist who bought and paid for women in order that they should do as he desired. Hunt can hardly be held personally culpable, of course, for this was the actual state of relations between the sexes, whether in marriage or without, and all the notions of romantic love could not camouflage it.

The painting was finished in January 1854, destined for the Royal Academy Exhibition; the moment it was completed Hunt departed for the Middle East, somewhat precipitately despite his long preparations, as if in a great hurry to get away. It is possible that, notwithstanding his moral principles, he and Annie did come

close to a sexual relationship during the period she was modelling
for him, and that he took fright and fled. Some such moral crisis
would explain the self-mortifying aspects of Hunt's Holy Land
travels and account for the fact that he stayed away until he had
completed his extraordinary painting of *The Scapegoat*,[16] banished
to a lurid desert in expiation of sin. I wouldn't go so far as to claim
that the goat resembles the painter[17] but there are several layers of
meaning in the choice of subject. Hunt placed the scapegoat,
ritually sent into the wilderness as a symbol of sinfulness, near the
biblical site of Sodom, destroyed for sexual sins, and he described
the Dead Sea scene as a literal vision of 'men's secret deeds and
thoughts . . . the horrible figure of Sin – a varnished deceit – earth
joys at hand but Hell gaping behind, a stealthy, terrible enemy for
ever . . .'[18] The picture, which was not a popular or marketable
subject, seems to have pressed its claims upon him, as if it required
to be done. When it was painted, Holman returned to Britain.

Annie, in his absence, had been left in Fred Stephens' charge to
learn her letters and her manners, the former from Sarah
Bradshaw, who lived with Hunt's landlady in Prospect Place and
had formerly been a governess,[19] and the latter from a real lady,
Mrs Bramah, aunt of a medical student friend of Fred's nearby in
Cheyne Walk. She was to teach Annie how to speak, stand, sit and
walk correctly, how to dress and do her hair, and how to conduct
herself in public and private – all of which she needed to know in
order to disguise her class origins. The lessons were paid for by
Hunt, and supervised by Stephens, who handled his friend's
affairs and was, as Diana Holman-Hunt justly remarks in her
biography of her grandfather, thereby 'condemned to the thank-
less role of the go-between'.[20] Annie did not receive an allowance
for herself, however, and seems to have continued to live at home
with her aunt and uncle. In order to earn some spending money,
Hunt allowed her to model for other artists. He left Fred a list of
approved painters, 'lest poor Annie should get into trouble';[21]
these mainly comprised Pre-Raphaelites and friends whom he felt
he could trust and to whom he must have confided something of
his intentions, for they regarded themselves obliged to find work
for Annie when she requested it. The chief aim seems to have been
to make sure that she did not go off the rails while Holman was
away; in the letters he received in Egypt and Palestine during the
first few months of 1854 his friends regularly stressed Annie's

'good' behaviour. In May Millais wrote: 'Annie Miller has been sitting to me and I have painted a little head from her. She is a good little girl and behaves herself properly.' Mike Halliday, a pupil of Hunt's, confirmed this, saying that Millais had done 'two or three beautiful little studies of Annie Miller' and that 'he and I have been giving her a lot of work to do lately'.[22] It is thought that the pictures for which Millais used Annie at this date were a small oil entitled *Waiting*, and *The Girl in the Pink Bonnet*, identified as a head study for the oil, though this may be only because the same bonnet appears; as it is clear from the correspondence that she did sit to him, it seems most likely that these were the result. Despite the small size of *Waiting*, the girl seems to me to have Annie's features, but I am less convinced by those of *The Girl in the Pink Bonnet*, where the face is more rounded and softer: Annie seems to have had stronger, squarer features, while here Millais painted a sugarplum.[23]

At the same date, *The Awakening Conscience* was displayed at the Royal Academy, and it is to be hoped that one of Hunt's friends thought to escort Annie to see it, though there is no record of this. Fred wrote to tell Hunt that he and Halliday had taken Annie out boating. She was about to go to work for Augustus Egg, and Fred had checked on the propriety of her modelling. 'I believe she is a good girl,' he wrote reassuringly. 'On my enquiring if any of our people had given her cause for complaint she said, we were a curious lot but none had been uncivil except one person who she had met at a studio, names she would not give.' However, there was some cause for concern, since 'she says she has been sitting to none but such as you named except one person, whereupon I administered a lecture to her and seeing the artist shortly afterwards informed him of the position in which you regarded yourself concerning her danger and put it pretty forcibly to him'.[24] The language of this curious passage reveals the ambiguous nature of Hunt's position: he regarded himself as Annie's guardian but behaved more like a traditional 'protector' or jealous lover. It is hard not to snipe at the way her obedience seems to have been demanded in exchange for a few lessons in elocution and etiquette, and impossible to see this as different in substance to 'buying' a prostitute or 'keeping' a mistress.

The 'one person' not on Holman's permitted list is presumed to have been Gabriel Rossetti, who was later accused of having led

Annie astray. From George Boyce's drawing, however, dated 27 February 1854, it is clear that she also sat to him, although he was not on the approved list. As his portrait strongly suggests the 'good little girl' described by Millais and Halliday there can have been little in it for Holman to object to. There is no firm pictorial or documentary evidence that she sat to Gabriel in 1854–5 while Holman was away. It may be possible to discern her features in the elaborate drawing *Hesterna Rosa*,[25] which was the result of Rossetti's idea at Sevenoaks based on the theme of women of easy virtue. In this, one of the harlots actually covers her brow in a gesture of stricken conscience while listening to music, with a closeness to Hunt's theme in *The Awakening Conscience*. This has not been noted before but may support the identification of Annie as model. In Pre-Raphaelitism, models often became associated with the moral character of the figures for which they sat, since artists and audience assumed a correspondence between nature and appearance. If Annie did pose for Gabriel, however, it must have been while Holman was still in London, for Rossetti completed *Hesterna Rosa* in 1853 before Hunt left for Palestine; it therefore does not provide evidence that Annie and Gabriel disobeyed Hunt's instructions in his absence. The drawing, incidentally, was given to Fred Stephens, which may suggest that he was responsible, as Hunt's agent, for arranging Annie's sittings to other artists.[26]

All the time that Holman was away Fred sent letters reporting on Annie's progress towards gentility with no suggestion that she might be misbehaving. He wrote in March 1855:

> I have a visitor this evening who sits opposite turning over *Pendennis* with a quaint turn of a head this every now and then as I write particularly as I have just said, 'Now Annie Miller I am going to write something about you.' Then she looks up. She seems rather more lively than usual tonight and I am about to make her put in this letter a few words about herself . . . She is I believe a good little goose enough . . . and looks very well having much reformed her hair dressing.

But he failed to persuade her to pen a few words, as 'from some unaccountable funk she says she "can't write" so I must fill up saying she hopes you are quite well and begs to be mostly kindly remembered'.[27] These were the phrases of middle-class politeness, no doubt taught by Miss Bradshaw or Mrs Bramah; they do not convey any sense of passion or flirtatiousness. Despite her 'funk', it appears Annie could write quite well, communicating with Stephens by letter. And she was obeying her instructions carefully. Some time in the summer of 1855, she was asked to pose for the daughters of Sir Julian Slade, whom Madox Brown was reluctantly teaching to draw. 'Gave my first lesson for a guinea and am no longer a gentleman,' he told his diary gloomily on 9 May.[28] As they were not on the approved list, Annie hesitated and twice called on Stephens for his advice only to find him away from home; eventually, 'entirely on her own judgement', she declined, exhibiting a scrupulosity that was surely beyond the spirit of Holman's ban, since posing for female artists could hardly present much moral danger, despite Fred's remark that the Slade household 'kept red-breeched flunkies and had swells hanging about, the smallest of whom might have upset A.M.'.[29] She was apparently thought to have no defences against those who would plot her ruin. She also refused to sit to F.B. Barwell, a painter known to Hunt but not on his list.

Perhaps she regretted her caution when at about the same time she quarrelled with her father, now living at the Royal Hospital, over a 'loan' of £2 that he refused to repay. She wrote urgently to Stephens, who replied by asking her to come and sit, 'paying for the same well', as he reported to Hunt, 'in order to break the loss a trifle' and 'of course counselled submission'.[30] Annie's display of filial respect, to a parent who appropriated her earnings and with whom she was not living, must be explained by contemporary views of daughters' correct, self-sacrificial behaviour, especially among the middle class, to whose values she was now being expected to conform. At a cruder level, until Annie came of age, any money she possessed belonged by law to her father. She did not pursue the argument, and it is interesting that a few years later, old Mr Miller himself became a model, posing in his uniform as a kindly Pensioner talking to a small girl in Francis Moody's picture *In Chelsea Gardens* in 1859; this time he earned his own beer money.

He boasted too, it seems, about the conquests his daughter had made among the artists for when, many years afterwards, Francis Moody's daughter spread Chelsea gossip that was heard by Rossetti, the tale was that both Hunt and Stephens had been infatuated with her; the innuendo was that both had behaved improperly.[31] As we have seen, Fred took Annie on the river but apparently tried to see no more of her than his duties as Hunt's agent required; he was well aware of her charms. She called Fred her Godfather, in affectionate allusion to the fact that he paid for her lessons and looked after her welfare.[32] At some unspecified date she went dancing with George Boyce and to Cremorne pleasure gardens with Gabriel. Both men enjoyed her company and she in turn found them witty, courteous gentlemen. She seems to have been aware that her position was somewhat anomalous: she was neither formally engaged nor free to encourage other admirers. And it was, again, a question of class as well as sex. Her sister Harriet, now a domestic servant in Kensington, was betrothed to a gas fitter, a respectable trade, but not at all compatible with Annie's new education and social milieu. She was being groomed to become a lady. Yet while her 'improvements' precluded marriage to a working man, her background still stood in the way of a higher match. Having created this problem, Hunt and Stephens became anxious and in the last weeks of his deputizing Fred voiced some 'nervous fears' to Holman, and took it on himself to raise the subject of matrimony with the young woman, pointing out to her 'the advantages of this holy institution in a jocular way so that she might think of it seriously . . . It seemed to have some effect.' He added significantly but hesitantly, 'She is, I believe, safe and good at the present time.'[33] This concern with her moral welfare was understandable, for in an attempt to 'save' her, Annie had been taken from her proletarian background and put directly into contact with bohemian life and the demi-monde; it was almost as if she was being urged to 'fall'.

It seems that at this point Fred, at least, did not think that Hunt was going to marry Annie, merely that he was saving her from degradation and the streets. In his letter to Holman he joked that of course all girls thought of nothing else but marriage. His advice that she should think seriously was reinforced by one of the few letters Holman wrote directly to Annie from Palestine, also 'recommending matrimony'.[34] It seems he had not yet identified himself as the prize. But maybe Annie had; her behaviour suggests that, like Mary Barton, she was now determined that 'her looks should make her a lady'.

Meanwhile, no such development was visible in Lizzie's relationship with Gabriel. It is often assumed that around this time, if not before, she had moved into the Chatham Place apartment as his unofficial mistress. This view is supported by William Michael's observation that she became 'such a settled institution in the Chatham Place chambers' that he and others stopped calling there casually, despite his follow-up remark that although the situation went 'beyond the conventional fence-line', there was nothing in it 'suspicious or ambiguous or conjectured by anyone to be so'.[35] This denial of any 'immorality' sounds frankly weak and unconvincing. The evidence, however, suggests that if Lizzie was frequently at Blackfriars during the autumn months of 1854, Gabriel was not. The success of *The Awakening Conscience* at the 1854 Royal Academy summer show provoked him to return to his own version of the Fallen Woman theme, on which he had long claimed copyright.

Originally based on a poem by W. Bell Scott, itself inspired by conversations with a young Edinburgh prostitute, Rossetti's *Found* depicts a bedraggled whore discovered in her finery at dawn in the city street by her former sweetheart, a young farmer, bringing a calf to market. As usual, Gabriel found the composition easier than the painting, particularly as he determined to outdo Hunt in this instance by painting his scene out of doors. In October he was in Chiswick, painting from a suitable brick wall, and by November he had moved in with the Browns at Finchley, sleeping in the parlour, in order to paint a calf, procured for him by Brown from a local farm. This, caught in a net on the back of a cart on its way to slaughter, functions in the unfinished picture both to identify the man's occupation and to symbolize the woman's sinful state, in an oblique but unmistakable reference to the conventional wisdom that saw the Fallen Woman's path as leading irrevocably from seduction through ruin, disgrace and despair to death. Painting the calf gave Gabriel immense trouble but he persevered and indeed only gave up shortly before Christmas when a combination of his casual habits, the Browns' lack of money and Emma's imminent confinement led to him being asked to leave. The house was small, and in the holidays accommodated Brown's elder daughter Lucy as well as himself, Emma and Cathy. There was barely room for the servant girl (who was obtained from the Barnet workhouse, presumably for little more than her keep) and very little for the monthly nurse whose employment was customary to assist with a new baby.

The only direct evidence of Lizzie's activities during this period is contained in Brown's diary. Calling at Chatham Place at the end of October after pawning all his valuables to raise £11 for household expenses, Brown found her there with Gabriel, 'looking thinner and more deathlike and more beautiful and more ragged than ever' but also 'a real artist, a woman without parallel for many a long year', and one who inspired Gabriel to 'wonderful and lovely' drawings – 'one after another each one a fresh charm, each one stamped with immortality'.[36] It is indeed true that the drawings of Lizzie done at this period are more delicate and impressive that the rather stiff little watercolours Gabriel also produced, and for her contribution to these she deserves much credit, but too much should not be read into their expression of intimacy. Lizzie was not living at Chatham Place. She was not there, for example, when Brown visited to welcome Thomas Woolner home from Australia, and was offered 'a whole bed upstairs' or 'at least half' of Gabriel's. After a fortnight struggling with the calf, Gabriel returned on what he called a flying visit 'to see Miss Siddall',[37] in order to finish a woodblock design he had long promised as an illustration for Allingham's poems, and Lizzie posed in triplicate for the three fairy women in *The Maids of Elphenmere*,[38] the picture that was so strongly to impress Edward Burne-Jones. Lizzie seems to have been working at Chatham Place, for on 19 November Gabriel, writing from Finchley, asked his brother to obtain tickets for a lecture on art to be given by Ruskin and 'send them to Lizzie at my place'.[39] She could then invite Barbara and Anna Mary to go with her, and thus repay some of their kindness. Significantly, Gabriel did not escort Lizzie to the lecture himself.

I myself doubt that the relationship between them was sexual at this date. It is easy to assume that it was, owing to the amount of time they spent together unchaperoned and to the fact that the course of their love was extremely uneven, but close examination of the available information, such as the arrangements for Lizzie to stay at Chatham Place only when Gabriel was away, suggests that certain proprieties were kept. The evidence is hard to interpret, but may suggest that the inhibitions were greater on his side than hers. Lizzie had, we may assume, been brought up with a firm

sense of morality and been warned of the dangers of 'loose'
conduct, and is unlikely to have entered a sexual relationship
before marriage, or at least not without a very definite promise for
the future. But she had overstepped other boundaries, and was
evidently not shocked by those who, like Emma Hill, had enjoyed
sex outside marriage. Indeed, it must be acknowledged that in
many social groups, and particularly the British working class,
pregnancy has often been regarded as the natural outcome of
courtship, with marriage only contemplated seriously when a
baby is on the way.[40] In this respect Lizzie may not have held very
different views from her contemporaries; the examples of Emma
and of Lizzie's own sister Lydia point in this direction. Chastity, I
suspect, was more of a problem for Gabriel. He was inhibited
partly by artistic idealism – as with Holman, it is almost
inconceivable that while depicting a Fallen Woman theme he
should have contemplated an act that he would have interpreted as
the seduction of an innocent girl – and also by his strict moral
upbringing. His mother would not have looked favourably on
Lizzie becoming pregnant. Furthermore, should she conceive,
Gabriel would be obliged to marry her and his earning power was
still limited. Like many artists he had a fear of premature financial
responsibility. So, when he was thrown out by Brown at
Christmas, he did not return to his own apartment but to his
mother's home, apparently to avoid inconveniencing or compromising Lizzie at Chatham Place.

Rossetti's poetry was often a transparent guide to his feelings,
the state of which seem to me to be well conveyed in a sonnet
written in August 1854, where the beloved is compared to a
sibling:

> Have you not noted, in some family
> Where two remain from the first marriage bed,
> How still they own their fragrant bond, though fed
> And nurst upon an unknown breast and knee;
> That to their father's children they shall be
> In act and thought of one goodwill; but each
> Shall for the other have, in silence speech,
> And in one word, complete community?
> Even so, when first I saw you, seemed it, love,
> That among souls allied to mine was yet

One nearer kindred than I wotted of.
O born with me somewhere that men forget;
And though in years of sight and sound unmet,
Known for my life's own sister well enough!

The use of sexually charged terms here indicates a combination of
sibling companionship and sexual love. Contemporary convention, however, allowed little place for such a type of affectionate
relationship. As has often been shown and discussed, women were
presented either in romantic terms as rosebuds and angels to be
adored and worshipped, or in the practical terms which encouraged young men to 'use' servants and whores sexually. Cohabita-
tion of the kind suggested by the poem was not socially
acceptable.

   The problems and contradictions caused by this may be seen in
the recurrence of the theme of the Fallen Woman among
Pre-Raphaelite painters, particularly in the early 1850s when they
were facing such conflicts themselves. Just as in the earlier phase of
their work they had expressed youthful interest in the theme of
young love and awakening romance, so *The Woodman's Daughter*,
Hesterna Rosa, *The Awakening Conscience* and *Found* can all be read
as reflecting the painters' interest in unsanctioned sexual relationships. This was a troubling area because the male-dominated
structures of power both prohibited and encouraged such relationships by making women socially and economically dependent
on men. The painters, so far as we know from their letters and
conversations, were aware of the unfairness of this. However,
they were also, as men, personally in a position to 'ruin' or destroy
women – Annie and Lizzie, for example, were 'at risk', both by
virtue of their sex and class. This anxiety, I suggest, expressed
itself obliquely in the art, and not only in the work of the
immediate Pre-Raphaelite circle. Another painter who tackled this
theme was W.L. Windus, with *Burd Helen* and *Too Late*,[41] both of
which deal with sexual betrayal, the one archaically, the other as 'a
subject of modern life'.

   In this context, it is worth noting that more often than not, the
Fallen Woman was not a professional prostitute but an 'unfortunate', a victim led astray by a wicked man's lust. However, this did
not disguise the fact that the message carried by this recurrent
theme was that of the dominant ideology, functioning to blame

and punish deviant women by presenting seduction (disobedience to social and parental instructions) as leading inevitably to prostitution, destitution and death, usually by drowning. This propaganda was reproduced in many other works of the time.[42]

Some examples were by women artists. Early in 1854 Anna Mary Howitt, for example, submitted a picture of Faust's *Margaret* to the British Institution and when it was rejected she started work on a similar, allegorical work, *The Castaway*, which was 'rather strong-minded', according to Gabriel, and contained 'a dejected female, mud with lilies in it, a dust heap, and other details; all symbolical of something improper'.[43] This was shown at the Royal Academy in 1855. And in the autumn of 1854 when Gabriel was working on *Found*, Lizzie started and completed a new drawing that was a careful illustration to a passage in Robert Browning's poetic drama *Pippa Passes*, when the heroine meets a group of 'poor girls' talking about their treats and reminiscing about 'he that seduced me when I was a girl'. (Another episode in the drama, incidentally, involves a young artist being tricked into proposing marriage to a beautiful but uneducated peasant, his model.)

Lizzie's own work progressed steadily at this period and contradicts the view of her as a weak and amateurish artist. She composed and drew a picture showing a pair of *Lovers Listening to Egyptian Girls Playing Music* in which the lovers bear more than a passing resemblance to herself and Gabriel and which was promised to William Allingham. By the beginning of 1855 she was working on two watercolours, one based on her original drawing for the poem 'We are Seven' and the other on Keats' 'La Belle Dame Sans Merci', a subject of unrequited romantic love much favoured by nineteenth-century painters and one which Gabriel had already attempted. Neither of these works of Lizzie's seems to have survived.[44] At the same time she seems to have joined with Gabriel in producing illustrations for an edition of Tennyson's poems, for which the publisher Edward Moxon had commissioned a number of established and promising artists, among them the three chief Pre-Raphaelite Brothers: Gabriel, Hunt and Millais. It is possible that Lizzie knew of this project when she composed her illustrations to 'The Lady of Shalott' and 'St Agnes' Eve' a year before and Gabriel lobbied hard but in vain for her to be accepted as one of the illustrators. She produced at

least two more Tennyson illustrations, *St Cecilia* (for 'The Palace
of Art') and *Lady Clare*. The latter is interesting because of what it
says about class and marriage, while the former resembles
Gabriel's own design for *St Cecilia*, as published by Moxon.
Lizzie's saint is shown with a portable organ inside a tower room;
in one sketch her head is thrown back in a gesture of holy rapture,
which is very similar to Gabriel's design. In view of his admiration
for Lizzie's powers of composition, it seems possible that when he
failed to persuade the publisher to use her work, he silently
incorporated part of her drawing into his, so that she should at
least have the satisfaction of seeing her work in print. An
alternative and not incompatible explanation could be that at this
period they were working very closely together, and it is not
always possible to separate their work. *Sir Galahad at the Shrine of
the Holy Grail* is an example of a joint project; it was inscribed
'EES inv. EES & DGR del'.[45]

Gabriel was certainly pursuing Lizzie's professional advancement with as much energy as his own. Ruskin, returning to
London for the winter and ignoring the scandal of the annulment,
was anxious to establish himself as Gabriel's patron. He viewed
Millais as a victim rather than a villain for alienating Effie's
affections, but it was clearly impossible to continue on terms of
friendship and Effie's remarriage in July 1855 finally broke all links
between her two husbands. Ruskin, who all his life searched for
disciples, was looking for a new protégé. Gabriel, who could be
equally demanding, was looking for patrons. It was therefore
agreed that Rossetti would produce for Ruskin a series of pictures
on themes taken from Dante and in addition Lizzie was put
forward as equally deserving of patronage. She had been working
hard, and on 8 March 1855 a collection of her work – comprising
to date about a dozen drawings and designs – was displayed to
Ruskin by Gabriel. She herself was not present. Excitedly, Gabriel
reported to Allingham that Ruskin

saw and bought on the spot every scrap of designs hitherto
produced by Miss Siddal. He declared that they were far better
than mine, or than almost anyone's, and seemed quite wild with
delight at getting them. He asked me to name a price for them,
after asking and learning that they were for sale; and I, of
course, considering the immense advantage of their getting into

his hands, named a very low price, £25, which he declared to be too low *even* for a low price, and increased to £30. He is going to have them splendidly mounted and bound together in gold and no doubt this will be a real opening for her, as it is already a great assistance and encouragement.[46]

In his enthusiasm, Gabriel included *The Lovers* in his sale and when Lizzie realized she wrote apologetically to Allingham promising to do him another drawing, based on one of his own poems.[47]

Having made her first professional sale, Lizzie was now launched on a career as an artist. But, inevitably, she was not to be allowed to succeed on her own terms. So systematically has her reputation been diminished, no one now believes her drawings were worth so much of Ruskin's attention or money. There is no doubt that Ruskin liked her work, as he claimed: it possessed a delicate, primitive quality that he admired even if the draughtsmanship was far from perfect. But his main purpose in buying up her drawings was to enlist Gabriel as his champion in the crusade against modern materialism and ugly art. Given the prevailing view of women and art, it was hardly conceivable that she should make an independent reputation on equal terms. To say this is not to attach blame to any individual, for the structures of organized gender discrimination were so strong that there were few of either sex who escaped them.[48] Furthermore, as well as the reduction of her work to a kind of appendage of Gabriel's, another downgrading mechanism was in force by which Lizzie's art became not a matter of professional pride and earning power, but an object of pity and charitable relief. Women who worked called into question all the bourgeois values of status, whereby those who belonged to the gentry were inhibited from earning: only lower-class women worked for money. Lizzie's position as a potential 'lady' was thus undermined by her need for financial support. But she could be safely patronized as a deserving case. The process may be clearly seen in a letter from Ruskin to his friend and fellow patron, Ellen Heaton, whom he advised on works of art. 'By the by,' he wrote some time in 1855, 'there is one of Rossetti's pupils – a poor girl – dying I am afraid – of ineffable genius – to whom some day or other a commission may be encouragement and sympathy be charity – but there is no hurry

as she don't work well enough yet and Rossetti and I will take care
of her till she does, if she lives.'[49]

Gabriel immediately capitalized on Ruskin's response by getting
him to write a letter of confirmation to Lizzie, commissioning
another picture (which he planned to circulate among other
influential people who would thus be induced to buy her work)
and also by securing an invitation to take Lizzie to tea with Ruskin
and his parents at Denmark Hill. This was wise, for the money to
purchase paintings came ultimately from old Mr Ruskin and his
social approval of the new artist was worth acquiring. She was
presented not as a young professional, however, but as a lady, and
judged not on her work but her manners. It was a crucial occasion
and by all accounts Lizzie's gentility and reserve had the right
effect. Old Mr Ruskin declared that she might have been born a
countess[50] while Ruskin himself, meeting Lizzie for the first time,
said she was 'a noble, glorious creature'. His mother, claiming
'much medical knowledge', took Lizzie upstairs to investigate her
health and reported that her illness was 'principally weakness, but
needing the very greatest care'. The guest thus scored high on all
counts. On their departure, Mrs Ruskin promised Lizzie some of
her own special ivory bone-dust, to be made into a jelly and eaten
as a restorative – the mid-Victorian equivalent of ginseng or
vitamin pills. The next day her son called at Chatham Place with
an offer which showed that the strategy had succeeded. He came
to discuss with Gabriel a plan to assist Lizzie. She was not there,
nor expected, nor consulted. As her health was poor and she
lacked the money either to look after herself or to develop her
artistic gifts, Ruskin proposed to help, either by buying each piece
of work she produced or by making her a regular quarterly
allowance, taking in exchange whatever she might manage to
draw or paint. He offered £150 a year, sufficient to support a
single girl in comfort if not luxury.

Gabriel was delighted and rushed off at once to tell Lizzie. This,
incidentally, is proof that she was not living at Chatham Place,
and suggests that she was back at home with her family; indeed,
she clearly had no money of her own, or from Gabriel, to pay for
independent lodgings. However, she was out and he had to return
in the evening to deliver the good news.

Lizzie favoured the first option, preferring to sell her work on
its merits, rather than enter a relationship that emphasized her

dependence. Later, Ruskin compared her pride to that of Walter
Scott's heroine, Flora MacIvor, saying Lizzie would refuse
consent 'to anyone's buying her drawings merely to help her'.[51]
Gabriel strongly favoured her taking the regular allowance. 'I
think myself the second plan the best,' he told Brown, 'considering that there may be goodish intervals when she cannot work and
might run short of money but she, to whom I spoke of it
yesterday evening, does not seem to like so much obligation and
inclines to the first plan. However, she will be sternly coerced if
necessary.' Otherwise, he was overjoyed. 'I love him and her and
everybody,' he wrote, 'and feel happier than I have felt for a long
while.'[52] He must have felt that he had discharged his responsibli-
ties towards his pupil rather well. And Lizzie, reluctantly, was
coerced, and agreed to be 'kept' by the gentleman from Denmark
Hill in return for services of an artistic kind, and for obedience.

For immediately she began receiving her quarterly payments,
Ruskin was writing with instructions that had less to do with
painting than with her proper behaviour as a sickly young lady.
She should leave London, he said, and go to the country for the
sake of her health and her art. He stressed that she should not feel
that taking his money 'involved a sort of pledge on your part' and
stated that she should not be worried or unhappy if she did not
produce as much work as she hoped, insisting that his allowance
was a free gift. But his conditions were firmly spelt out:

> I should like you to go to the country immediately. The
> physician whom you consult will probably give you some
> suggestions, but doctors nearly always have some favourite
> watering-place . . . I shall be most happy to meet the expense
> (which will not be great) of your journey to any point
> recommended by you, but I *strongly* would oppose your
> thinking of *Italy* which would be so fearfully exciting to you
> that I believe you would be thrown into a fever in a week. South
> of France might perhaps be well; but if you were my own sister,
> I should plead hard for a little cottage in some sheltered Welsh
> valley.

It is not clear whether Lizzie had expressed any desire to go to
Italy, a common ambition among artists, or whether Ruskin was
recalling with pain Effie's flirtatious enjoyment of social life in

Venice. He continued, with a happy disregard of the then unknown tubercle bacillus:

> Once established with someone to take care of you in a cottage –
> if possible near a cattle shed – you must try and make yourself as
> simple a milkmaid as you can, and only draw when you can't
> help it . . . What you do you are to send me, whether you think
> it good or bad, nothing or something . . . Work as much as
> possible in colour. I do not care whether they be separate
> drawings or illuminations, but try always to sketch with colour
> rather than with pencil only . . . Be sure to travel
> comfortably.[53]

But she resisted these attempts to organize her life and Ruskin had to write again, both to persuade her to take his money and to urge her to follow his advice. She had evidently protested that she did not want his allowance except in the form of commissions or payments for specific works, and suggested that it was really Gabriel whom Ruskin wished to help. He agreed, and added:

> If you do not choose to be helped for his sake, consider also that
> the plain *hard fact* is that I think you have genius; that I don't
> think there is much genius in the world; and I want to keep
> what there is, in it . . . Utterly irrespective of Rossetti's feelings
> or my own, I should simply do what I do, if I could, as I should
> try to save a beautiful tree from being cut down, or a bit of
> Gothic cathedral whose strength was failing. If you would be so
> good as to consider yourself as a piece of wood or Gothic for a
> few months, I should be grateful to you.[54]

Having no viable alternative, Lizzie accepted £150 a year, which was a relatively large sum of money and compared favourably with what Gabriel was earning, although by the beginning of 1855 his income, mainly from or through Ruskin, had also risen. Now, with independent means and not as his impoverished, lower-class 'pupil', she could safely be presented to Mrs Rossetti, a momentous event that took place on 14 April 1855. After lunch, Lizzie arrived at Chatham Place, where Brown was waiting to escort her to Robersons, the artists' suppliers in Long Acre, for Gabriel had decided that the first things she was to buy with Ruskin's money were brushes and paints of her own, and he was too much in debt to Robersons himself to take her. They went on to the Pantheon to meet Gabriel 'who of course was not to be found', as Brown commented irritably; but he eventually turned up and they then proceeded to the Rossetti home in Albany Street, which Brown told his diary was 'Miss S's first interview' with Gabriel's mother. They had a meal and Brown accepted an invitation to stay the night while Gabriel escorted Lizzie home.[55] It is assumed, from the slightness of their later relationship, that Lizzie did not get on with the formidable Frances Lavinia Rossetti and her pious daughters Maria and Christina, but there is no direct evidence that this visit was less successful than that to the Ruskins, although a possibly significant silence surrounds it. It was, of course, in the nature of a trial, but the visit was by no means a total disaster. Like Mrs Ruskin, Mrs Rossetti took an active interest in Lizzie's health and offered to introduce her to her own doctor, which seems a friendly gesture. Perhaps Lizzie responded in a prickly manner; she may not have liked being on display, particularly when she had just obtained an income that meant no one could look down on her as just a shopkeeper's daughter or milliner's assistant. She did not take up Mamma's offer. A few days later Gabriel wrote to his mother saying it was difficult to fix a date for the consultation. But when it could be arranged, he would ask her to give Lizzie a bed for the night, 'which I'm sure you will do like a good old buncum. We will come that night to take tea again; and I'll let you know in time.'[56] Gabriel's letter on this occasion provides the first reliable evidence as to where Lizzie was living, for in it he wrote, in allusion to the proposed visit to Dr Hare, that Lizzie 'could hardly get down to Albany Street from Burnsbury Park so early as 10 a.m.', hence the request for a bed. There is in fact no such place in London, but the location must be the more familiar 'Barnsbury Park' in Islington where Lizzie's aunt Lucy lived with her husband, grocer William Day. They, it is known, kept a shop in which Lizzie's sister Lydia worked before her marriage,[57] and it must have been here that Lizzie was staying.

Her presentation at the Rossetti home had the effect of making everyone speak of Lizzie in new terms; that is, as Gabriel's 'intended' or prospective wife. On hearing of Lizzie's success in securing Ruskin's patronage, Brown told his diary that 'Rossetti once told me that, when he first saw her, he felt his destiny was defined. Why does he not marry her?'[58] And on 24 April Ruskin himself addressed a very delicate letter to Gabriel, asking 'whether you have any plans or wishes regarding Miss S., which you are prevented from carrying out by want of a certain income, and if so what certain income would enable you to carry them out?' He received an ambiguous reply to which he responded, 'My feeling at the first reading is that it would be best for you to marry, for the sake of giving Miss Siddal complete protection and care, and putting an end to the peculiar sadness and want of you hardly know what, that there is in both of you.'[59]

Not long afterwards, Holman Hunt was urging the advantages of matrimony on Annie Miller. Thus she and Lizzie were both steered towards marriage. For women, in 1855, there was scarcely any other desirable option.

4

There was much concern in the mid-nineteenth century about the condition of middle-class marriage. The 1851 Census revealed a larger than expected proportion of unmarried adults and a relatively late marriage age – 26 for men and 24.5 for women. This tendency was felt to be particularly marked among the gentry, and was associated with the idea of 'prudent marriage' whereby couples did not come together formally until the husband was capable of maintaining a household within the class to which he belonged.[1] This delay, it was thought, was one reason why the population was growing faster among the lower classes than the middle classes and was a great cause of Victorian worry, lest the 'better' sections of society be swamped by the worse. It was also identified as a main cause of the century's other great evil, prostitution, by encouraging young men who were not yet in a position to marry to seek sexual relief elsewhere.

The cause of 'the increasing dislike to marriage which is said to exist among young men in general but especially among the more refined and educated of the middle class'[2] was diagnosed as economic: the high cost of keeping a family according to modern standards of comfort and cleanliness. For a fraction of what his married cousin spent on household expenses, a bachelor could occupy a high place in society and enjoy the good life. This principle held for all grades within the very wide catchment of the term middle-class, which covered all those in non-manual occupations spending between £100 and £1,000 per annum. Correspondence in *The Times* in 1858 on the subject of marriage, sparked off by the formation of yet another anti-prostitution league, showed that a young clerk could keep a wife, child and servant on £230 a year, while a company employee, with housing provided, spent £393 14s 1½d maintaining a wife, three children and three servants; and a man who aspired to membership of a Pall Mall club and a social position to match needed two or three times that amount to keep a family in appropriate style. A single man could live well on £200.

The blame for this state of affairs was placed, by some, on wives and young women who were said to demand, through ambition and vanity, unrealistically high levels of expenditure. This was almost certainly untrue, since most young women were in no position to refuse to marry on the grounds that the income was insufficient, much as they may have desired to spend money on clothes and carriages, but it did touch on a key feature of middle-class marriage. The growth of the bourgeoisie in Britain, as an urban middle class dependent on salaries, dividends and rents but not normally land, resulted from economic expansion and consolidation. Increased wealth created more leisure and led women and richer men into roles where their chief function was consumption and display. This, though undoubtedly restrictive to women in many ways, was not necessarily unpleasant; it was a condition that many could and did envy, aspire to and enjoy.

With the development of the bourgeoisie came its supporting ideology, which reinforced the notion of the 'good' marriage as one which aimed to reach a higher, secure and admired social state. The ideal middle-class marriage was, accordingly, one contracted between a young man with either an inheritance or a prospective career and a younger woman of similar social standing, pleasing appearance and moral virtue. Among 'the middling sort' of earlier periods, the wife became an effective if not legal partner in the family business or household, looking after apprentices, visiting the parish or helping with the social aspects of the business; this was not the case by 1850 when the separation of work and home was well under way and it was indeed one index of middle-class respectability that women were – less and less – expected to work. Their role was to spend, however judiciously, rather than contribute to the making of money. Young men worked hard in their twenties and thirties either going out into the world or living frugally as juniors, assistants, curates and the like before succeeding to the older generation's places. They were sometimes heard to calculate when, if ever, they could afford to marry. It was asserted that no man should marry before the age of twenty-five, while bachelors of over forty were regarded as highly eligible. By marrying a man at this stage in his life, a woman moved at once to a household at a similar level and avoided loss of comforts.

Many men did in fact delay marriage for economic reasons; hence the intolerably long Victorian engagement and the familiar pattern of men marrying girls half their age. However, this was not universally admired, and it was feared that the practice of prudent marriage, if carried too far, would result in fewer marriages and thus more unmarried women. From the middle of the century 'surplus females' were seen as a distinct demographic problem. Prudence was also opposed by the growing idea of romantic love, fuelled by literature and the arts, which also accorded with the spirit of the age, albeit in a contradictory manner. The establishment of the middle class required the virtues of thrift and prudence, in emotional as well as economic matters, but at the same time the century was an age of competition, initiative, innovation and mobility. These latter qualities both contributed to and resulted from industrial development and social change; they may be seen as the economic counterpart to personal romance. Inspired by love, young men strove to succeed rather than wait for their elders to retire or die. They pursued fortunes in commerce or the colonies, supported by loving, loyal women who might either wait patiently for the hero's return or accompany him, forsaking family and friends, to the ends of the earth. It can be argued that prudence and romance were not, however, mutually exclusive: a combination of prudential marriage and romantic love supported the entrepreneurial activity of nineteenth-century capitalist development. This is not a cynical observation: in many ways this form of marriage served the middle class well, providing support, sympathy and security in a world that, despite the general class progress, could at an individual level be anxious and uncertain.

One of the effects of changing marriage patterns was that inheritance and parental consent declined in importance in the matter of the choice of a spouse. Romantic love encouraged social as well as geographical mobility; economic ambition went hand in hand with marital hopes. This was especially true of women, for while men were, at least in theory, able to change their class position through education or hard work and opportunity, for women marriage represented virtually the only means of upward mobility. Another practical effect, however, was the restricted choice allowed to middle-class women, who were expected to marry (even worse than not being married, Alice James remarked in mock despair, was the shame of never having had an offer!) but given little part in the choosing. To protect them from the risk of marrying down for love, they were strictly segregated and chaperoned and, even within their own social circle, were made to wait rather than act. Only men could propose. For marriage was not merely a matter of love but a serious legal responsibility and a proposal was regarded as a contract: if it were rescinded a woman could sue for breach of promise and receive damages for the loss of a prospective provider. Despite its manifest disadvantages for women, in the very inequality of this system lay an equilibrium of male responsibility, which could sometimes be onerous, and ·female dependence, from which nothing could be asked. Married women, as is well known, had no legal identity.

The dual impulse may be illustrated by two quotations from verses addressed to the young middle-class male in the mid-century. The first is from a popular advice manual:

> Shun not th'expenses of a wedded life
> Although they be not small. They rouse the man
> To new exertion and fresh energy
> And oft develop capabilities
> The owner never dreamed of . . .

> . . . with care
> Prudence and forethought, first prepare thy home.
> For 'tis not manly to allure a girl
> From peace and comfort and sufficiency
> To a sad cheerless hearth and stinted board.[3]

The second is from the perhaps even more popular 'Angel in the House',[4] written by the Pre-Raphaelites' friend Coventry Patmore:

> He meets by heavenly chance express,
> The destined maid; some hidden hand

Unveils to him that loveliness
Which others cannot understand.
Her merits in his presence grow,
To match the promise in her eyes,
And round her happy footsteps blow
The authentic airs of Paradise.

He prays for some hard thing to do,
Some work of fame and labour immense,
To stretch the languid bulk and thew
Of love's fresh-born magnipotence.

At any given moment, romance or prudence might be in the ascendant and it was within the constraints of both that individual conduct operated. The Pre-Raphaelite painters exhibited the attitudes and behaviour of their sex and class, heavily influenced by romanticism and idealism, and also acutely aware of prudential considerations, coming as they did from the poorer end of the middle class, without inherited wealth. They were, too, alarmed at the extent of the responsibility marriage entailed, and the financial aspects of acquiring a wife and children. And in addition to all this, they were influenced by arguments, apparently originating in France, that creative artists should not dissipate their talents through marriage and breeding. Ironically, this was a Romantic idea serving to free artists from conventional bourgeois responsibility; in effect it supported the side of prudence.

Not surprisingly, the Pre-Raphaelite painters' attitudes to marriage were fraught and ambivalent. As we have seen, although much concerned with the matter, Holman Hunt effectively removed himself from the scene with his trip to Palestine in 1854–5. But he hoped to return triumphant from this, with something more substantial to offer 'the queen of his heart', as he wrote to John Millais, than a clutch of unsold paintings.[5] In justifying his trip, he remarked, 'I have a notion that painters should go out . . . and bring home precious merchandise.'[6] His implicit if not acknowledged choice of Annie Miller as potential bride may have accorded with his notions of romantic love, freed from all mercenary considerations; at the same time, coming from such a poor background, she would be unlikely to make excessive financial demands on her husband. He would therefore be freed from the fear of being unable to maintain his wife, in the resonant phrase of the time, in the style to which she was accustomed.

John Millais, in the autumn of 1853, had been roused to romantic love by the plight of a maiden (so it sadly proved) in distress and he came to her rescue. A year after her release from Ruskin was secured, Effie and Millais were married, a proceeding that both alarmed and excited him. On the eve of the wedding, Millais wrote to a friend of his fears. 'There are some startling accompaniments, my boy, like the glimpse of the dentist's instruments – my poor brain and soul is fatigued with dwelling on unpleasant probabilities.'[7] Of the ceremony itself Effie wrote in her diary that 'he cried dreadfully, said he did not know how he got through it, felt wretched; it had added ten years to his life and instead of being happy and cheerful he seemed in despair'.[8] Yet within a few months all was well, and Millais was urging all his friends to follow suit. 'I cannot help touting for matrimony, it is such a healthy, manly and right kind of life,' he wrote to Holman, adding, 'I cannot enumerate the advantages now – *Man was not intended to live alone*' and disposing of the argument that wedlock was inimical to art by stating, 'Marriage is the best cure for that wretched *lingering* over one's work, which seldom betters it, and racks the brains and makes miserable . . . I would immensely like to see you all *married* like myself and anchored.'[9] Ironically, in view of his high hopes, it was this aspect of marriage, encouraging him to paint for quick and certain returns, which did so much to diminish the general quality of Millais' work; once married, he steadily ceased to paint in a Pre-Raphaelite manner, preferring to exploit his facility for the sake of high prices and easy money. In addition, at Effie's request, he withdrew from the Pre-Raphaelite social circle, which is one reason why, despite her marriages and role as model, Effie cannot properly be described as a Pre-Raphaelite woman. In any case, her story has been well told elsewhere.[10]

Finally, Gabriel Rossetti had also fallen in love, but felt in no position to marry. By dint of borrowing, from his own family or the even needier Brown, he managed to live on a low income without recourse to employment or the potboiling that artists despised but often depended on. He had only recently left home and was enjoying the full freedoms of a bachelor's existence. In addition, he cherished his professional independence and refused to accept Ruskin's offer of a 'competence' or regular income since this would have meant an obligation to paint as his patron desired, rather than according to his own wishes. It is evident that Gabriel's reluctance to marry, which has often been remarked, was very real. Equally significant, at this date, however, was Lizzie's sense of independence and pride, which seems to have been reinforced by certain contemporary objections from women to marriage as a form of licensed slavery.

This early feminist agitation was in fact undertaken by women whom Lizzie knew and admired as friends and fellow artists, and was at its height during the mid-1850s. During 1854 Barbara Leigh Smith compiled a pamphlet giving 'A Brief Summary in Plain Language of the Most Important Laws Concerning Women'. Under common law a wife was her husband's property: all her belongings and earnings as well as her body and her children were legally owned by him, even if he was neither living with nor supporting his wife. One woman, for example, became an actress when abandoned by her spouse, only to find that the theatre was obliged to hand over her wages to him. Even in happy marriages, the situation was inequitable: Mr Gaskell received all the money earned from her books by his wife, to whom he gave the usual allowance for her personal spending. The injustice of the situation had given rise, among the aristocracy, to legal marriage settlements, in order to protect wealthy women from being left penniless by spendthrift husbands, so that there was in effect one law for the rich and another for the rest of the population. On a small tide of indignation, a committee came together under Barbara's leadership, with the participation of Mrs Howitt (who was a working writer) and Bessie Parkes, among many others. A petition was organized, calling on Parliament to reform the legislation relating to married women's property, pointing out that there were laws against beating wives but not against robbing them, and drawing attention to 'well-known cases of hardship suffered by women of station and also by professional women earning large incomes by pursuit of the arts'.[11] A total of 24,000 signatures was collected, of which Barbara herself gathered 3,000, including those of Jane Carlyle, Elizabeth Gaskell and Elizabeth Browning. In the process she and her colleagues discovered that the legal oppression suffered by women was far worse than they had thought.

It is claimed that as a result of her work, Barbara's revulsion to men and marriage was such that her mental equilibrium was disturbed, and she was ordered to spend the winters abroad, where incidentally she could do no agitating. In fact, she scandalized her family by giving serious thought to a proposal to live in unmarried union with the publisher John Chapman and was as a result packed off to Algeria. Here she later met and married Dr Eugene Bodichon, a Frenchman of equally independent views who did not require submission from his wife and allowed her to live half the year in England, as she wished, pursuing her own activities and social life.[12]

The response of the Leigh Smith family illustrates the widespread hostility even to modest attempts to reform the position of women. The Married Women's Property Bill of 1857, based on the petition, fell at the first reading in Parliament and the law was not amended until 1870, after which followed additional legislation; and something of a male counter-attack emerged, acknowledging some of women's grievances but above all stressing female difference and dependence. As we shall see, Ruskin was a key exponent of the new 'separate and supportive' creed with regard to women, but perhaps of equal significance was the work of Alfred Tennyson, the most famous and revered contemporary poet, who took issue with the feminists in *The Princess*, published in 1854. In this poem the heroine, Princess Ida, reigns over a feminist estate set in a kind of outdoor college, whose members refuse marriage and devote themselves to education, self-government, science and art. The college is infiltrated by men and although Ida beats off the prince-hero to whom she was betrothed in infancy, she eventually succumbs to a mixture of gallantry and suffering, thus enabling the poet to reinforce the status quo and endorse his view of marriage as a holy partnership in which the wife's role is

> to live and learn and be
> All that not harms distinctive womanhood,
> For woman is not undevelopt man,
> But diverse: could we make her as the man,
> Sweet Love were slain: his dearest bond is this,
> Not like to like, but like in difference.
> Yet in the long years liker must they grow;

The man be more of woman, she of man;
He gain in sweetness and in moral height,
Nor lose the wrestling thews that throw the world;
She mental breadth, nor fail in childward care,
Nor lose the childlike in the larger mind;
Till at the last she set herself to man,
Like perfect music unto noble words.

It is very probable that Lizzie was asked to sign Barbara's petition and that she associated herself with its views. She was certainly introduced to George Eliot who, from 1854, lived unmarried under the name of Mrs Lewes and was reviled for doing so; and it was surely with reference to Tennyson's poem that Ruskin bestowed on Lizzie the name of Ida, not because she was deemed as refined and gracious as a princess. The significance of this appears to have gone unremarked. There is, too, a reliable tradition, descending indirectly from Madox Brown, that Lizzie was reluctant to marry. This states, for example, that in relation to the problematic question of her 'engagement' 'at Miss Siddal's request the contract was kept secret, and its first publication to Rossetti's close friends seems to have been contrary to her wishes . . . In 1857 the engagement was openly mentioned, though even then its promulgation was opposed by Miss Siddal.'[13] But later writers have either dismissed the idea altogether or treated it as evidence of Lizzie's perversity rather than of her independence: what woman would not have leapt at the chance of marriage to the wondrous figure of genius, poet and painter combined, known as Dante Gabriel Rossetti? Lizzie of course knew him before the days of his fame and perhaps did not look with such eyes on the prospect of being married to him; she wished first to pursue her career.

It is my guess, therefore, that all these factors combined to keep Lizzie and Gabriel from marriage. For the time being, Ruskin's allowance made it unnecessary. However, Lizzie began to feel what it was like to be dependent on a man who, by virtue of his role as provider, expected obedience. Ruskin's letters were full of advice and invitations, urging her 'as the weather comes finer, to come out here sometimes and take a walk in the garden and feel the quiet fresh air, and look at a missal or two' and telling her how she should draw. He wanted her to stop designing 'fancies' or

imaginary scenes and instead said, as he did to all his protégés, that
she should 'be made to draw in a dull way sometimes from dull
things'.[14] At this, Gabriel admonished him, saying that in future
all criticism of Lizzie's work should be transmitted through him,
her teacher, and thenceforth Ruskin offered no more comments.
He did, however, tell her to give up dabbling in spiritualism,
saying, 'you are a very good girl to say you will break off those
disagreeable ghostly connections of yours'.[15] Spiritualism was as
fashionable in the 1850s as astrology in the 1960s. It intrigued
many otherwise sane people, particularly women to whom, in
certain respects, it offered a plausible alternative to the oppressive
masculine rationality and male power structures of the age. The
most impressive medium of all time, D.D. Home, arrived in
London in the spring of 1855, when seances and table tapping
became all the rage.[16] The point here is not that Lizzie was silly
enough to take up spiritualism – many other creative women such
as Elizabeth Barrett Browning did so too – but that Ruskin
assumed the right to tell her to drop it.

And, now prevented from pronouncing on her painting, he
redoubled his efforts to get her away from London. He suggested
first Jersey and then Devon and when both met with no response,
he insisted that Lizzie at least travel to Oxford to be medically
examined by his old friend and eminent physician, Dr Henry
Acland, then Radcliffe Professor of Medicine. Again, Lizzie
resisted his plans although, since they were ostensibly for the
benefit of her health, it was difficult to do so except on the
grounds that she did not want to be beholden, nor to perform
social duties. 'You shall be *quite* independent,' replied Ruskin,
persuasively. 'You shall see no one. You shall have your little
room all to yourself. Only once put your tongue out and let him
feel your pulse.' He assured Lizzie that she would not be expected
to see more of Mrs Acland and the children than normal civility
required and was insistent to the point of bullying, going on to
make the arrangements so that she would seem discourteous to
break them. 'Could you get one of your sisters to go down with
you on Monday?' he asked,[17] and Lizzie gave in.

To Acland Ruskin briefly outlined her situation, as told him by
Gabriel. 'She is the daughter of a watchmaker. Rossetti first got
her to sit for his higher female faces and thus found out her talent
for drawing, taught her and got attached to her, and now she is

dying unless the rest and change of scene can save her. She is five and twenty.'[18] This was one of the more accurate accounts of her age; it would be interesting to know whether his other comments, on her family's disapproval of art obliging her to work in an unheated bedroom, were also based on fact or on a sense of drama and embellishment, which seems to have been the origin of his stark statement 'now she is dying', which she was not. It is possible that Ruskin unconsciously wished her to do so, since he concluded his letter to Acland by saying that Lizzie's death might either devastate Rossetti entirely or free him to concentrate on his far more important art.

Under protest, Lizzie went to Oxford, and found Acland himself a friendly soul. In what must have been a gesture of thanks, she gave him her drawing, *We are Seven*, and also sent him a photo or postcard after her visit, which he still kept a decade later.[19] But she did not enjoy the rest of the visit, complaining that 'everyone bothered her greatly . . . and made arrangements on her behalf'. Social engagements were fixed for her and the Warden of New College, as well as showing her medieval manuscripts in the Bodleian, invited her 'to a special treat at his own house' which turned out to be comparing a black beetle as drawn by Dürer with 'a real one fetched up from the kitchen' and examined under a microscope. This, the sort of thing Ruskin himself liked, was something Lizzie 'never went to enjoy', as Gabriel reported to his mother.[20] She was introduced to many members of University society including a Miss Pusey, sister or daughter of the great Tractarian, but she was not impressed and in some unrecorded manner offended Mrs Acland, to whom Ruskin felt obliged to write and apologize, describing her as 'that wilful Ida'. He excused her behaviour on the grounds that she was 'not ungrateful but sick' and therefore 'sickly headstrong',[21] but all the evidence suggests that she was both rude and ungrateful. It is clear, however, from other sources that Oxford was a particularly narrow, snobbish and unappealing place in the 1850s. Holman Hunt recalled its scornful philistinism and mawkish religiosity,[22] while Josephine Butler, who lived there from 1852–7, found it intellectually limited, uncompassionate and highly class-conscious.[23] Acland himself, campaigning in the late 1850s for sanitary reform to reduce the incidence of cholera in poor quarters, met much indifference and even hostility. It was a small

town, but one where Mrs Acland's house-guest was only likely to
have met young Janey Burden, then a fourteen-year-old stableman's daughter living hard by New College, in the shape of a
scullery girl or housemaid.

When Lizzie returned to London, with Gabriel to escort her,
since it was still deemed improper for ladies to travel alone,
Ruskin continued to reprimand her, sending her a pile of
'uninteresting' books and telling Mrs Acland she deserved to be
soundly whipped and sent supperless to bed like the naughty
children in the nursery rhyme.[24] To Lizzie, he lamented her
intractability, sighing, 'there is no knowing how to manage
you'.[25] The only excuse for her behaviour was ill-health, and so
although it is clear that Acland had found no organic disease,
Gabriel wrote that his diagnosis showed that her condition was
very serious and required great care. There were no actual
symptoms and 'her lungs, if at all affected, are only slightly so'
and there was 'no really unarrestable or even infixed disease *as yet*'.
Nevertheless, she was undoubtedly ill. 'The leading cause of her
illness' was identified as 'mental power long pent up and
overtaxed',[26] which reads like a classic male indictment of female
activity as abnormality, and the advised treatment for her
non-existent condition was rest. She should leave London and
stop drawing. Acland's medical prescription, according to Gabriel, was that Lizzie should 'abstain from all work for some
months'. This put her in a difficult position, for only by accepting
the role of invalid could she be sure of retaining male support and
sympathy; if she disputed it, she might be obliged to fend for
herself. At the same time, if she gave up her art, there would be no
reason for them to look after her; she would cease to be of interest.
But inevitably, since everyone insisted on her frailty, Lizzie too
believed it and accepted disease and debility as part of her own
self-definition. Illness was, after all, a condition of her quarterly
allowance.

The allowance made possible her summer holiday which,
rejecting Jersey and Devon, she took in June 1855 at the seaside
resort of Clevedon in Somerset, probably alone, although it is
possible that her sister Lydia went too. Gabriel, who liked Lizzie
not least for her wit and sense of the ridiculous, reported on some
of her amusements there, including the donkey rides on the beach,
where a talkative twelve-year-old was in charge. This deserves to

be quoted in full, since so few of Lizzie's own accounts of her experiences survive; it gives a vivid and unexpectedly lively picture of her at Clevedon.

The donkey-boy opened a conversation by asking if there was any lions in the parts she comed from. Hearing *no*, he seemed disappointed, and asked her if she had ever ridden on an elephant there. He had last year when the beastesses was here, and on mounting the elephant for a penny, he felt so joyful that he was obliged to give the man his other two-pence, so he couldn't see the rest of the fair. He wished to know whether boys had to work for a living there, and said that a gentleman had told him that in his country the boys were so wicked that they had to be shut up in large prisons. He never knew hisself no boy what stole anything, but he supposed in that country there was nothing but fruit-trees. He pulled a little blue flower growing out of a rock, and said he liked to let flowers grow in the fields, but he liked to 'catch' one when it grew *there* and take it away, because it looked such a poor little thing. He had a project for leading donkeys without beating, which consisted of holding a handful of grass within an inch of their noses, and inducing them to follow it. Being asked whether that would not be the crueller plan of the two, he said he had noticed that donkeys would always eat even when they were full, so he had only to fill his donkey first. All that could be got in an explanation of why he thought Lizzie some outlandish native was that he was sure she comed from very far, much farther than he could see.[27]

She explored Clevedon and its surroundings and when Gabriel came to escort her home towards the end of the month they took 'several longish excursions' together and visited the grave of Arthur Hallam, Tennyson's beloved friend lamented in *In Memoriam*. On their return to London, they took with them some golden water flags to plant in pots on the Chatham House balcony. There was a good deal less in Gabriel's letters about her lack of health but it was understood that she would spend the winter abroad, on Ruskin's advice.

For his part Ruskin was active on Gabriel's behalf, trying to interest Charles Kingsley in his work, and putting forward his name in connection with the decoration of the new University Museum at Oxford. Gabriel tried to promote Lizzie equally but Ruskin said Kingsley would think her drawings 'morbid'[28] and although a sketch of hers was sent, no commission to design for the new Museum resulted.[29]

One of the first people Lizzie saw on her return to London in August 1855 was Emma Brown, who was living at Finchley in straitened and not altogether cheerful circumstances. Her son Oliver, known as Nolly, had been born on 20 January, and the costs of a doctor and a monthly nurse meant frequent recourse to the pawnshop; at the end of the year ten shillings were raised from Brown's dress clothes and Emma's silk wrap and brooch.[30] Money worries were temporarily alleviated on 22 February, when Brown borrowed £50 from Tom Seddon's father; after paying the household bills, he took Emma to the mercer's to buy new baby clothes, which cost £7 15s. 'I am an ass,' he told his diary ruefully.[31] Early in March Emma was allowed to buy a new dress and bonnet for herself; with the departure of the monthly nurse she resumed her household duties with the assistance of a servant girl and, as well as looking after the baby, Katty and Lucy, she frequently sat for the 'emigrant picture' (*The Last of England*) as painting proceeded. On 24 March she took Oliver to visit her mother and there was the first of many recorded marital disputes. Brown gave Emma £1 and told her to return by bus the same day; to his annoyance she stayed the night and came back in a cab, 'breaking all promises as usual and spending more money'.[32]

It is unfair, but unavoidable, to use Brown's diary as evidence of Emma's domestic behaviour; I do so because it is the only available source and bearing in mind that, whatever defects others observed in her character, her husband was always kind and affectionate. His own deep anxieties about money and success made him difficult and irascible, and it is as likely that their quarrels were due as much to his moods and ill-temper as to her 'extravagance' and her tendency to neglect the household. And the frictions of their relationship were surely commonplace. For example, on the day after he took Lizzie to buy paints, he stayed overnight at the Rossettis' and returned home at 2 p.m. to find, in his words, Emma 'pretending to be sulky'.[33] Four days later she had recovered and the whole family, including the servant girl, had an outing to a tea garden in Mill Hill, at a cost of 3s 6d.[34]

A more serious quarrel took place at the beginning of July. Brown was depressed and angry. 'Emma began the day quarrelling,' he recorded, 'so I determined to give her a dose of it otherwise she becomes unbearable.' He stopped speaking to her. In return she took Lucy into her bed and locked the door against him. The following morning she 'started off to London without letting me know before I was up, borrowing two shillings of Lucy and more of the servant'. She came back late and went to bed without saying hello and the next day took Nolly and Katty out. Brown was in despair and wrote a letter of reconciliation, or ultimatum, 'the answer to which our fate seems now to hinge on . . . what would become of my children if I were to finish my wretched existence and what is to become of me if I do not. O God! have mercy on me.' He woke on the sofa at 4 a.m. and went upstairs to see Emma asleep with the baby. 'Saw him trying to get the breast in his sleep. Poked it into his mouth and slipped out of the room again.' In the morning – four days after the initial quarrel – Lucy brought an answer 'to last night's note. Emma gives in so we are all happy again.' To celebrate, he took her to the draper's.[35] These episodes strongly suggest that Emma had much to tolerate from Brown's black moods. Later in life, she was renowned for her placidity. 'When my grandfather flew into a rage,' her granddaughter Juliet recalled, Emma 'used to smile and say "Ford, Ford", and he was quiet at once and began smiling.'[36]

Early in August Brown visited Stafford House, the grand London residence of the Duke of Sutherland which was periodically opened to the public to display its works of art and rich decoration. This roused Brown's democratic sympathies, and he railed against 'such heaping up of bad taste, such gilding of hideousness'. He also, incidentally, saw 'Miss Siddall, beautifully dressed for about £3, altogether looking like a queen'. He had been told that the Duchess and her daughters dressed so vulgarly that they looked like whores.

On 13 August Lizzie and Gabriel went to stay with the Browns for the weekend. And here we run into another Pre-Raphaelite myth, which blames Emma for inciting Lizzie to discontent with Gabriel. The evidence, such as it is, suggests that the incitement, if any, was mutual. Lizzie slept in Brown's room and Gabriel was

put up at the Queens Head, a nearby inn. They persuaded the
Browns to go with them on a carriage ride to Totteridge where,
'with Gabriel's assistance', Brown spent more money than he
could afford. The next morning, before Gabriel got up, the two
women went off into town together, at which he complained
loudly, accusing Emma of 'always trying to persuade Miss Sid
that he was plaguing her etc.'. Brown laughed at his fury, before
telling him where to find them, since Betsy the servant girl was
due to take baby Oliver to meet Emma in Kentish Town, perhaps
at her mother's or sister's house. When Gabriel left, Brown settled
down to his painting, only to be disturbed at 4.30 in the afternoon
by a note asking him to meet the others at the theatre. He followed
them to Chatham Place and to Astleys, a place of light
entertainment and circuses, and waited in a coffee shop until the
end of the performance, when he retraced his steps to Blackfriars;
here he 'found Gabriel gone and Miss Siddall in bed'. Emma had
departed to stay with her mother, so Brown found himself an
uncomfortable overnight lodging and went home in the
morning.[37]

Emma seems to have enjoyed these outings and it is probable
that she went into town to spend the day with Lizzie more than
once. On one occasion Brown was again summoned to join them
at the theatre. Only two tickets could be obtained, which were
allocated to the Browns, who then suffered 'discomfort and heat
fierce and intolerable acting (English operatics)' before returning
to Chatham Place for the night. The following day Brown was
running a fever and so he, Emma and Oliver were obliged to stay
'in the midst of all manners and squalls and discomfort, Emma
having to nurse Nolly who did not seem to relish the change'.
Ruskin called and Gabriel ignored his temporary lodgers, while
the baby gave 'an occasional squall from the next room'.[38] Lizzie
does not appear to have been in the house.

She was preparing to go abroad, at Ruskin's expense. It had
been agreed that she should spend the winter in the South of
France, travelling with a Rossetti relative named Mrs Kincaid,
whose presence made it possible for Gabriel to consider joining
the party. Lizzie wanted to go only to Paris and fought hard to be
allowed to stay there. Ruskin eventually agreed on condition she
proceed swiftly to the South. There were two views of Paris: as
the home of the best and most up-to-date fashions, and as the

origin of overblown art in the decadent Academic manner and a place of vice. By the time of Lizzie's departure from London, there was a minor panic about money, as she had already spent most of the current quarter's allowance, having 'lent' £20 to Gabriel, which he could not repay. However, it and more were borrowed from the faithful Browns and Lizzie left England on 23 September with £40 in her pocket. The week before she left, Gabriel visited the Siddall home for the first time, and spent the evening with Lizzie and her sister 'at her native crib, which I was glad to find comfortable'.[39] This was followed by a farewell party at Chatham Place attended by Mr and Mrs Kincaid, Mamma and William Michael Rossetti, Gabriel and Lizzie. Mrs Kincaid stayed the night and they left the next day by boat from the London docks at 7 a.m. for Le Havre.

After they had been in Paris for nearly six weeks, seeing the sights and studying the fashions, Gabriel came for a ten-day visit, accompanied by his Pre-Raphaelite friend the sculptor Alex Munro, ostensibly to see the International Exhibition. On display at the Exhibition was Millais' *Ophelia*, with Lizzie floating in the water. Ruskin was annoyed at Gabriel's visit to Paris: he had promised Gabriel payment for colour sketching in Wales and when he found it had been spent on going to Paris where Lizzie still lingered, he wrote, 'Tell Ida she must go south directly. Paris will kill her or ruin her.'[40] However, he sent the next quarter's allowance. 'We enjoyed Paris immensely,' commented Munro, 'in different ways of course, for Rossetti was every day with his sweetheart, of whom he was more foolishly fond than ever I saw lover.'[41] To raise money, Gabriel had hastily completed a picture of *Paolo and Francesca*,[42] the illicit lovers from Dante's *Inferno* whose embrace may have reflected his own feelings. Eventually Lizzie and Mrs Kincaid set off for Nice. 'She is sanguine of being able to paint there,' wrote Ruskin.[43]

There is virtually no information about how Lizzie spent her time on the Riviera, apart from one fragmented letter to Gabriel that again reveals a lively sense of observation and comment. In it she described the local bureaucracy:

On your leaving your boat, your passport is taken from you to the Police Station, and there taken charge of till you leave Nice. If a letter is sent to you containing money, the letter is detained at the Post Office, and another written to you by the postmaster ordering you to present yourself and passport for his inspection. You have then to go to the Police Station and beg the loan of your passport for half-an-hour, and are again looked upon as a felon of the first order before passport is returned to you. Looking very much like a transport, you make your way to the Post Office, and there present yourself before a grating, which makes the man behind it look like an overdone mutton chop sticking to a gridiron. On asking for a letter containing money, Mutton-chop sees at once that you are a murderer, and makes up its mind not to let you off alive; and, treating you as Cain and Alice Gray in one, demands your passport. After glaring at this and your face (which has by this time become scarlet, and is taken at once as a token of guilt) a book is pushed through the bars of gridiron, and you are expected to sign your death-warrant by writing something which does not answer to the writing on the passport. Meanwhile Mutton-chop has been looking as much like doom as overdone mutton can look, and fizzing in French, not one word of which is understood by Alice Gray. But now comes the reward of merit. Mutton sees at once that no two people living and at large could write so badly as the writing on the passport and that in the book, so takes me for Alice, but gives me the money, and wonders whether I shall be let off from hard labour the next time I am taken, on account of my thinness. When you enter the Police Station to return the passport, you are glared at through *wooden* bars with marked surprise at not returning in company of two cocked-hats, and your fainting look is put down to your having been found out in something.[44]

(Alice Gray was a famous felon, 'a good-looking woman of swindling proclivities' who frequently featured in British news-paper reports.)

Lizzie's letter reminds us that this was her first trip abroad, and despite her complaints she may have enjoyed the experience. But she does not seem to have spoken French and she did not get on with Mrs Kincaid. The weather was good and she sent cheerful reports but six months must have been a long time away. Gabriel missed her and on 15 February 1856 wrote a tender, comic verse:

Yesterday was St Valentine.
Thought you at all, dear dove divine,
Upon the beard in sorry trim
And rueful countenance of him
That Orson who's your Valentine?

He daubed, you know, as usual.
The stick would slip, the brush would fall:
Yet daubed he till the lamplighter
Set those two seedy flames astir;
But growled all day at slow St Paul.

The bore was heard ere noon; the dun
Was at the door by half past one:
At least 'tis thought so, but the clock –
No Lizzie there to help its stroke –
Struck work before the day begun.

There were three more disconsolate verses before the last:

Come back, dear Liz and, looking wise
In that armchair which suits your size,
Through some fresh drawing scrape a hole.
Your Valentine and Orson's soul
Is sad for those two friendly eyes.[45]

Receiving such a missive, Lizzie must have felt secure in his affections, and certain of the love between them. Perhaps she was deceived, however, for despite his words Gabriel was a good deal less lonely than he made out.

5

When he returned to Britain at the beginning of 1856, Holman Hunt found several of his friends newly married: John Millais, Tom Seddon, Arthur Hughes. Charley Collins was about to marry and even the staid William Michael Rossetti was engaged.[1] The same was rumoured of Gabriel and Lizzie, according to Fred Stephens,[2] although in Brown's view Gabriel was far from committed and indeed he 'still prudently holds aloof from any measure of the kind likely to break in upon his artistic and poetic reveries'. Otherwise, it seemed that in coming home Hunt was 'only hastening to a sort of maelstrom of matrimony' into which he would himself sooner or later plunge.[3]

We may note Brown's use of the term 'prudently' here. Hunt had business and family matters to attend to, chiefly the completion and sale of his Holy Land pictures, which left little time or inclination for courtship. He enjoyed being back in town and playing the role of the Intrepid Traveller and arranged to share a bachelor establishment in Pimlico with fellow artists Mike Halliday and Robert Martineau rather than rent a large house with room for a nursery, as Millais advocated, hoping for the proximity of his old friend in 'a pleasant society, if our wives wouldn't quarrel'.[4] It was a commonplace among men that marriage imposed restrictions on their social life, which became increasingly formal, and Millais was already aware of some of the penalties of matrimony. His friends were no longer welcome to drop in on him casually but had to go through the rituals of visiting cards and written invitations. The friend who felt this most keenly was Wilkie Collins, brother to Charley, who in December 1856 published a story in *Household Words* entitled

'Bold Words by a Bachelor' describing how marriage froze a man's relations with his erstwhile friends.[5]

Owing to her annulment, Effie's position in society was difficult. There was gossip about the exact state of her virginity and the reason why Ruskin had not exercised his conjugal rights. In view of her later aspiration to be presented at Court, it is easy to ascribe to Effie the snobbish values that persuaded Millais to cut his links with Pre-Raphaelitism and to drop his former friends. To do her justice, however, it should be said that Wilkie Collins, who, as his story showed, suffered most from the cold shoulder, from February 1856 had lived unmarried with Caroline Graves, a woman from a lower class whom he declined to marry, partly because the *mésalliance* would upset his mother and partly because Caroline's position in society would be extremely awkward if not impossible. The arrangement also enabled Wilkie to enjoy the benefits of married and bachelor life, for he was still welcome in society – except at the Millais' house. The chief objector was his old friend: 'I see *nothing* to prevent him from getting rid of this disreputable kind of secret connection,' wrote Millais to Hunt in disgust. 'Why should this stupid fellow go and tie himself to such a woman?' He should find himself a proper wife without delay.[6]

This response to a situation similar to that depicted in *The Awakening Conscience* is illustrative of a strong strand of the early Pre-Raphaelites' moral attitudes, which were closer to the standard middle-class code than to that generally attributed to bohemia. The conviction that there was no justification for sex outside marriage informed Thomas Woolner's unpleasant attack on G.H. Lewes and Thornton Hunt as 'hideous satyrs' and 'stinkpots of humanity'[7] and later in the year of his return Holman Hunt discoursed to Brown on the subject of artists' immorality, gossiping about the Academicians and how Mulready at the age of seventy had got a model with child and how 'old Pickersgill in his own house is found on the rug en flagrant délit by the maid who fell over him with the coal scuttle'.[8] In this context it is clear that 'Holy Hunt', as he was later nicknamed, would not have contemplated an irregular relationship with Annie or any other girl. Marriage was the only option. Yet he did not propose.

Indeed, for some time after his return, he seems to have paid Annie very little attention and I suspect that he did not really know what to do now the initial fantasy of raising her from degradation had been realized. He had embarked on the venture without thinking it through, for unless he was to marry her himself he had to find her a suitable husband, which would not be easy. It was a grave dilemma and for a time he did nothing. It seems, in fact, as if it was Annie who took steps to resolve the situation, although the exact course of events is not clear. The relevant chapters of Holman's autobiography, which does not otherwise allude to Annie, are prefaced with epigraphs that appear to contain a coded account of their relationship. That for 1856 reads, 'It is said that jealousy is love . . . but I deny it . . . for though jealousy be procured by love . . . yet jealousy extinguishes love.'[9] The truth was perhaps not so simple, but it began with jealousy. In the spring of 1856, when Lizzie was still in Nice, Annie went to model for Gabriel, sitting for one of the attendants in his picture of *Dante's Dream at the Time of Beatrice's Death*.[10] The likeness is very similar to that in George Boyce's drawing of two years earlier. By the summer, Holman was made aware that she was being escorted by other men, apparently as a result of this sitting. Gabriel took her to Bertolini's dining and dancing rooms, and Gabriel and Boyce took her to Cremorne Gardens, where she actually danced in public with Boyce, and even William Michael took her out on the river. There was nothing immoral in any of this, except that in Hunt's rather puritan view lower-class dissipations were represented by drinking and dancing. However, there was also a rumour, which only reached Hunt later, that some time in 1856 Annie was seen in the company of a 'swell Regent Street whore'.[11] This was a serious allegation, the accuracy of which is hard to attest. In Holman's eyes any woman of loose behaviour could have been termed a whore and the individual in question may have been a fashionable woman on the fringe of the demi-monde or in the theatre. In any case, her company was not evidence of similar immorality on Annie's part. But it could nevertheless ruin her reputation and her conduct at this period, particularly her evident delight in being taken out by a variety of escorts, strongly suggests that she was either very naïve or deliberately provocative. Certainly her flirtations with the Rossetti brothers read like a simple expedient to stimulate more attention from her 'guardian'.

Hunt later asserted that the 'fault' lay with Gabriel, who had made advances to Annie, and William Michael confirmed that his brother was to some degree culpable. But while personal as well as professional rivalry was strong between the two painters, this version of events fails to consider Annie's role in the affair; we are so used to thinking of Pre-Raphaelite women as passive objects of male attention that their own capacity for action is ignored. It should be remembered that Annie had her own career to think of, and that her behaviour in the summer of 1856 can be interpreted in this light.

The fact that Pre-Raphaelite men were attracted to women of a lower social class has often been remarked and this was indeed the situation of five out of the six women whose lives are chronicled in this book. However, I would suggest that the women's upward mobility may be explained less in terms of the men's choice than the women's initiative. We have already seen how Lizzie took the opportunities to move into the painters' circle and how Emma and Annie accepted lessons to remedy deficiencies in their education. In addition, Annie's success with men was to be her chief means of self-improvement. As is evident, these women were not passive. They had talent, personality and ambition and were capable of exerting control over their own destiny.

They were also women of their age, when the way to control their lives was through marriage. Women could better their social status only by marrying 'up' and this was therefore the aim of many ambitious working-class girls. The main avenue of achievement lay through appearance and a pretty girl was frequently urged to improve her situation (and incidentally that of her family) by marrying a gentleman. Statistics for exogamous class marriage are not available and it cannot have been a common event, but social mobility through marriage did occur and sometimes on a very dramatic scale. The servant class seems to have been partly sustained by Cinderella stories of kitchen maids marrying aristocrats. One or two examples were sufficient for the daydream to flourish; one such was recorded by Munby, when in 1862 Lord Robert Montague married nursemaid Betsy Wade. London Society, in which Munby moved, was disgusted with Lord Robert's 'degradation', while Betsy's friends and fellow servants, who included Munby's servant-wife Hannah, were both envious of Betsy's good fortune and proud of her 'as a champion of her class'. In the servants' hall where the matter was discussed, it was the view that no servant girl would decline such an offer on the grounds that she already had a sweetheart of her own class.[12] In this context, the apparently widespread tales of gentlemen seducing maidservants perhaps owed as much to the marriage aspirations of the latter as to the lust of the former. It was worth the risk to become a lady.

Annie's ambitions were probably similar to Emma's – to move into a higher social sphere, to wear good clothes and enjoy outings and entertainment. In view of her background, with its poverty, dirt, ragged clothes and crowded rooms, this was understandable and was indeed what Holman had intended when he began her education; it was unfair of him later to accuse her of being 'so bent on getting out of your own sphere' that she forfeited his regard.[13]

This is not to deny that there was a strong emotional attraction between Annie and Holman. She provoked a response with her flirtations, according to an agitated conversation Brown had with Hunt in July 1856, all about 'Annie Miller's love for him and his liking for her, and perplexities and how Gabriel like a mad man increased them by taking Annie to all sorts of places of amusement which he had implied if not stated should not be'. Giving his summary of the affair to date, Brown recalled how Annie had sat for 'that picture of the swell and his mistress' and how Holman, in his own words, had

> promised to be like her guardian and she should never sit to any [but] him or those he should name lest poor Annie should get into trouble and having allowed her to sit to Gabriel while he was away Gabriel has let her sit to others not on the list and taken her to dine at Bertolini's and to Cremorne where she danced with Boyce and William takes her out boating forgetful it seems of Miss R., as Gabriel, sad dog, is of Guggum.

Both Rossetti brothers were supposed to be attached to other women and Brown concluded, wonderingly, 'They all seem mad about Annie Miller, and poor Hunt has had a fever about it.'[14]

Hunt's fever, actually recurrent malaria, was doubtless aggravated by his jealousy, but his vocabulary reveals the complicated nature of the relationship. He spoke of Annie's 'love' for him, but only of his 'liking' for her; of his role as 'guardian' and also of his 'perplexities'. He seems to have been trying to conceal his attraction to her. However, the whole business did make him pay her more attention and it seems that after he had been to the coast to recuperate, Annie was invited to the studio in Pimlico, perhaps to pose. Arriving there one morning, Brown helped Hunt escort her to the steamer for Chelsea; she was, he reported, 'looking most siren-like'.[15] At the same time, she gave up seeing Gabriel and William Michael, and the rift was closed, if not wholly mended.

Not long before this, Lizzie had come back from France. Around the beginning of April she had written to Ruskin expressing dissatisfaction with Nice, to which he replied, 'I *hate* Nice myself . . . but I didn't know what you would or wouldn't like, when you went off to Paris instead of Normandy.' He urged her to go to the Swiss Alps for the summer, where there was 'soft and pure air, clear water, mossy rock and infinite flowers – I suppose you like that?'[16] But even while trying to steer her away from London and Gabriel, to whom he wrote a gloomy misogynist letter suggesting that Lizzie and Mrs Kincaid between them had run up more debts than they would admit, Ruskin acknowledged her desire to return home.

This she did. Her first objective, on reaching Britain early in May, was to resume her painting. She at once retrieved a drawing, *Clerk Saunders*,[17] she had prepared for Allingham's projected ballad book and set out to reproduce it in colour. The story is macabre and concerns a young man who, while lying asleep with his beloved, is murdered by her brothers; it is essentially a tragic tale precipitated by a woman's assertion of independence in choosing a suitor not approved by her family, and ends in her inevitable suicide. The stanzas Lizzie chose to illustrate relate how Saunders' ghost returns to visit May Margaret:

> My mouth is full cold, Margaret,
> It has the smell now of the ground;
> An' if I kiss thy comely mouth,
> Thy life days will not be long.
>
> Up she has ta'in a bright long wand,
> And she has straked her trouth thereon;
> She has given him out at the shot window
> Wi' mony a sad sigh and heavy groan.

In the original drawing, the male figure is wrapped in a sort of shroud and appears through a keyhole-shaped door, while Margaret stands, holding a rod to her lips. In the finished watercolour, in which the whole image appears reversed, Saunders is in medieval dress and Margaret kneels on her bed, with a bible prominent on a prie-dieu in front. Through the alterations the composition lost some gaucherie and gained in sentimental intensity, the lines of tension moved from the figures' arms to their eyes, and the total effect became less strange. Strikingly, the aspect of the faces resembles that in Gabriel's *How They Met Themselves*, also a 'ghost' picture, which was completed some four years later and may be further evidence of his debt to her work.

In the summer of 1856 Lizzie led an independent social life, secure in her allowance. She took rooms in Weymouth Street, an upmarket area in the West End off Portland Place,[18] and one of her first calls was on Emma, who was now expecting her third child. Brown's situation was becoming slightly more prosperous and in the autumn of 1855 the family had moved to a larger house in Fortess Terrace, Kentish Town. Here they were able to afford servants to assist with the housework and the child care, for which Emma, constantly pregnant or nursing, had little energy or inclination. Soon after this baby was conceived, at the beginning of 1856, it was arranged that Lucy, now aged twelve,[19] would board with the Rossetti family and be instructed by Maria, who had been a teacher and governess, for a fee of £40 a year.

Lizzie stayed the night with the Browns and in the morning took Emma off to see her new lodgings. When Gabriel arrived, expecting to find her at Fortess Terrace, he again accused Emma of inciting Lizzie against him, and set off with Brown in pursuit. This was the first recorded quarrel in a series that was to blight the whole summer. On arrival at Weymouth Street, Gabriel was still angry and did not greet Emma, on the grounds that she 'puts Miss Siddall up to being discontented with him'. This, as Brown indignantly pointed out, 'she does not, for poor Miss Sid complains enough of his goings on not to require that sort of thing'.[20] The dispute was of short duration, however, for Gabriel sent the apology Brown demanded and then came with Lizzie to spend an evening with the Browns. The next day Emma was again with Lizzie in town, and she and her husband had supper at Weymouth Street, where they were shown a 'superb Indian opera cloke [*sic*]' which Lizzie was to wear to the theatre, where an acclaimed production of *The Winter's Tale* was running. Brown's comment was simple: 'They had better marry.'[21]

The evidence suggests that it was Lizzie's independence that annoyed Gabriel for when at the end of May she decided to accompany Emma on a short holiday to Ramsgate and was staying the night prior to their departure, he arrived and tried to persuade her not to go. Brown was angry with both, for Lizzie had borrowed £6 for the trip. The journey, by sea, was rough and it was raining when they arrived. Two days later Emma lost all her money and soon they were back in London, where the quarrelsome summer continued. On 10 June Emma and Brown came home and found Lizzie and Gabriel already in the house. 'I was very cool to them,' Brown recorded, 'for I am sick of them coming here and his rudeness to Emma.'[22] For some weeks he did not see Gabriel at all, as he told Hunt when asked to intervene in the matter of Annie Miller.

This would seem to be one of the 'goings on' of which Lizzie complained, and on 15 July Emma, calling to see her before dining with the Rossetti family, found her 'very ill and complaining much of Gabriel', who appeared to have transferred his affections to Annie and was singing her praises to everyone. 'He is mad past care,' commented Brown.[23] Perhaps Gabriel's motive, like Annie's, was to provoke jealousy and a proper sense of respect, but the whole affair soon blew over; at the same time as Brown reported meeting Annie in Pimlico, he noted that Gabriel and Lizzie were 'on the best of terms now', since Gabriel had 'forsworn flirting with Annie Miller', Lizzie having 'rebelled against it'.[24] He reported that she was again busy painting.

This was probably her version of the Ladies' Lament from 'Sir Patrick Spens',[25] another watercolour based on a ballad text, showing a group of women and children looking out to sea from a sandy cove beneath a low grassy cliff. It is signed 'E.E.S. 1856' and is a pleasant, original design of figures in a landscape, considerably less claustrophobic or fanciful than her other compositions and attractive in colour. It relates to the lines from the ballad:

> O lang lang may their ladies sit
> With their fans into their hand,

> Or ere they see Sir Patrick Spens
> Come sailing to the land.

Perhaps its most striking aspect is that it depicts a scene where the action is absent: the female group of women and children looks out of the picture towards the missing men. Through subject and presentation, the women are defined as marginal, waiting figures, reacting to events and lamenting. This image may be seen as a metaphor of the position of women as perceived (and as experienced) by the artist. This is, of course, only part of the meaning contained in the painting, but it strikes me that there is an emotional correspondence between the painting and life. Being women, both Lizzie and Annie were expected to play subordinate roles and men were offended when they stepped into the limelight.

On 16 September 1856 Emma gave birth to her second son. Katty was now nearly six and Nolly two and a half. The baby was named Arthur Gabriel and Lizzie and Gabriel were asked to be his godparents, in recognition of their friendship. Calling on Emma a few days later, Lizzie perhaps reflected that marriage and motherhood were not compatible with painting, but she may equally have envied her friend, for in some ways babies are more satisfying than pictures. It would anyway be a mistake to attribute simple responses to any of the women whose lives are outlined here; like our own, they must have been a mixture of conflicting and complementary desires. Something however seems to have precipitated more definite thoughts of marriage than ever before, for soon after little Arthur was born, Gabriel arrived unexpectedly at Fortess Terrace late one evening, where William Michael was posing for the head of one of Christ's disciples, and while his brother snored on the sofa, he announced to Brown that he 'intended to get married at once to Guggum and then off to Algeria!!'[26] Brown's surprise, or disbelief, was registered in the exclamation marks.

According to Lizzie's later account they did speak seriously of marriage at this date. Gabriel said he was only waiting for the money from a picture he had sold in order to fix a day for the wedding. He was still concerned about her health and the need for her to winter abroad – hence the notion of Algeria, which was that year's fashionable prescription and where Barbara Smith was being sent with her sister and brother. Lizzie did not like the idea, but both Algeria and the wedding day proved chimerical, for when his money arrived, Gabriel called on Lizzie with the news 'and told her all he was going to do with it but never a word about marriage'.[27] Lizzie's response was to pack her bags and take her sister off to Bath, upset and angry with Gabriel, and determined, in Brown's words, 'to have no more to do with him'.

This incident dramatically illustrates how, despite their relative freedom and initiative, the Pre-Raphaelite women were also women of their time, constrained by the structures of social and sexual power that determined women's roles. Up to a point they could shape their own lives, define their own destinies, in a wealthy, expanding economy. But there were limits. They could not, like men, make active choices of when and whom to marry, nor pursue high-profile professional careers. And so we see that ultimately their lives were defined more by gender than by talent.

There was resistance and rebellion to male dispositions, but it could not prevail. Annie's situation in the autumn and winter of 1856–7 was comparable. Her self-appointed guardian resumed his role, instructing her on how to behave and indicating that she should strive to be both grateful and worthy of his efforts on her behalf. It is now almost impossible to reconstruct more than an outline of events in the autumn of 1856, although the general shape of the relationship is reasonably clear. Annie resisted Holman's attempts to turn her into the type of woman he desired. Having once cast her in the role of Fallen Woman, perhaps he could not, psychologically, recast her as a fit wife; but he did not yet know this, and persisted in setting standards of correct ladylike behaviour and obedience, which Annie did not wish to attain. He did not mention matrimony, and she was not inclined to obey his orders merely to please him. In addition, she may have come to feel that life with him lacked gaiety. She declined to see him, which upset him. Her stopping away, he remarked ruefully to Fred, was 'most uncomplimentarily indifferent'.[28]

He was in fact frequently working in South London at the Crystal Palace, on the background of *Christ in the Temple*, his projected *chef d'oeuvre*, and he again employed Fred Stephens as intermediary, sending him instructions on how to handle Annie.

'You cannot of course hold yourself out to her as a prize for exertion on her part,' replied Stephens, uncomfortably aware that he was describing the situation with some accuracy, and commenting, 'In fact I fancy she expected the golden apple was going to drop into her mouth and that you would marry her without further trouble or interest on her part.'[29]

Holman wanted to send Annie to school, apparently to cure her 'wretched false pride' and 'fatal indolence'. Evidently Annie's idea of being a lady was finery and leisure. She did not like his criticisms and sat stonily through one interview with him during which he gave a lengthy assurance of 'unlimited – unended interest in her good' only breaking silence with the fierce exclamation: 'I wish I were dead!' Hunt's gloss on this was that she was wilful: 'she must either have life without the control of one vanity, or would not have it at all'. However, he was the more determined; having set out to save her, he would carry on 'for years . . . rather than be the first to give up the attempt'.[30] She *should* do as *he* wished.

He sent Fred to deliver an ultimatum: would Annie agree to go to a young ladies' academy at his expense? There was no mention of marriage as a possible outcome, so Fred, by his own account, represented Hunt as 'a most anxious and sincere friend who was desirous of benefiting her so that she might obtain a happier position from her own exertions'. Either from pride or disappointment that no proposal was in sight, Annie replied that she did not care what Holman or Fred wished her to do; their concern was none of hers. She added that 'she did not care about painting and never did' and had told Hunt so long ago. Fred, 'knowing the beneficial effect a cup of tea has upon the female mind', induced her to stay a little longer and renewed his attack; eventually Annie agreed to think it over, and give an answer the following week. 'I trust she may come to her senses tomorrow,' commented Fred, adding that in his view Annie's feelings were 'too shallow' for her ever to be worthy of being Mrs Holman Hunt; he had, he remarked, urged on her the 'duty she owed to others and her family' to improve her position but 'this she almost laughed at'.[31]

The following week Annie sent her reply, which has not survived, but was sufficient to send Hunt from Sydenham to the Miller home. Annie was out but he spoke to her aunt 'who seemed a reasonable woman and professed great interest in the hope to educate her niece. She told me that Annie had been fretting very much, but seemed ready to do anything that I should recommend.'[32] By involving her family, Hunt put pressure on Annie from another direction, for his offer to support her constituted a net gain to the household and one they were in no position to decline. So Annie agreed to go to school. She secured one compromise: she was not to be sent away – Hunt had been inquiring about Emma's education at Highgate[33] – but to a day establishment. Hunt agreed to this, and it appears that he also decided to use Annie as a model again. Although she had received no proposal, perhaps she had gained some ground. The following year, her twenty-second, passed relatively smoothly.

In February, Lizzie returned to London after spending three months in Bath, where Gabriel had joined her for a short stay just before Christmas. It would be only partly unfair to say that Gabriel preferred her absence, because although he was un-doubtedly fond of her, he enjoyed his freedom and was increasingly liable to sudden passions for women he saw in the street or at the theatre – such as his admiration for the actress Ruth Herbert whom he first saw on the stage in the winter of 1856 while Lizzie was in Nice.[34] This admiration was as much aesthetic as erotic but clearly marriage or an engagement or even the regular company of his 'intended' would have interfered with its free expression, and it seems that his infatuation with Lizzie had cooled. He told people she had gone to Bath because she was 'terribly ill', and perhaps she had indeed become so, although her chief symptoms were loss of appetite and weight – Brown was told in January that she 'says she has not eaten for a fortnight'[35] – and sound more emotional than physical. She had, of course, a vested interest in being ill, for then Gabriel's care and concern increased, but my suspicion is that this period of emotional distress marked the start of her laudanum addiction. An opium derivative in liquid form, laudanum possessed the property of dulling physical pain, emotional unhappiness and hunger. It was also addictive, so that, once established, any disturbance or interruption of the habit resulted in genuine physical symptoms such as vomiting, sweating and delirium. Used moderately, opiates are not lethal, and the use of laudanum in the nineteenth century was comparable to that of tranquillizers today. It is not surprising to learn that the majority of users were women. The stress Lizzie was experiencing was visible in the quarrels with Gabriel once she was back in London and revolved around the vexed issue of his stubborn but tacit refusal to get married.

A large part of his reluctance stemmed from the fact that he was enjoying a revival of his student days, with the admiring company of two new friends. Edward Burne-Jones and William Morris took the old rooms he had once shared with Walter Deverell in Red Lion Square and were training to be painters under his supervision – which was as much social as professional and involved a lot of London's nightlife. In addition, the young painters were beginning to enjoy rising prestige and to be invited for example to Arthur Lewis's famous 'bohemian' bachelor parties in Campden Hill and to gatherings at Little Holland House, hosted by the lion-hunting Mrs Prinsep. These delights had to be measured against those of marriage, and at this moment the idea of a small society or colony of artists and their wives, first raised by Millais, was revived, mainly by Brown. He was clearly feeling more than usually sociable and was perhaps aware of Emma's isolation from congenial friends, for it may have been at this date that she began to drink; certainly her ability to keep house began to deteriorate. The idea of shared accommodation, however, triggered off one of the worst rows between Lizzie and Gabriel.

Soon after her return to London, Gabriel mentioned the notion to Lizzie, presenting it as a range of studios and saying nothing about the projected 'married quarters'. Gathering, perhaps from Emma, that she did not much favour the idea, Brown walked over to Lizzie's new lodging in Hampstead one evening in February, surprised that she had not been consulted and ready to explain his scheme. He found both Gabriel and Lizzie's mother there with her, and began to outline his plan, speaking of 'two married couples' to start with. It transpired, however, that he did not mean Gabriel and Lizzie as the second pair. Nor did Gabriel say anything to correct him. He claimed later that he had expressly told Brown that he would be married 'by the time it came into operation' and would therefore require appropriate accommodation, but significantly Brown had either not heard or not remembered these words and Lizzie herself had been told only of the plan for adjacent studios. It is hard to resist the inference that Gabriel had given no indication to anyone that he would soon be in need of married accommodation. This made Lizzie 'more than usual incensed' against him, as Brown noted,[36] and the following evening there was a fierce argument. Gabriel said he had not spoken up the previous day because she had 'lately shown so much displeasure at my mentioning our engagement'. This was hardly surprising, since it was so insubstantial; more to the point, perhaps, he had carefully avoided mentioning it before her mother who would have been a material witness to a declaration that he had yet to make in public. He told Brown he hoped her anger was 'attributable to illness', a clear example of the way unacceptable female emotions could be deflected and indeed turned back on themselves by a man: it was not he but she herself who was the cause of her resentful feelings, if they were the result of an illness. To Lizzie he insisted he was willing to marry, and had discussed it with Brown with a view to sharing accommodation; she replied that he had not consulted her and, moreover, had appeared to be ready to make arrangements that would involve her living in close proximity to Hunt, which was intolerable. Gabriel affected not to understand her objection, despite the well-documented tiff over his flirtation with Annie only six months earlier; he added disingenuously, if she disliked the college idea he would have nothing more to do with it: her wishes were his. But Lizzie was not to be placated; she remained 'embittered and estranged' and Gabriel, whose behaviour belied his considerate words, confessed that she made him 'most unhappy' about it all.[37]

The argument continued over the following two days and finally he seems to have worn her down, at least partly by the simple method of regarding all her complaints as symptoms of disease. Brown was told that things were getting better and Gabriel was no longer angry with Lizzie for making such a fuss, as she had been 'kind and patient' with him many times before, 'more than I have deserved'. He trusted that the present trouble between them was over: it had been caused by ill-health. She was still not eating; it was 'but too natural that her mind should be anxious and disturbed'. Thus her very real distress at his behaviour was transformed into a feature of her weakness: rage was defined as mental disturbance, just as Annie's angry independence had been described as wilful ingratitude. Gabriel even appropriated Lizzie's anguish, saying he felt 'most wretched' about her and was in 'constant pain' at her suffering. However, to his relief the crisis passed, and Lizzie, defeated, went to stay with her sister.[38]

Brown, who was drawn into the affair as a friend of both parties, was so perturbed by the quarrel that he began keeping his diary again after a long gap. His account is the nearest thing to an objective, contemporary viewpoint and while it may not be wholly accurate it does show that the winter of 1856–7 was characterized by Gabriel's repeated promises of marriage and repeated failure to carry them out. After being 'settled to marry' when he had mentioned Algeria (in October), he had, as we have seen, put it off for lack of money and failed to raise the subject again. Having followed Lizzie to Bath, he had 'again some little while ago promised marriage immediately, when since he has again postponed all thoughts of it until about a fortnight ago', that is, at the end of February when, after the row over the artists' colony, he once more went to Brown 'and talked seriously about it and settled all he was to do'. The next morning he called again 'and said the only thing that prevented his buying the licence was want of tin, upon which I said if it was this that prevented it I would lend him some'. Gabriel accepted the offer and a few days later called 'and borrowed £10 but spent it all somehow', without arranging any wedding. Indeed, he even came back to cadge another pound. Lizzie, who had been staying at the Browns' and must have felt as close to the altar as she had ever been, was well and truly let down; her distress was alarming and on 14 March Brown wrote, 'she is I fear dying'.[39] Understandably, he thought, 'she now seems to hate Gabriel in toto'. Brown himself was still resentful, calculating that, between them, Gabriel and Lizzie owed him a total of £42 10s; he noted that Gabriel 'had quite lost her affection through his extraordinary proceedings'. One thing, however, was clear: Gabriel was not going to get married.

The fraught situation continued. On 15 March, which was a Sunday, Emma took Lizzie back to Hampstead and Brown was detailed to look after Gabriel who was 'so unhappy' that he would not be left alone. On Wednesday Emma and Brown walked over to see Lizzie, who still continued to abuse Gabriel. All this emotional turmoil was taking a lot of Brown's painting time, but the next day he went to Blackfriars to tell Gabriel what Lizzie had said. This upset Gabriel even more and 'in much affliction' he went home with Brown with the idea of walking over to Hampstead and asking to see her. Emma suggested she go first and let Lizzie know he was coming. But this effort at reconciliation failed for when the men arrived at Lizzie's lodging she refused to let them in. 'At length,' Brown recorded, 'I was admitted, but could obtain no favourable speech from her and so Gabriel and I came away leaving Emma.' In the evening the men went off to a meeting at the Working Men's College at which Ruskin was speaking and on their return to Fortess Terrace found that Emma had brought a note from Lizzie saying she would see Gabriel the next day. He and Emma then went off in a cab, while Brown attended to business in town and returned to Hampstead for dinner – 'after which such a scene of recrimination as never'. But overall Lizzie seemed to be relenting. Eventually Brown took Gabriel home, leaving Emma with Lizzie. Arthur, who was not yet aged six months, was despatched with a servant to spend the night with his mother. The crisis appeared to have passed, and Brown gave up his diary again.[40]

In fact Lizzie had lost the battle and there were few further references to marriage. In April, Arthur's christening was due, but Gabriel failed to attend, preferring to stay in Wales where he was discussing a commission for Llandaff Cathedral.[41] He sent a message to 'Dear Guggum', promising to call on her as soon as he returned, but otherwise his letters contained little mention of her, and the distinct impression is that they were much less frequently together than before. However, Lizzie had other things to occupy her. Brown was busy organizing a small, private Pre-Raphaelite exhibition, to be mounted in Russell Place, where Lizzie's work was to be shown in public for the first time. It was an important event in her career and she undertook to pay her share of the expenses, in company with Millais, Hunt, Rossetti and other much better established artists than herself. She submitted three watercolours: *We are Seven*, *The Haunted Tree* and *Clerk Saunders*, a selection of drawings based on Browning and Tennyson, and a *Study of a Head* which was perhaps her self-portrait.

It was not an immensely successful show but Lizzie's contributions received favourable comments. Holman Hunt, who had not previously seen her work, compared it with that of Walter Deverell, which was meant as a compliment although Gabriel took it as a slight, insisting that it was 'a thousand times better than anything he ever did!'[42] The *Spectator*, probably in the pen of William Michael, remarked that her designs were 'quite unlike anything which the manner of lady artists has accustomed us to',[43] and she was also mentioned by the *Saturday Review*. She also made a sale. Her watercolour, *Clerk Saunders*, was bought by Harvard professor Charles Eliot Norton, whom Ruskin brought to the Russell Place gallery.

It may have been this sale that induced her to give up Ruskin's allowance, which she did in the summer of 1857, when it appears she felt she could not go on accepting his money while attempting to sell her pictures elsewhere. Ruskin did not protest. 'I shall rejoice in Ida's success with her picture, as I shall in every opportunity of being useful either to you or to her,' he told Gabriel. 'The only feeling I have about the matter is of some shame at having allowed the arrangement between us to end as it did.' He would have been happy to continue, with Lizzie 'simply accepting it as she would have accepted a glass of water when she was thirsty and never thinking of it any more',[44] but he had long since ceased to regard her as his protégée and ended by asking Gabriel and Maria Rossetti to Denmark Hill, an invitation that significantly did not include Lizzie. I would like to see Lizzie's decision to give up Ruskin's money as an assertion of pride and independence, showing confidence in her earning ability – her work was also to feature in an exhibition of British art due to be shown in the United States – were it not for the fact that such a gesture implies a moral scrupulosity she did not otherwise display. Months afterwards, Brown was still waiting for her share of the costs of mounting the Russell Place exhibition, and there is no evidence that she ever repaid what she owed him. So while she was no doubt glad to be free of Ruskin's advice and interference, I suspect that relinquishing his allowance had more to do with her private war of attrition with Gabriel, who after all had coerced her into accepting it in the first place, evidently to relieve himself of the responsibility of supporting her.

She worked hard in the months following her return, and some time during this year she completed a watercolour version of her earlier *Lady Clare* composition.[45] It was signed 'EES/57' in a new, elaborate monogram, and the subject, interestingly, was that of marriage across the classes. The poem by Tennyson on which it was based is a Romantic ballad, apparently designed to counter the tragic nature of traditional love ballads like 'Clerk Saunders'. It presents a medieval-style tale of a fair lady and heiress who is about to marry a noble kinsman when her attendant Alice reveals that the Lady Clare is really of humble birth, Alice's own child, substituted in infancy. Against Alice's advice, Clare rides off to tell Lord Ronald and give him the opportunity to break the engagement, on the grounds that she is not what she has claimed. Happily, Lord Ronald responds like a Romantic hero, dismissing her servile origins and reaffirming his promise to marry her. As she says:

> He does not love me for my birth,
> Nor for my lands so broad and fair,
> He loves me for my own true worth.

The ending is therefore happy and through marriage if not birth Clare retains her status and her lands.

Without wishing to read a literal biographical meaning into this choice of subject, it seems to me that there was poignancy in Lizzie's decision to return to this theme in 1857.[46] She depicted Alice on her knees imploring Clare not to reveal her low origins, while Clare covers Alice's face with her own hand, expressing rejection, and turns her head away in a gesture of painful decision, towards a stained-glass representation of the wisdom of Solomon, an archetype of the triumph of true feeling. The resonance of the Lady Clare theme in Lizzie's own situation is clear. The emotional issues are first, marriage between persons of different social classes and second, threat to and doubt in a relationship of long standing. They present a significant correspondence between life and art. Maybe Lizzie was no longer sure that she was loved for her 'own true worth'.

This is perhaps why, in August, she left London for Sheffield. Shortly before, as will be recalled by those who have read the many books and articles on the second phase of Pre-Raphaelitism, Gabriel had arranged to spend the summer in Oxford with his new friends Ned Jones and William Morris, enjoyably but unprofitably painting scenes from Malory's *Morte d'Arthur* on the ceiling of the new Union debating chamber. It is obvious that, as a woman, Lizzie could not have participated, but it may have been galling that several of those whom Gabriel enthusiastically recruited to assist were men of much less artistic experience than herself and in some cases of none. This did not really matter: the whole adventure was one of male camaraderie, humour and high jinks, a mixture of the art-student atmosphere of the original Pre-Raphaelite Brotherhood and the undergraduate world Ned and Topsy (as William Morris was always known) had only recently left. Thoughts of marriage played little part in this atmosphere and rather than remain alone in London, Lizzie decided to go north to visit her Siddall relatives.

The Browns were deserted by their two friends in the midst of trouble, for in July Arthur suddenly sickened and died. Emma, again pregnant, suffered a miscarriage and was confined to bed, ill and unhappy, for several weeks. This was bad enough, but when one reads of Brown having to borrow money in order to bury his baby son, one wonders at the heartlessness that allowed Lizzie, as well as Gabriel and Millais, to fail to reimburse the money owing on the exhibition. In time, however, Emma recovered, and as it later turned out, proved a good friend to the new generation of Pre-Raphaelite sisters.

6

Very little is known, unfortunately, about the time Lizzie spent in Sheffield. She seems to have stayed, together with her sister Lydia, at the home of their relative William Ibbitt, a silversmith, who lived in Durham Street. He had a daughter named Sarah Ann and a son William who was a draughtsman and, it is said, had an interest in art. He was impressed that his cousin from London was not only a painter herself but also a friend of the great critic Ruskin. Lizzie evidently intended to pursue her career, for she enrolled in some classes at the city's School of Art.[1] One day in September, she went, with other students, on a rail excursion to the great 1857 Art Treasures Exhibition, on display in Manchester. At around the same time, the Browns treated themselves and Lucy to a visit, to lift their spirits after their distressing summer. Not long after, Brown went on his own to Oxford, to see the celebrated Union murals, and heard the news of Gabriel's discovery of a new 'stunner'.

The emergence of Jane Burden from the obscurity of ordinary life into the Pre-Raphaelite glare is another legendary tale, not unlike that of Lizzie herself. One evening in the last week of September or the first week of October, Jane and her sister Bessie, aged eighteen and fifteen respectively, went to see a show presented by the touring company of the Theatre Royal Drury Lane, then playing a summer season in a converted gymnasium in Oxford. The plays on offer in the repertoire were *Hamlet*, *School for Scandal*, *Jane Shore* and *Ben Bolt*, the last a popular musical drama staged to revive flagging attendances and of a type likely to appeal to girls of the Burden sisters' age and education.[2] They sat in the gallery, where seats cost 1s, and were seen from the more

expensive seats below by Gabriel and Ned Jones. Gabriel was a
keen, if casual theatregoer who often annoyed Ned by leaving
before the end; on this occasion he spotted the two girls and
accosted them after the performance, asking Jane if she would
come the next day and model for the murals at the Union. 'She
probably did not know what he meant,' was Ned's later
comment, and perhaps Jane thought this a novel sort of
proposition for although she agreed, the following day she did not
appear. Maybe her mother warned her against accepting invitations from unknown gentlemen. However, a few days later Ned
happened to see her again in the town and he renewed the request;
after some negotiation with her family, she duly appeared at 13
George Street, where Gabriel, Ned and Morris were installed in
picturesque old lodgings.[3] This was the start of her Pre-Raphaelite
career.

The background to Jane's encounter with the painters lay in the
special circumstances of the Oxford Union venture, which
marked the second phase of Pre-Raphaelite companionship and
has been so often described that there is no need to repeat it here,
except perhaps to list the participants. As well as his young
disciples Ned Jones and William Morris, Gabriel had enlisted
Arthur Hughes, a well-established member of the Pre-Raphaelite
school; Val Prinsep, student son of the Prinseps of Little Holland
House; J. R. Spencer Stanhope, who was to take a studio at
Chatham Place; and J. Hungerford Pollen, an Oxford scholar who
had already worked on frescoes for Merton College chapel. It
was, as they all recognized, a light-hearted vacation enterprise and
involved a group style of banter, in-jokes, teasing and the
consumption of large quantities of soda-water. One suspects that
the work was not taken altogether seriously and certainly there
was time for other pursuits. Topsy in particular finished his panel
quickly and, inspired by the Arthurian themes they had selected,
extended his antiquarian interest in medieval armour. The others
were more interested in the search for female models.

This was a difficulty, for while they could sit to each other for
the male figures and faces, there were no professional models in
Oxford and hiring whores could have caused a scandal; moreover,
the Union had agreed to supply materials, board and lodging but
no wages. There was also much talk of 'stunners' or beautiful girls
such as goes on typically among young men. Gabriel was the most

outspoken on this subject and the deliberately provocative nature of his presentation may be judged from the shocked reaction of a young student drawn briefly into the charmed circle at the Union, who heard them argue persuasively but amorally, that if Madeline Smith, then on trial for poisoning her lover, should be found guilty of murder, she should not be hanged since she was so good-looking. 'Oh! you wouldn't hang a stunner!' they chorused.[4] Madeline Smith, incidentally, was acquitted and later married the general manager of the Morris & Co partnership and thus, by a curious twist of fate, actually came to meet her youthful champions.

Gabriel encouraged the others in the search for models who should also be stunners. On one occasion he despatched Morris, who never mastered figure drawing, to sketch a local beauty known as the Stunner Lipscombe whose father kept the inn at Godstowe, a picturesque village upriver from Oxford. 'But the daughter had never sat,' explained Val Prinsep later, 'and Morris was certainly not the man to persuade any mother that he was an artist of sufficient eminence to make a sitting an honour; and moreover it happened that Stunner Lipscombe's mother was painfully aware that the good looks of her daughter were so many snares to many amorous undergraduates.'[5] She sent him packing, which meant that his Iseult on the Union wall retained the aspect of an 'ogress' and the following words were pinned to the unsuccessful painter's bedroom door:

Poor Topsy has gone to make a sketch of Miss Lipscombe
But he can't draw the head and don't know where the hips come.

It was one more demonstration of Gabriel's supremacy. All the group sank their individuality 'in the strong personality of our adored Gabriel', and joined in the hunt for 'the legendary stunner with auburn hair'.[6] Characteristically, however, he maintained his leadership by confounding his followers: setting up rules and then changing them. For the girl he accosted at the theatre had not the bright locks of Lizzie or Ruth Herbert; she was dark-haired and by conventional standards the reverse of stunning.

There is no doubt that in contemporary eyes Jane was not perceived as pretty; a Holywell neighbour later commented that her sister Bessie was considered better-looking.[7] Jane's unusual looks were described in Morris's early poem about her, which specifically celebrates her appearance in terms that do not correspond with the conventional attributes of beauty. Her skin, said the poem, had the pallor of ivory; 'colourless' was an even less flattering comment by Georgie Burne-Jones.[8] Her hair was 'not greatly long', 'thick and crisped' and 'dead as though it had been forged . . . of some strange metal, thread by thread'. Her eyes were large and her lips curled up; her neck was prominent and her fingers long and bony. To speak plainly, her complexion was pallid, her eyebrows heavy and her hands and feet large and ungainly. This last feature, according to the pseudo-scientific classification of human types then popular, and accepted by the painters, was an indication of her 'lower' origins. The 'higher' type of female was delicate and refined, with tiny hands and feet while those of proletarian, Irish and 'savage' stock were heavy-limbed, coarse and sensual.

It was therefore somewhat perverse to pick Jane as a representative of female beauty.[9] A large part of Rossetti's genius, it appears to me, lay precisely in this ability to persuade others to accept his prescriptions, a power that is still potent, as any of the popular and many of the scholarly works on Pre-Raphaelitism testify. Since the concept of female beauty is entirely a social construct, it isn't quite true to say that he made us believe an ugly girl was pretty, but almost single-handed he enlarged the definition, so that Jane Burden's looks became a standard of feminine appeal, evolving through the later idea of the *femme fatale* and vamp into the sultry and enigmatic Hollywood star.[10] The initial impulse, I would suggest, was akin to the 1960s promotion of Twiggy as a fashion model.

If Jane was plain she was also poor. She was indeed ashamed of her social origins and discouraged later enquiries. At this distance, concealment seems unnecessary, particularly since there is no suggestion of illegitimacy, but it was a sensitive subject whose details probably cannot now be recovered. Robert Burden and Ann Maizey, her father and mother, were born in villages to the west of Oxford early in the century and migrated to the city during the agricultural decline that followed the Napoleonic wars. Robert's brother was a college groom and it was probably through this connection that Robert found work as an ostler or stablehand. He and Ann, who was illiterate, were married in 1833, and subsequent Census records show them constantly shifting from small dwelling to small dwelling in the courts and alleys off Holywell Street, where Robert worked. Their first child, Mary Ann, was born in 1835, followed by son William in early 1837, Jane, born 19 October 1839 and the first to be entered under the registration system, and finally Elizabeth or Bessie, born in 1842. At the time of Jane's birth, the family lived in St Helen's Passage, one of Holywell's least salubrious alleys containing five tenement houses without water or sewage facilities, 'several unwholesome dirt heaps' and a central cesspit with a wooden trapdoor. This description of 1848 states that St Helen's had been 'much improved within the last few years', so its condition when Jane was born must have been considerably worse, although it was probably not exceptional. Until Lizzie's friend Dr Acland and others successfully agitated for sanitary reform, the living conditions of Oxford's poorer classes were for a long while a source of scandal and cholera.

In 1841 Robert Burden was described as a 'male servant', a term that encompassed both indoor and outdoor service, and he may already have been working at Symonds' Livery Stables along the street. In 1849, when Jane was nearly ten, her fourteen-year-old sister Mary Ann died of TB, which must have been a practical as well as emotional loss, for at that age she was ready to go into service and start earning, or to provide valuable domestic assistance at home. Two years later Jane's brother, by then fourteen himself, was working as a college messenger boy, a secure and sought-after position. The Burdens were now living in Kings Head Yard, behind the pub, in a cottage said to be little larger than the loose boxes it faced. Jane and Bessie, aged eleven and nine, were entered in the 1851 Census as 'scholars' and were probably attending the Holywell parish school. Archive material from a similar school in Oxford at this date indicates the vocational bias of the curriculum: girls spent the whole afternoon in needlework or ironing and every pupil took part in 'scouring a room' on Saturdays. The education of parish children was designed to fit them for employment as superior servants, clean, literate and semi-skilled, in the homes and institutions of the University, as William Burden's career illustrated.[11]

When, fifty years later, her husband's biography was being prepared, all the information that Jane would volunteer about her own childhood was that she 'used to pick violets on the Iffley Road'.[12] Later, her reticence went further. It was proposed to include in the book a picturesque back view of Holywell that showed 'the bit of old Oxford . . . in which she lived before her marriage',[13] thus linking Morris's time at Oxford with his marriage. Jane vetoed the proposal and when her old friend Philip Webb, who claimed kinship with Jane on the basis of having also been born in Oxford, was enlisted to persuade her she sent a letter that led him to reply that he was 'almost glad I unwillingly gave you some pain . . . now that you have opened to me your real reason for objecting'. He noted how 'both our families had their rather sad lives' in the same town,[14] and the offending drawing was quietly dropped.

The nature of the 'sad life' of which Jane did not wish to be reminded can now only be surmised. Part of her objection may have been based on the fact that her husband's friends all seem to have believed that her childhood home was at 65 Holywell, the address on her marriage certificate, whereas she seems to have lived there only briefly, if at all. In 1857, the year she met the painters, she was living at the other end of the street, opposite the Music Room, as Topsy and Ned clearly recalled.[15] Ned indeed said she was living 'in a little cottage-like house in an alley' with her mother and sister.[16] He thought her father was dead, which is odd, for he must have remembered that Robert Burden gave his daughter away at her wedding eighteen months later. By 1859 her brother William had taken part tenancy of 65 Holywell and it is likely that Jane at least went to live there in the weeks before her wedding; it was a 'better' address from which to be married than a squalid cottage in an alleyway.

When Jane first went, at the age of nearly eighteen, to sit to the painters, presumably for a fee, she posed mainly, if not exclusively, for Gabriel. It was noted by his companions that he spent little time actually working in the Union chamber and preferred to draw and sketch in his lodgings. For his mural subjects he had chosen aspects of the Holy Grail legend and it is argued that Jane was the model for Guenevere in one of his surviving studies for *Lancelot's Vision of Sanct Grael*[17] in which the Knight's adulterous passion for the Queen prevents him from reaching the Grail. This is, however, not obvious from the drawing and the subject had been designed some weeks earlier, at the start of the Union painting. Nor does Jane appear in Gabriel's second projected mural, showing Galahad, Bors and Percival attaining the Grail.[18] However, in the month after her introduction to the painters, Jane's features steadily gained ground in Gabriel's pictures, displacing Lizzie's, whose aspect is seen in the several watching angels of *Lancelot's Vision*, suggesting that her influence was still present, and Jane was indisputably the model for the highly finished ink drawing of *Lancelot in the Queen's Chamber*[19] and the careful study for this showing her with her hands up to her throat.[20] At the same time she sat for a study of her face inscribed 'JB Aetat XVII / DGR Oxoniae primo delt. Oct. 1857'[21] and, I believe, for a watercolour of *The Wedding of Saint George and Princess Sabra*[22] where 'in a confined space crammed with accessories' the couple embrace as Sabra cuts a lock of her black hair. It would be reading too much biography into art to claim that Jane inspired this choice of subjects dealing with adultery, love and marriage, although there is a clear shift from the spiritual themes of the Grail. But it is not without significance that *The Wedding of Saint George* was the first of Gabriel's paintings for a long time to contain a dark-haired heroine.

For most of the month of October 1857 Jane was sitting to Gabriel in the upstairs sitting room at 13 George Street. Some discretion appears to have been practised by the other painters, for her presence does not seem to have been registered by those outside the immediate circle, such as Ned's friend Crom Price, who kept a diary of the period, or the London visitors such as Ruskin and Hunt, who each arrived in Oxford to see the famous frescoes for themselves. Madox Brown turned up on the last day of October, had too much to drink and wrote a tipsy note to Emma. Perhaps he did remark on the rise of a new star in Gabriel's sky, for within a fortnight of Brown's return to London, Gabriel had been summoned away to Derbyshire by Lizzie, who was now at Matlock Spa. He left Oxford abruptly, leaving his friends surprised and deserted, to say nothing of his new model. One by one the painters finished or abandoned their work and returned to normal life. All except Morris.

Together with Ned Jones, Morris had fallen heavily under Gabriel's spell, becoming his ardent disciple or, in the courtly terms they so admired, his devoted squire, ready to follow and serve. He had given up architecture and started painting because

Gabriel told him to and had entered fully into the spirit of the Oxford Union enterprise, even to the extent of having a helmet and chainmail made as props by a local blacksmith. It is this aspect of medieval make-believe that in my view holds the key to his early relationship with Jane. Medievalism and the cult of chivalry were important features of upper-middle-class culture in the Victorian age and the Pre-Raphaelite interest was by no means unusual or even particularly intense: other groups got up elaborate tournaments or lived out courtly roles in real life. In *The Return to Camelot: Chivalry and the English Gentleman* (1981) Mark Girouard details the passion for the middle ages which spread out from Walter Scott's novels to reach the aristocracy and the monarchy – Victoria and Albert chose medieval parts for costume balls and portraits – and promoted the ideals of gentility and honour in order to sustain the institutions of the church, state and empire. In industrial and imperial Britain, codes of conduct modelled on archaic, Arthurian sources were adapted so as to mould a master class capable of self-denial and probity rather than one given to indulgence and dissipation; thus the needs of business, the armed forces and the colonial service were met. The public schools played a major part in helping to cultivate a cluster of ideas about male comradeship, loyalty and idealized love, whose chief features were constancy and deferred gratification. Romantic love and prudence were thus merged: the courtly romance, translated into nineteenth-century terms, saw a long period of devoted service to a chosen lady as a positive aspect of a gentleman's life.

A good deal of this medievalism was transmitted through art and in literature it pre-dated the Pre-Raphaelites and indeed influenced them. While students at Oxford, Ned and Topsy discovered and devoured books like Kenelm Digby's *The Broadstone of Honour*, La Motte Fouqué's *Sintram*, Wilhelm Meinhold's *Sidonia von Bork* and Malory's *Morte d'Arthur*, then only recently reissued. In 1853 Charlotte Yonge's *The Heir of Redclyffe* appeared and it has been pointed out how Morris seems to have identified with the hero Guy de Morville in his determination to quell a ferocious temper.[23] These Gothic stories, set in a distant age far from the modern world, were as popular with the mid-Victorian generation as were Tolkien's tales of Middle Earth in the hippie culture of the late 1960s, particularly among men. It is not difficult to see how the strong masculine institutions, such as the public

schools, colleges, regiments and clubs were emotionally reinforced by the stories of the companionship and prowess of the
knights of the Round Table, and something very similar was
clearly in progress at the Oxford Union, where the small band of
heroes was actually engaged in painting scenes from the *Morte
d'Arthur*. It was a small step to acting out its legends and it was
perhaps inevitable that Morris should fall in love with Janey. He
had already chosen to follow Gabriel unconditionally; when Ned
warned him against forfeiting his individuality, Morris is supposed to have replied, 'I have got beyond that. I want to imitate
Gabriel as much as possible.'[24] So if Gabriel said that Jane was the
loveliest being in the world, Topsy would adore her too, just as a
medieval squire in the courtly tradition would defend the lady
whom his knight loved. And when the knight was called away to
Matlock in Derbyshire, the squire would continue to worship and
protect his lady, first through his master's medium of paint and
eventually through the proposal of marriage which the knight,
being otherwise committed, could not make himself. For this was
not a tale but the real world of Victorian England and if she did
not marry, Jane's future was unappealing. After a few weeks of
worship, she would have no choice but to return to life in the
Holywell slum.

Many years later, Jane claimed never to have loved her
husband[25] and it has been suggested that she was persuaded to
accept his offer despite her own reluctance by pressure from her
family who recognized the value of the connection, and who were
encouraged by other stories of university gentlemen falling for the
pretty daughters of humble townsfolk,[26] of which Stunner
Lipscombe's mother was evidently also aware. But Jane herself
was probably moved by material considerations too. Her actual
feelings are hard to discern. Years later after Morris's death she
tried to explain something of what she felt by saying, 'I suppose
that if I were young again I should do the same again.'[27] It seems
likely that she was overwhelmed by her introduction to the
Pre-Raphaelite group, and lost her heart to Gabriel, who had
chosen her and charmed her and told her she was beautiful; when
he vanished and she heard of his attachment to another woman, a
sure instinct kept her in contact with his friends, fastening in
particular on the one whose sense of chivalry made him most
susceptible. Morris, acting as Gabriel's gallant stand-in, could not

cast her off; instead he retained her as a model, struggling to paint her in the sitting room in George Street and eventually asking her to marry him. How far she encouraged him and how far he fell in love with the idea of rescuing a damsel in distress rather than with Jane herself are interesting but unanswerable questions. Jane, who seems to have felt later that she had always loved Gabriel, probably only knew that to be so courted was vastly better than life at home. Morris's offer could not be refused, whatever her feelings.

The courtship began with a picture, the well-known oil now in the Tate Gallery entitled *Queen Guenevere*.[28] It shows Jane standing in a chamber tying the girdle of a medieval-style gown; behind her is an unmade bed on which a little dog lies curled up and in the distance beyond the hangings a minstrel is playing and singing. As a picture it attracts and disturbs through the ambiguous posture and expression of the figure and is frankly far better than it should be, given Morris's difficulties with figure drawing. It is said that both Rossetti and Brown also worked on it but it is not known to what extent. The title is another mystery, for it should be called *La Belle Iseult*, as Jane herself confirmed many years later.[29]

At this date Morris was as much taken with the Tristram stories as Gabriel with those of Lancelot; his first picture, begun early in 1857, was said to depict 'Sir Tristram after his illness in the garden of King Mark's Palace recognized by the dog he had given Iseult'.[30] The subject of his Union mural was 'How Sir Palomydes loved La Belle Iseult with exceeding great love out of measure and how she loved him not again but rather Sir Tristram', a choice that can almost be said to be clairvoyant, so closely did it correspond to the later emotional triangle of Jane, himself and Gabriel. In fact the wall painting pre-dated Jane's appearance by some two months; perhaps in an obscure way it compelled Morris to act out the tale he had chosen, by declaring his love for a woman who, like Iseult, loved another, whom she was unable to marry. In any case, it is not surprising that he took a related subject for his new easel painting, although the obscurities and confusions surrounding *La Belle Iseult* are almost as great as those in the traditional tale of Tristram and Iseult and unfortunately the iconography of the picture is not sufficiently clear to identify an exact source passage in the *Morte d'Arthur*. The little brachet on the bed surely confirms

the figure as Iseult and perhaps the unmade bed represents that in
which Tristram was taken naked by Sir Andred and his twelve
knights. On the other hand, Jane/Iseult's sorrowing face may
convey a meaning more psychological than narrative, as she
mourns Gabriel/Tristram's departure.

This is similar in theme to Morris's celebrated poem to Jane, 'In
Praise of My Lady', written during this courtship phase, which is a
hymn of sorrowful devotion rather than mutual affection. The
lady is beautiful, and sad, but she is not pining for the poet:

> Her great eyes, standing far apart
> Draw up some memory from her heart,
> And gaze out very mournfully;
> > *Beata mea Domina!*
>
> So beautiful and kind they are,
> But most times looking out afar,
> Waiting for something, not for me –
> > *Beata mea Domina!*

The poem is usually read as a simple avowal of Morris's love for
Jane, whereas it is better seen as a dramatic rendering of the
feelings of a squire who does not expect to attain the lady, but
simply worships from afar. It was written, according to Morris's
friend, Richard Dixon, before or during Morris's hasty visit to
Manchester just before the end of the Art Treasures Exhibition;
this suggests that it dates from the time before Gabriel had left
Oxford to join Lizzie and that Morris's 'imitation' of his master
was so thorough that he adored his beloved before he was in a
position to court her himself. This accords with the emotional
pattern of the relationship. It is also a very sexually charged poem
and it seems that when Topsy stepped into Gabriel's place he
inherited, as it were, a good deal of feeling. Perhaps he felt too
strongly. Val Prinsep recalled Morris bending the prongs of a fork
in rage when one of the company spoke disrespectfully of Miss
Burden, who was, after all, only a model and an ostler's daughter,
with no pretensions to being treated like a lady. And the persistent
rumour that Gabriel encouraged Morris to marry her may have its
basis in a similar joking remark, or in the humorous caricature of
Topsy presenting Jane with a ring, scribbled by Gabriel on the

back of one of his mural studies.[31] It seems probable that the
painters teased Topsy about his chivalric devotion, until they
realized that he was serious.

It was several months before an engagement was announced,
partly perhaps because both Morris and Jane were shy and
inarticulate. Another of Prinsep's recollections of the Oxford
period was venturing into the George Street sitting room where
the two were together and finding Topsy reading *Barnaby Rudge*
aloud to his beloved. This has been taken as a sign of ineptitude
but there are other interpretations, for reading aloud filled several
functions in nineteenth-century society. It could be the equivalent
of today's family television viewing, with jokes and comic
sequences relived over and again, or a gesture of affection, more
along the lines of an invitation to the cinema. Reading aloud to
loved ones was a mark of devotion and may have been so for
Morris. One story is that it took him so long to progress from
painting to proposing that while Jane was posing he wrote on his
picture: 'I cannot paint you but I love you.' This may be a fair
representation of his difficulties, for all contemporary observers
were united in their perception of Morris as brusque and rough in
manner, unable to muster many graces even when women were
present. This fact is not without significance in relation to Jane
who, at the age of eighteen, found herself affianced to a man of
twenty-four who had most of the attributes of the eligible
bachelor, being young, wealthy and unattached, but who lacked
certain crucial qualities. It was difficult to think of him as
handsome or charming.[32] He was short, squat, bespectacled,
untidy and grubby, with 'a head that appeared too big' and 'dark
matted locks' often bespattered with paint. He presented, Val
Prinsep said, 'a truly grotesque figure' who could not sit still but
was always writhing and fidgeting.[33] He was good-natured and
willing to stand a phenomenal amount of teasing but he also flew
into sharp and uncontrollable rages with explosions of violence
and bad language. In company he could be tongue-tied and
diffident, often appearing rude and ungracious. In short, he was
rather an unprepossessing suitor.

It seems clear that at this date Topsy compared unfavourably
with Gabriel; and probable that Jane knew from the start whom
she preferred. Much later, when living with Jane at Kelmscott,
Gabriel wrote a brief outline of a story for a picture that seems to

me to offer a shared, retrospective version of events which implies that Jane had loved him all the time. The essence of this story, 'The Cup of Water', is in its beginning, and the characters need no elucidation:

> The young King of a country is hunting one day with a young Knight, his friend; when, feeling thirsty, he stops at a Forester's cottage, and the Forester's daughter brings him a cup of water to drink. Both of them are equally enamoured of her unequalled beauty. The King, however, has been affianced from boyhood to a Princess, worthy of all love, and whom he had always believed that he loved until undeceived by his new absorbing passion; but the Knight, resolved to sacrifice all other considerations to his love, goes again to the Forester's cottage and asks his daughter's hand. He finds the girl has fixed her thoughts on the King, whose rank she does not know. On hearing it she tells her suitor humbly that she must die if that be her fate, but cannot love another. The Knight goes to the King to tell him all and beg his help, and the two friends then come to an explanation. Ultimately the King goes to the girl and pleads his friend's cause, not disguising his own passion, but saying that as he sacrificed himself to honour, so should she, at his prayer, accept a noble man whom he loves better than all men and whom she will love too. This she does at last . . .

This may represent only a vague outline of the emotions involved but does suggest some interesting things about Gabriel's view of himself. It is possible however that when they were both in London at the end of 1857, Gabriel heard of Morris's suit and gave it his blessing. It is certain that at this date he did not wish to marry Jane himself. Jane's desires, as always, are more obscure; but one line of speculation is that she married Topsy, warts and all, in order to stay in the Pre-Raphaelite circle and she may therefore have done so with more awareness than she is generally given credit for.

She had, first of all, to overcome the objections of his friends and family. Marriage to a stableman's daughter was not a connexion that the Morris family could be expected to welcome. Topsy's widowed mother had already weathered his several abrupt changes of career, and probably thought it a dreadful *mésalliance.* Some of his friends were equally aghast. The response of young Algernon Swinburne, who had joined the circle of painters while the Union project was in progress, may have been representative in its double edge. Jane was a 'most perfect stunner', he wrote to a fellow student in February, 'but the idea of his marrying her is insane. To kiss her feet is the utmost men should dream of doing.'[34] This hit neatly at the confusion of romance and reality and at the social pressures against class exogamy. One hint that Jane may have faced social isolation, if not direct hostility, is a note recorded by Morris's biographer immediately after copying the details of the marriage register, to the effect that the Prinseps were 'kind in taking J. up'.[35] This refers to Val's mother, Sarah Prinsep, the unconventional hostess of Little Holland House, who evidently smoothed Jane's path into London society during the first few, awkward months of her married life. Morris himself was not one to pay attention to such social difficulties. Whatever the obstacles to the match they were soon cleared, and the engagement was announced in April 1858.

At this date Lizzie was still at Matlock, where she spent the winter after summoning Gabriel in November. He had left Oxford hurriedly, telling his friends only that she was 'terribly ill' again and failing to inform his mother altogether. An anxious letter from Mrs Rossetti was forwarded by Ned but in his reply from Mr Cartledge's boarding house at Lime Tree View, where he and Lizzie were staying, Gabriel neither explained why he was there nor mentioned Lizzie's presence. He described a visit to Haddon Hall and promised to be in London before long. He asked his brother for 'the loan of as many pounds as you can manage';[36] an account dating from 1860 shows that staying at Lime Tree View cost around 30s a week.[37] It is impossible to know who paid Lizzie's bill. And there is little information about what she and Gabriel did during the months at Matlock. He returned to London for Christmas, when he and Topsy both attended a party at what was now Ned's studio in Red Lion Square before departing again to their respective 'stunners'.

At Matlock Gabriel completed two watercolours, *A Christmas Carol*,[38] dated 'Xmas 1857' and showing a Lizzie-like figure playing a clavichord, and *Before the Battle*,[39] with a lady tying her banner to a knight's lance. These, together with *The Chapel Before the Lists*,[40] seem to derive directly from the previous summer's medievalism and it is tempting to ascribe the same date to Lizzie's little watercolour of *A Lady Affixing a Pennant to a Knight's Spear*,[41] which shows a blue-robed woman helping a black-gowned knight fasten a red pennant to his lance.

By April 1858 Gabriel was anxious to return to London. To Brown he wrote mainly of penury and boredom, saying he missed metropolitan gossip 'in these solitudes'. Of Lizzie he said, 'all is much as when I last saw you'.[42] To other correspondents he did not even mention her and it is hard to assess the state of their relationship. On the one hand, they were together in Derbyshire for several months, away from everyone else. On the other hand, when Gabriel left for London in May, Lizzie was not to see him again for nearly two years and their relationship was effectively broken.

This fact has been seldom acknowledged and indeed was slurred over by many when it became necessary to insist on a steady, if lengthy, engagement from the early 1850s onwards for the sake of their posthumous reputations. William Michael was chiefly responsible for the false impression but even he was sometimes made uncomfortable by romanticized versions of the Gabriel–Lizzie story. He half-corrected the memoir of Walter Deverell for example. To the manuscript phrase 'financial difficulties prevented the marriage from taking place for many years', he added 'not to speak of other obstacles'; and he deleted the sentence reading: 'During that long engagement Rossetti's devotion never wavered.'[43] Hall Caine, who was Gabriel's companion at the end of his life, was more specific. 'Then came a separation,' he wrote.[44] It does not now seem possible to discover what happened, or what Lizzie subsequently did: information about her life, as with so many women, ceased when she was no longer in contact with the famous man.

I would like to connect their parting with the following lines by Gabriel:[45]

> But before going out, she took her stand
> At the wide door, and struck him with her hate
> Full on the cheek; and the scorn did not bate
> Nor the strength failed an instant. With one hand

She heaped her fallen tresses in their band
And with the other, turning, closed the gate.

But there is no evidence to support this, and all that is known is that Gabriel returned to London and was no longer seen in her company. Whether she stayed in the North, or went back to her family in Southwark, is not known.

Gabriel's work in the months following their separation effectively confirms that Lizzie had been deserted by her beloved. In the latter half of 1858 he picked up the subject of Hamlet and Ophelia, which he had first tackled some years earlier, now altering the design and message and filling the picture with details that invite biographical interpretation. The intricate and highly finished ink drawing *Hamlet and Ophelia*[46] depicts the moment in the play when Hamlet's rejection of Ophelia is most explicit. She arrives to return his betrothal gifts and he says abruptly, 'I loved you not,' to which she replies, 'I was the more deceived.' A lengthy quotation from this scene is in fact painted on to the frame, thus making it clear that the subject is the breaking of an engagement, the denial of affection and the pain of rejection that leads, in Ophelia's case, to insanity. The figure of Ophelia is based on Lizzie but this does not imply that she sat for it, since Gabriel had many studies of her, sitting in similar attitudes, and could no doubt draw her face from memory. The drawing contains some biblical and Blakean symbolism and in the distance behind the couple is a curious double snake staircase whose two flights curve together and apart in what may be read as a fanciful, half-conscious allusion to the on–off nature of the artist's relation to his model.[47] This picture is contemporary with a number of poems Gabriel wrote lamenting the death of love. The most expressive of these was 'Even So', which took its central image from an observation he had made many years ago at Hastings, during his second visit there with Lizzie, when he remarked that 'sometimes through the summer mists the sea and sky are one',[48] with the fishing boats looking like flies:

So it is, my dear.
All such things touch secret strings
For heavy hearts to hear.
So it is, my dear.

Very like, indeed:
Sea and sky, afar, on high,
Sand and strewn seaweed –
Very like, indeed.

But the sea stands spread
As one wall with the flat skies,
Where the lean black craft like flies
Seem well-nigh stagnated,
Soon to drop off dead.

Seemed it so to us
When I was thine and thou wast mine,
And all these things were thus,
But all our world in us?

Could we be so now?
Not if all beneath heaven's pall
Lay dead but I and thou,
Could we be so now!

Lizzie's feelings may be judged from her own verses, which
were probably written in 1858 and the few years that followed.[49]
'Love and Hate' seems to express the emotions aroused in her by
the endlessly postponed wedding:

Ope not thy lips, thou foolish one
Nor turn to me thy face;
The blast of heaven shall strike thee down
Ere I will give thee grace.

Take thou thy shadow from my path,
Nor turn to me and pray;
The wild wild winds thy dirge may sing
Ere I will bid thee stay.

Turn thou away thy false dark eyes
Nor gaze upon my face;
Great love I bore thee: now great hate
Sits firmly in its place.

All changes pass me like a dream,
I neither sing nor pray
And thou art like the poisonous tree
That stole my life away.

'The Passing of Love' reflects bitter disillusion:

O God, forgive me that I ranged
My life into a dream of love!
Will tears of anguish never wash
    The passion from my blood?

Love kept my heart in a song of joy,
My pulses quivered to the tune;
The coldest blasts of winter blew
    Upon me like sweet airs in June.

Love floated on the mists of morn
And rested on the sunset's rays;
He calmed the thunder of the storm
    And lighted all my ways.

Love held me joyful through the day
And dreaming ever through the night;
No evil thing could come to me,
    My spirit was so light.

O Heaven help my foolish heart
Which heeded not the passing time
That dragged my idol from its place
    And shattered all its shrine.

Lizzie's verse is usually characterized as slight, derivative and melancholy but it seems to me that there is a good deal of fierce, even violent, feeling in these lines and a painful irony that beams through the poetic conventions, undercutting the invocation of Love in a technically accomplished manner. The simplicity and directness of expression is very attractive. It seems that once again her talent has been critically subsumed in that of Gabriel's, and again judged inferior. It has, however, its own power and individuality and although her total output was small, consisting

of some sixteen poems, it deserves to be compared with that of
Christina Rossetti – who was especially impressed with 'Dead
Love' which she described as 'piquant with cool, bitter sarcasm'.[50]
In its biting use of the same endearment this could almost be a
response to the smooth regret of Gabriel's 'Even So':

> Oh never weep for love that's dead,
> Since love is seldom true
> But changes his fashion from blue to red,
> From brightest red to blue,
> And love was born to an early death
> And is so seldom true.
>
> Then harbour no smile on your bonny face
> To win the deepest sigh;
> The fairest words on truest lips
> Pass on and surely die,
> And you will stand alone, my dear,
> When wintry winds draw nigh.
>
> Sweet, never weep for what cannot be,
> For this God has not given.
> If the merest dream of love were true
> Then, sweet, we would be in heaven
> And this is only earth, my dear,
> Where true love is not given.

The strength of feeling that plays across the light control of the
verse here seems to me to belie not only Lizzie's reputation as a
feeble, imitative writer but also the generally held view that she
was emotionally feeble, characterized by weak health, debility and
lassitude. The unspoken inference of this view is that she, with so
little to offer, had no 'right' to hold the brilliant, lusty Gabriel to
an engagement that had outlived its impetus. Such a judgement is
neither true nor fair. Lizzie's invalidism was foisted on her by
others and used to suppress her natural talent and spirit. And now
she was rejected. In the 1850s a woman who had been jilted, at the
age of nearly thirty and with neither family nor fortune, had small
chance of happiness, as both she and Gabriel knew. Ophelia's fate
stared her in the face. Lizzie's poems indicate that when Gabriel
abandoned her she felt first angry and then despairing.

PART TWO

Marriage

7

In the New Year of 1858 two women who, by their membership of the Pre-Raphaelite circle, fill out the cast-list of this story passed close to each other in London, without meeting. Since they represented two very different aspects of Victorian womanhood it was hardly possible for them to meet; the men whom they both knew constructed their social world in such a way as to keep them apart. One was Fanny Cornforth, a professional prostitute; the other was Georgiana Macdonald, a Methodist minister's daughter.

So far, the women whose lives are under scrutiny here 'have formed a sort of group, with similar origins and aspirations. Their tricky but rewarding routes upwards in society illustrate two key processes in the nineteenth century: the growth of the middle class and the fluidity of the social formation. A fuller picture of the position of women in general and that of the Pre-Raphaelite circle in particular is provided by the histories of Fanny and Georgie, who modify the simpler picture produced by Lizzie, Emma, Annie and Jane. In January 1858 both were, separately, at the Red Lion Square studio occupied by Ned Jones, Fanny as model and Georgie as prospective wife.

Fanny Cornforth's name, age and origin are all somewhat uncertain, reflecting the nature of her life. It would be interesting to pinpoint such facts as her date of birth with greater accuracy than seems possible, but might not add much to our knowledge of her. For the uncertainties provide a more important fact: that Fanny did not consider herself defined by the past, but constantly redrew the changing shape of her life.

She claimed to have been born about 1835–6 in Sussex, and her

real name is said to have been Sarah Cox. Later accounts identified
her date of birth as 1824, her father as a blacksmith and her place of
origin as Steyning, a large village on the edge of the South Downs
but much of this information is based on a misapprehension and
may be misleading. She was probably born in the 1830s,
somewhere in Sussex.[1] Her accent by the time she met the
Pre-Raphaelite painters was distinctively cockney, which suggests
long residence in London, and it seems probable that she was in
fact a village girl, perhaps of uncertain parentage, who went into
service at an early age and after some time as a skivvy decided to
put her good looks to better use and 'went on the streets'. The
drawings of her done between 1858 and 1860 suggest that she was
then in her mid-twenties, which accords with the age of
twenty-seven that she gave the Census enumerator in 1861.

There was never much doubt about her profession. It is often
hard to distinguish between fact and moralists' fantasies when
writing about prostitution but the practical choice I have imputed
to Fanny was by no means unusual. The accepted view of
prostitution, often supplied by the practitioners themselves,
evidently aware of what society wished to hear, was that women
became prostitutes after being seduced, in order to obtain finery
and leisure without hard work; after a brief period of prosperity
they sank into inevitable degradation and despair, and frequently
ended their lives by suicide. In fact, at least some women found it
a pleasant and profitable occupation, with no drudgery and
relatively good prospects. For others, it was an occasional means
of earning, when work was scarce. It compared favourably with
employment as a domestic servant or 'slopworker', sewing
garments for pitifully small wages. And since the transmission of
disease was hardly understood and TB and cholera were far more
deadly, the risk of contracting venereal disease was less of a
deterrent than it later became. It may be that the hostility towards
prostitution that was aroused in the Victorian age was due in part
to the fact that the career of a 'swell Regent Street whore' could in
fact be successful and glamorous.

Some examples of 'career prostitutes' were recorded by A.J.
Munby in his remarkable diary. One was a farmer's daughter
from Chesterfield who came to London 'nominally to be a
draper's assistant, but really to become of her own accord what
she is', a professional prostitute working the Oxford Street area.[2]

Another was Sarah Tanner, whom Munby first met as a maid-of-all-work, 'a lively honest rosy-faced girl' scrubbing steps, and whom he next saw in Regent Street, 'arrayed in gorgeous apparel'. 'How is this?' asked Munby. Sarah answered frankly:

Why, she had got tired of service, wanted to see life & be independent; & so she had become a prostitute, of her own accord & without being seduced. She saw no harm in it: enjoyed it very much & thought it might raise her & perhaps be profitable. She had taken it up as a profession, & that with much energy: she had read books, & was taking lessons in writing & other accomplishments, in order to fit herself to be a companion of gentlemen. And her manners were improved – she was no longer vulgar: her dress was handsome & good, & she was, & is still, a fine-looking girl, with good features.

Three years later, when Munby met Sarah again, she was dressed soberly, 'like a respectable upper servant' and told him she had left the streets and settled down, having invested her earnings in a coffeehouse by Waterloo Bridge.[3] Finally there was Nelly Turner, daughter of a Dorset gamekeeper, who had begun her career as a general servant in London, had been seduced and later became 'gay', as prostitutes styled themselves. Her sister, a lady's maid, had married her master's son, an Army Captain, and Nelly herself had a 'friend' who was a Major in the 3rd Buffs, but she intended marrying a respectable tradesman, a collar-and-harness-maker, who knew all.[4] From these examples it is clear that prostitution did not lead inevitably to destruction.

The one generally undisputed fact about Fanny was that she was exceptionally good-looking. With unusual fulsomeness, the prim and elderly William Michael later recalled her as 'a pre-eminently fine woman, with regular and sweet features, and a mass of the most lovely blonde hair – light golden or harvest yellow'.[5] She was a real stunner who had otherwise 'no charm of breeding, education or intellect'. She was, according to another source, 'an authentic and undeniable trollop'.[6] That she was not the predicted raddled wreck indicates that her chosen trade had treated her well. If any confirmation of her profession were required, it is provided by the fact that as well as being handsome, she was forward: in all the stories of her meeting with Rossetti, which range geographically from the Strand to Victoria and Vauxhall, she is said to have accosted him first, in public. No respectable Victorian woman, of whatever class, would have so approached a strange man without some kind of introduction.

They met in what was known as a 'night garden' – according to Fanny, during a firework display at the Royal Surrey Gardens,[7] a resort similar to Cremorne. 'As they passed each other on the path she cracked a nut between her teeth and threw the shell at him': an interesting style of soliciting. Fanny herself gave a different story, in which she was chaperoned by an elderly cousin and accidentally bumped into Gabriel and his friends, thus dislodging her magnificent hair, but this rings less true than the tale of the nutshell.[8] The most likely date for the meeting seems to be the period of Christmas and New Year of 1857–8 when Gabriel was briefly in London. Around 20 January, Brown called on him at Chatham Place and the two then proceeded 'on to Jones' at Red Lion Square, where Brown 'saw there Fanny, their model'.[9]

Fanny herself, however, placed her meeting with Gabriel in the summer, which would suggest it occurred after his return from Matlock. She recalled how, in the conversation that followed the 'accident' to her hair, it was arranged that she should go the next day to Gabriel's studio, where 'he put my head against the wall and drew it for the head in the calf picture'.[10] This was of course the unfinished *Found*, Gabriel's reply to Hunt on the fallen woman theme which had lain untouched since the struggle to paint the calf at Finchley at the end of 1854. Meeting Fanny seems to have rearoused his interest in the subject, reinforcing his new deter-mination to produce 'important' works in oil rather than pretty watercolours, and she sat for an expressive pen-and-ink sketch of her head, leaning as she said against the wall, her eyes averted and her brow puckered in shame. This image was then painted on to the first, panel version of *Found* and later on to the larger canvas version.[11]

Fanny's occupation as a prostitute was not merely incidental to her role as a model, but played an active part. Whether as cause or result of her acquaintance, the Fallen Woman theme re-emerged in the painters' art and lives during 1858. Gabriel made little progress with *Found* but returned to a similar subject, *Mary Magdalene*, depicted in Western hagiology as a repentant harlot elevated to sainthood – a religious means of dealing with a 'forbidden' subject. Below him in Chatham Place, Spencer Stanhope, one of the companions of the Oxford Union, was newly installed in a studio and engaged on a picture showing 'an "unfortunate" in two different crises of her life'.[12] This, however, was in June; in January Ned Jones had a real-life encounter with such a female, when his compassion was roused by 'a poor miserable girl of seventeen he met in the street at 2 a.m. the coldest night this winter, with scarce any clothes and starving *in spite of prostitution*', as Brown emphasized with indignation.[13] Ned gave her some money and told her to call at Red Lion Square the next morning, which she did, telling him her parents in the country were willing to take her back but she was too shabby to go. With the assistance of the apartment's cheerful and resourceful servant, known simply as 'Red Lion Mary', Ned arranged for Emma Brown to buy a new set of clothes for the poor girl, which Brown duly delivered to the studio. Much later, in words that seem to refer to this incident, Georgie commended Mary's kindness in helping 'a woman whose goodness was in abeyance'.[14] As it happens, we know that Mary became friendly with Fanny, whom she met at Red Lion Square, and perhaps Georgie's remarks offered an oblique comment on the number of 'unfortunate' women who visited that address. Of course, as Georgie also pointed out, Ned's behaviour was entirely honourable and kind: he was not the kind of man or artist to take advantage of a poor girl's plight. There is incidentally some evidence that part of Gabriel's initiation of Ned and Topsy into the ways of the metropolis was to push them among prostitutes – perhaps in the name of 'experience'. Many years later Ned told the story of how, when he was new to London, Gabriel once teased him by paying a prostitute five shillings to follow him, telling her 'I was very shy and timid and wanted her to speak to me. I said no, my dear, I'm just going home – I'm never haughty with those poor things, but it was no use, she wouldn't go, and there we marched, arm in arm down Regent Street', with Ned terrified lest any friend should see him.[15] A year or so later, however, he was buying clothes for a fallen girl and drawing Fanny Cornforth. In the same period, Val Prinsep recalled how Gabriel took his young friends to visit the *poses plastiques* or semi-nude shows in Leicester Square to chat to the artistes, and also to the Argyll Rooms at Piccadilly, where whores and their clients drank and danced late in the night.[16]

In 1857 there were, according to the Metropolitan Police, some 8,600 professional prostitutes in London, about 40% of whom were defined as 'well-dressed' or prosperous whores, operating from expensive premises; the rest were called 'low' and catered for less wealthy clients.[17] The total is not a large figure for a city of London's size and some commentators believed it to be a severe underestimate: the 'circulating harlotry of the Haymarket and Regent Street' alone was thought to number about the same.[18] The total may have been many times higher but facts, as opposed to assertions on the subject, are hard to come by. A full account of the reality of nineteenth-century prostitution, rather than official attitudes to it, remains to be written, but there is some evidence that the decline in rural employment owing to the agricultural depression in the 1820s and 1830s, together with the phenomenal growth of London, its accompanying prosperity and concealing anonymity[19] led to an increase in girls entering urban prostitution. Another factor, believed at the time, may have been the numbers of middle-class young men deferring marriage; but there is little information on the customers of 'the social evil', which was supposed to be gnawing away at the fabric of society, and many came from the same class as the women themselves.[20] One suspects indeed that much of the alarm generated by the subject was due not to increasing numbers of whores but to evangelical fervour and rising bourgeois morality, which found prostitution's visibility offensive. In order to advertise their services, 'gay' women in London's West End wore 'gaudy' clothes modelled on the fashionable dress of wealthy ladies, rather than the sober servants' wear appropriate to their class position, and often went without bonnets or shawls, two items that denoted 'correct' femininity. Much indignation was also aroused by the public nature of the places where prostitutes operated: on the pavements and in fashionable 'nighthouses' such as Kate Hamilton's, the Argyll Rooms and the Holborn Rooms, where customers and prostitutes could drink, dance and make arrangements. One woman described a typical evening's work thus:

I get up at 4 o'clock, dress and dine; after that I may walk about the streets for an hour or two, and pick up anyone I am fortunate enough to meet with, that is, if I want money;

afterwards I go to the Holborn, dance a little and if anyone likes me I take him home with me, if not I go to the Haymarket and wander from one cafe to another, from Sally's to the Carlton, from Barn's to Sam's.[21]

In addition, the guardians of public morality, who denounced what was both popular and profitable, may also have been outraged by prostitutes' high earnings, which far exceeded servants' wages, still largely based on board and lodging. As already noted, many whores hoped to amass capital and purchase property or to marry into relative comfort. Rates of pay spanned a wide range, with top West End prostitutes able to earn between £10 and £12 a week, those in Lambeth averaging between £3 and £4 and even the cheapest obtaining a shilling per client. It is true that, unlike servants, they had to pay for accommodation and that in fashionable districts this could cost up to £4 a week, but at the same time, most house servants received cash wages of between just £10 and £20 per year, while social surveys showed thousands of slopworkers toiling all hours of the week at tailoring and shirtmaking, to earn a total of five shillings. 'I don't leave off this sort of life,' commented one prostitute, 'because I'm in a manner used to it, and what could I do if I did? . . . Then if I had to sit hours and hours all day long and part of the night too, sewing or anything like that, I should get tired.'[22]

Finally, as well as being relatively well-dressed and well-paid, prostitutes enjoyed an independence and freedom from male control unknown to their sisters subordinated to the authority of fathers at home and employers at work; indeed, it is sometimes hard to understand why more girls did not take to the streets. Those who did, it may be noted, often lived together and supported each other in various ways, and it was not until late in the century that pimps and the oppression of 'organized vice' appeared, partly in response to the moralists' determination that any woman not visibly under the protection of a man could be defined as a prostitute. The inhibiting factor was the sense of shame, vigorously promoted through the 1840s and 1850s and continuing for the rest of the century and shared by all ranks of society except perhaps the very lowest. This social disapproval was reinforced by ostracism, which also served to strengthen the growing Victorian ideology of the family: parents were

encouraged to expel their 'erring' daughters and women in all classes
combined to ensure that prostitutes, however successful, could
never be received in 'respectable' circles. The shame of prostitution was so well inculcated in bourgeois thinking that to this day it
is regarded as something to be feared, avoided and pitied; peering
through the ideological obfuscation, however, it appears that in
the nineteenth century it had much to offer a poor, ambitious girl.
Doubtless it had disadvantages and dangers, but the lurid pictures
drawn in popular literature and art of debauchery and degradation
leading inevitably to disease and death did not so much depict
reality as attempt to shape it.

Some women combined prostitution with other employment;
many seem to have left it after a few years. In York, for example,
three quarters of the prostitutes known to the police were under
twenty-six years of age.[23] The older ones had given it up. Fanny
Cornforth, at the time she met the Pre-Raphaelite painters, was
perhaps thinking along these lines.

Her experience on the streets, however, had moulded her
personality as well as the attitudes of those who met her. As a
result, her relationship with the painters was distinctive, possessing a quality that is well expressed in a charming drawing by
Gabriel, showing George Boyce seated at an easel with Fanny
leaning forward from behind his chair, her arms clasped round his
neck in a gesture of easy intimacy.[24] Both faces are in profile
against the window and both are looking intently at the easel; the
embrace is only the secondary matter in hand. On the wall is a
small framed portrait of Ruth Herbert, to whom Gabriel gave the
drawing, and it is deduced that the picture illustrates the
companionable atmosphere in the company of women who, like
prostitutes and actresses, were not constrained by rigid notions of
what was proper or improper between men and women, but were
able to behave with easy affection and touch. For Gabriel, Fanny
normal attractions were enhanced by the fact that for her an
embrace, a kiss, and even sex were not acts strictly forbidden
except within the context of marriage.

Georgiana Macdonald was, by contrast, a 'good girl'. She came
from a respectable, religious household, whose income placed
them on the lower fringes of the middle class, but whose members
were unquestionably ladies and gentlemen in terms of behaviour
and acquaintance. Within the Macdonald family, where father and

grandfather were Methodist ministers, the greatest sin was a spiteful remark; reading Shakespeare and theatregoing were forbidden on the grounds of immorality. Born in 1840, Georgie was the fifth of the eleven children born to Hannah and George, whose plain-living and right-thinking family is remembered for the fact that four of the daughters made 'important' marriages and two were mothers of major twentieth-century figures: Stanley Baldwin and Rudyard Kipling. As usual, the women were defined by their menfolk, but had social conditions been different they might have found recognition in their own right, for the family was strongly matriarchal and the women were independent in their views, morally decisive and mutually supportive: an inheritance due in part to the size of the family and in part to the fact that in accordance with Methodist practice they moved to a new station every three years, thus strengthening family cohesion. Eight of the children survived infancy; another, Caroline, died at the age of fifteen.

The eldest boy, Harry, enjoyed supremacy over the rest, as was his right by virtue of age and gender; his sisters vied for the honour of taking him his breakfast when he was home from school. Since the family had no income beyond that from the ministry, there was little to spend on luxuries, but from the beginning 2s 6d was put aside weekly for Harry's education. Luckily he was a bright lad and from King Edward's School, Birmingham, won a scholarship to Oxford, where, apparently unable to live up to his family's expectations, he began a 'drop out' process that led him eventually to America. The daughters were treated differently; as Georgie put it, 'girls, in those days, had small chances of education. It is true we were sent to the usual "Young Ladies' School" or a daily governess came to us, but few fresh ideas reached us that way';[25] the Macdonald sisters relied on their brother and his friends for intellectual stimulation. Their father was 'an efficient help to the studies of his sons, but had not time also to direct those of his daughters'. He was indeed frequently away from home most of the week on preaching engagements, which he adored. His wife Hannah was thus left 'almost as lonely as a widow in the struggles of daily life'.[26]

The girls helped with the household tasks, learned to sew and mend and make their own clothes, and practised their 'accomplishments'. In these, according to the masculine bias of the family biographer, 'their talents were more interpretative than creative',[27] although as we shall see, this probably simply reflected the social conditions which valued men's art more highly than women's. None of the girls was fitted by upbringing for any future but marriage and this was evident to them from an early age, even if they never heard any friend or neighbour commiserate with their poor father, with so many daughters to wed. Many of the sisters' earliest recorded conversations concerned marriage. Carrie, aged five, asked, 'What is marriage?' to which Georgie, aged four, answered, 'It is staying at home.' Carrie dissented: 'No, it's going out to breakfast and getting a husband.' Alice, aged seven, pointed out that 'Papa is married and he has no husband,' and Georgie finished the discussion by announcing that, whatever it was, she definitely intended to marry.[28] Later, Aggie wrote sagely, 'Truly it is advisable for us to marry if the right thing turns up.'[29] The girls' upbringing might have been designed to attract precisely the 'right thing'. They were bright and resourceful but not too clever or well-educated; they were lively and cheerful, never silly or snobbish; they had a keen sense of humour built on a solid moral foundation; and they neither despised money nor the lack of it. All in all, they grew up to be ideal wives-and-mothers, perfect partners for professional young men making their way in the world.

With this future in mind, the Macdonald girls learnt early to worship their brother's friends, known as the 'Birmingham Set' at university. 'They all made upon us the impression of being gifted, interesting and amusing beyond words,' wrote Georgie later.[30] Thus it came about that three of Harry's schoolfriends, including Ned Jones, paid court to Macdonald sisters, who were in London between 1853 and 1859 while their father held successive ministries in Sloane Street and Marylebone. The dying Caroline was visited by Wilfrid Heeley, while Alice twice broke her engagement to William Fulford. The parents' faith was not transmitted to all the children and it was perhaps Fulford's ordination that made Alice reject him: to her belongs the most telling story of the family. During one of their many moves, she came across a faded envelope containing a precious relic, a lock of Charles Wesley's hair, which she promptly threw into the fire with the words: 'See! a hair of the dog that bit us!'[31] The most memorable anecdote of Georgie's youth concerned a heated argument as to whether, in extremity, one could eat a mouse. Wilfrid Heeley said he would, but when Alice cooked a little mouse pie he failed to respond to the challenge. Georgie, however, who was later to display great moral determination, ate a mouthful.[32]

Her artistic talents were for music – she sang and played the piano and enjoyed arranging words and music – and for drawing, at which she was thought good enough to attend classes at the School of Design, located in South Kensington. Later she dismissed her talent almost entirely, writing: 'I had a certain deftness of hand, but I did not learn anything vital',[33] but she took it seriously at the time, and once combined with a fellow student to purchase a print to copy out of school.[34] Her interest in art went hand in hand with interest in Ned Jones, one of Harry's friends whom she had long idolized, even though she had been barely out of the nursery when they first met. The only son of an unsuccessful Birmingham tradesman who lovingly pushed his son to scholastic advancement, Ned left Oxford untidily at the end of 1855, arriving in London with the idea of becoming a painter. He worshipped Rossetti and spent a good deal of time with him, but with his close friend Topsy still in Oxford, he was frequently lonely and grateful for the warm welcome he found at the Macdonalds' house. I think, too, he was partly appalled by the world of prostitutes and homeless vagrants that Gabriel showed him in their late-night walks around town and felt the need of a solid, moral anchor. The Birmingham Set, Georgie wrote, were all very idealistic, desiring to improve the world and live decorously. They had no 'conquering' airs towards women and were, she believed, certainly virgins before marriage.[35]

Ned was twenty-two and Georgie fifteen in 1856 when, after escorting her to the Royal Academy summer exhibition and sometimes meeting her on the way home from her drawing class, he formally asked her parents for permission to marry her. This was the 'correct' way to do things. Afterwards Georgie was summoned by her mother to be told the news and to be given her parents' blessing. Looking back, Georgie remarked on her father's freedom from mercenary considerations, since Ned's prospects were not great, but of course the Macdonald family was in no position to ask for better terms; in any case they believed that true affection was infinitely more valuable than money. With Georgie so young and Ned so poor, it promised to be a long engagement, but it is likely that for some time at least neither wished it any different. Ned was able to use the Macdonald home almost as his own in the evenings and otherwise to channel all his energies into his work. Georgie lived for the times she was alone with him and stared wide-eyed at the glimpses into the artistic world he showed her. His first gifts were his own favourite books, La Motte Fouqué's *Minstrel Love* and Rio's *The Poetry of Christian Art*. *The Arabian Nights*, which Morris presented to her sister Aggie as a sort of present for the whole family, was a more popular choice, read and reread aloud. Georgie first met Morris at the Royal Academy in 1855 and he called in correct fashion a year later with an engagement gift, Turner's *Rivers of France*, but though he was Ned's nearest friend, she did not much take to him; 'we were not much the nearer for this meeting,' she remarked of the man who after her husband was to mean the most to her.[36]

Awestruck, she was introduced to Gabriel at Chatham Place (but not to Lizzie) and taken to see Millais' studio. At the end of 1856 Ned and Topsy moved into the Red Lion Square studio and gradually the bohemian ways of the artistic world were revealed. Georgie had, she remarked, 'no precise idea of what the profession of art meant, but felt it was well to be amongst those who painted pictures and wrote poetry'.[37] Looking back, she tried to recall its impact:

> I wish it were possible to explain the impression made upon me as a young girl whose experience so far had been quite remote from art, by sudden and close intercourse with those to whom it was the breath of life. The only approach I can make to describing it is by saying that I felt in the presence of a new religion. Their love of beauty did not seem to me unbalanced, but as if it included the whole world.[38]

In the spring of 1857 Georgie was introduced to Ned's father in Birmingham and also to his former nurse Miss Sampson, who had cared for him since his mother's death soon after he was born, and whose jealous affection was such that 'an angel in heaven would have been unworthy' of being her darling boy's wife. True to her upbringing, Georgie did not drink wine, and when Ned made a small, charming ceremony by pouring water from a height into her glass so that it would sparkle, Miss Sampson was heard to mutter against such flirtatious absurdity,[39] but in general Georgie made a good impression, showing a modest pleasure at her good fortune. From Birmingham they went to Oxford, to meet Ned's friends the Maclarens, in whose garden Topsy was endeavouring to paint, and on their return to London they saw the small Pre-Raphaelite exhibition mounted in Russell Place. Still Georgie was not introduced to Lizzie, although as an art student she might have had an interest in meeting the only female exhibitor. Later, Gabriel took Ned to Little Holland House to meet an older generation of famous sisters, born Pattle and now married in various distinguished ways, before whisking him off to paint the Oxford Union murals. Ned's theme there was Nimue luring Merlin, showing woman as enchantress, a subject to which he regularly returned but one which was hardly inspired by the patient, self-denying Georgie, waiting quietly at home. She represented, rather, Eurydice or Alcestis, the loving, supportive, dependent wife.

She saw Ned briefly after Christmas, when he came to London and, as it seems, shared Fanny's services as a model. On the eve of Gabriel and Topsy's respective departures to Matlock and Oxford, there was a small evening party at Red Lion Square. 'Do come,' wrote Ned to Brown, promising 'victuals and squalor at all hours, and a stunner or two to make melody'.[40] This was a reference to Georgie and her sister, and a piano that was specially hired for the evening so they could entertain the company; Georgie's rendering of old troubador songs was particularly admired. Ned then left again for Oxford to finish his fresco. Before he went he took Georgie to meet the Browns. This was a day or two after the incident involving the seventeen-year-old girl 'starving in spite of prostitution' but Brown refrained from asking any questions, rightly divining that Georgie, who was the same age as the poor girl, had not been told of it. She was introduced to Brown as an art student. 'This little girl,' he commented warily, 'seems to threaten to turn out another genius,'[41] but he agreed to give her lessons, which she shared with Emily Seddon, whose brothers were Thomas and J.P. Seddon, painter and architect respectively. Georgie described these lessons as 'Madox Brown's incredible kindness in allowing me . . . to come and try to paint from a model in his studio',[42] and she professed herself prouder

that, when Emma was again ill in the summer of 1858, perhaps
suffering from the effects of a second miscarriage, she was allowed
to take three-year-old Nolly home for a few days. She liked
children and long remembered Nolly, unfamiliarly dressed in
white embroidered cambric, travelling by bus to meet her family.
Emma's amiable, indulgent style of childcare had produced a
robust, untamed infant who must have caused Hannah Macdonald
some qualms as he trod on a pie left on the windowsill to cool or
jumped on to the middle of a new-made bed, but the visit was
generally considered a success. It marked, however, the end of
Georgie's attendance at what Ned called Brown's 'little Academy'
of lady pupils.[43]

Ned himself was spending most of his time at Little Holland
House, having been 'rescued' from illness and depression at Red
Lion Square by Sarah Prinsep, Val's mother and patroness of
painters. Her home contained G.F. Watts and his studio and
functioned as a centre of artistic culture and cultivated
unconventionality.[44] Here Ned met Mrs Prinsep's beautiful and
talented sisters, Maria Jackson, Julia Cameron, Sophie Dalrymple
and Virginia, later Countess Somers. To Georgie it represented an
alluring, fashionable world against which Ned might find her own
attractions modest; she later wrote, 'I could not then realize as I do
now what this visit to Little Holland House must have meant to
him.'[45] Mrs Prinsep and Lady Somers actually called on the
Macdonalds in a visit that 'was felt to be one of inspection as well
as courtesy' and the two women seemed to come from a different
world. Georgie and Alice were invited to a dinner party at Little
Holland House, where they wondered at the 'dimly lighted, richly
coloured rooms', with 'dark passages opening into lofty studios'
and a table spread with 'boundless welcome'.[46] It was all very
different from the careful economy of a Methodist minister's
household. It was equally distant from the world into which, by
the end of 1858, Fanny had moved, modelling and now mixing
socially with Gabriel and his companions.

It is now necessary to introduce more fully George Price Boyce,
who has previously featured in this history of Pre-Raphaelite
women only in relation to Annie Miller, whose portrait he drew
while Hunt was in the Holy Land and whom he and Gabriel had

so scandalously escorted to Cremorne. Boyce was a personable young man, now aged thirty-two; the son of a prosperous pawnbroker, he began as an architect before turning to painting, mainly in watercolour. His sister Joanna was also an artist, whose work was highly regarded.[47] Boyce lacked the moral idealism associated with the Pre-Raphaelite school; he was openly interested in the physical charms of female life models and enjoyed the freedom of his bachelor status as an artist about town. He may be seen as a classic example of the reluctant bridegroom, not marrying until the age of forty-seven, by which time he had moved from a service apartment to a house of his own; he seems to have been driven to look for a wife by the difficulty of dealing with servants. His chief importance in the Pre-Raphaelite story lies in the fact that his diaries, kept largely as a record of his social engagements, provide a valuable contemporary source of information, particularly in respect of Fanny, whom other histories tend to ignore, and of whom Boyce was, in his way, very fond.

She met him for the first time at the end of 1858, when he called on Gabriel. 'We went off at dusk and dined at the Cock,' the diary entry reads, 'and afterwards adjourned to 24, Dean St, Soho, to see "Fanny". Interesting face and jolly hair and engaging disposition.'[48] The following day Boyce called on Spencer Stanhope, in the studio below Gabriel's, who was still occupied with his picture of 'a gay woman in her room by side of Thames at her toilet', for which Fanny was modelling. The finished painting, *Thoughts of the Past*,[49] shows a girl in a dressing gown, holding a hairbrush and standing before a window looking out on to the river and its busy traffic. She looks out of the canvas with a direct but abstracted gaze, and only those well versed in the iconography of Victorian painting can immediately 'read' the accessories that refer to her occupation: a walking stick and discarded posy on the bare floor, coins on the untidy dressing table, a torn curtain, straggling plants and the rest. The girl's face does not resemble Fanny's but there are signs of repainting and she was clearly the model for Stanhope's careful ink study[50] where the head is shown in profile. She looks young and handsome.

At this stage, Boyce wrote Fanny's name in quotation marks in his diary, evidently aware of its 'professional' nature. She was living in Soho, a favourite area for prostitutes owing to its proximity to the Haymarket and Argyll Rooms (and thus relatively expensive), which indicates that she was still plying her trade, although friendship with Gabriel and the modelling opportunities he found for her may soon have provided sufficient alternative income. She was already on terms of some intimacy with Gabriel; as Boyce noted, when she finished sitting to Stanhope, she went upstairs 'to Rossetti'.[51] She evidently flirted with Boyce too and a few days after Christmas he met her at the Argyll Rooms and took her to dinner, where she was 'in considerable trepidation lest Rossetti should come in – and lo! he did'.[52] From these fragmentary records, one gets a picture of two men in jocular rivalry for a woman's favours; but there is a hint that, for Fanny, things had a more serious edge.

Her next recorded appearance among the Pre-Raphaelites was in February 1859, when she was about to leave Dean Street to move to a new lodging in Tenison Street on the South Bank.[53] This was less central than Soho, probably cheaper, but within easy reach of Gabriel's studio at Blackfriars and Boyce's just across the river in Buckingham Street, and it seems that she was installed there partly under their protection and possibly with their financial support; Boyce at least was relatively well-off. Her relationship with her two new gentlemen friends is well conveyed in selected entries from Boyce's diary for 1859:

> February 11. Went to see Fanny and gave her a sovereign to help her in the furnishing of her new house.
> March 24. Rossetti came and we went to Tennyson St. [sic] and picked up Fanny, and thence to Zoological Gardens, where he wanted to draw a fawn for his Magdalen drawing. We stayed there 3 or 4 hours, much amused by the brown bear, wombat and some owls.
> April 2. To Tennyson St. to tea with Fanny and DGR. Took with me a little oil sketch . . . as a present for the former.
> April 11. Called on FC in Tennyson Street and gave her a silver thimble I had promised her, and made a slight pencil sketch of her.[54]

It is clear from Fanny's later life that she measured affection in gifts, a mercenary trait deplored by those who saw her as a blight on Gabriel's life, but one early understood and accepted by him. It has been suggested that she was maintained by Gabriel in Tenison

Street in exchange for sexual favours,[55] but it seems more likely that this arrangement was with Boyce. He was essentially a libertine, responding to a pretty face or a sexy look but never losing his head or his heart. In contrast, Gabriel had a deep and responsive sympathy towards people which, however badly he behaved otherwise, was genuine at the point of contact and aroused strong affection in others. To Fanny, whose other relationships were probably not marked by depth of feeling, his attention and very real affection were probably devastating. She may have liked Boyce, but she was soon in love with Gabriel, and their subsequent relationship suggests that she never ceased to love him. In her own fashion, she remained faithful to him for the rest of his life.

Their affair seems to have blossomed in the summer of 1859. Lizzie had not been seen for over a year and Jane, whom he had seen only once on a flying visit to Oxford the previous year, was now irrevocably married to Topsy. Gabriel used Fanny as his model in several paintings at this period[56] and in July 1859 he began a spectacular picture of her that was unequivocal. It was called *Bocca Baciata*[57] which means, simply, 'the kissed mouth' and is taken from a reference in Boccaccio to lips that are used many times still remaining fresh. It is in oils and is the first major work in the 'sensuous' mode that is now considered typical of his art. Up to this point his work, if not always as bloodless as some of his religious subjects, was remote and romantic in approach; his depiction of the passionate kiss between Paolo and Francesca, for example, had been far from voluptuous. *Bocca Baciata* is an avowedly sensual work. It contains an apple, symbol of sexual temptation, and various indications of vanity and lust. The background was filled with marigolds, or '"them behind's merrygoes" as the fair original might say in her striking rendering', to quote Gabriel.[58] Since Rossetti's art so frequently offers 'a running commentary on his emotional life'[59] it is reasonable to infer that, whatever the reasons for painting Fanny, she brought him release from the 'stale virginities' of his youth. This is not a popular view of Gabriel, who is usually presented as a Casanova or Don Juan, but the evidence that Fanny provided his first full sexual experience is strong. If one were writing his biography solely from his work, one would have to conclude that *Bocca Baciata* and the other pictures of Fanny that followed marked an important event in his life. His letters show he was always grateful to her, as if she perhaps helped him shed the sense of guilt and shame that surrounded the subject of sex, seen as an animal passion. This interpretation is supported not only by his painting but also by a resurgence of poetic composition, which always tended to accompany his periods of emotional tension. Gabriel's most sexually explicit poem is 'After the French Liberation of Italy' in which copulation is used as an elaborate metaphor for the political situation:

> As when the last of the paid joys of love
> Has come and gone: and with a single kiss
> At length, and with one laugh of satiate bliss
> The wearied man one minute rests above
> The wearied woman, no more urged to move
> In those long throes of longing, till they glide
> Now lightlier clasped, each to the other's side,
> In joys past acting, not past dreaming of:
> So Europe now beneath this paramour
> Lies for a little out of use – full oft
> Submissive to his lust, a loveless whore,
> He wakes, she sleeps, the breath falls slow and soft.
> Wait: the bought body holds a birth within,
> An harlot's child, to scourge her for her sin.

This was written in 1858, soon after he met Fanny. His next poem, 'Jenny', presented prostitution more directly and in a new way, outside the punitive constructions of the Fallen Woman theme, although we may note that in order to reduce her contaminating influence, Jenny herself remains safely asleep in the poem, which consists of the narrator's random thoughts on her profession. She is rendered partly in the conventional terms of faded lilies, besmirched clothes, despair, decline and death, but also in terms usually reserved for love poetry:

> Fair Jenny mine, the thoughtless queen
> Of kisses which the blush between
> Could hardly make much daintier;
> Whose eyes are as blue skies, whose hair
> Is countless gold incomparable:

and her charms are described in a very physical manner:

> all your wealth of loosen'd hair
> Your silk ungirdled and unlac'd
> And warm sweets open to the waist,
> All golden in the lamplight's gleam . . .
>
> Poor beauty, so well worth a kiss!

This deliberate ambiguity of attitude is felt throughout the rambling poem, which offers a rich confusion of thought and imagery on what is evidently a 'difficult' subject, in a discourse that adopts several points of view. It is suggested that Jenny is glad of a moment's rest

> From the heart-sickness and the din
> Where envy's voice at virtue's pitch
> Mocks you because your gown is rich;
> And from the pale girl's dumb rebuke
> Whose ill-clad grace and toil-worn look
> Proclaim the strength that keeps her weak . . .

and that whores are made by men:

> Jenny, looking long at you,
> The woman almost fades from view.
> A cipher of man's changeless sum
> Of lust, past, present and to come,
> Is left . . .

and that other women combine to confirm their outcast status:

> Like a rose shut in a book
> In which pure women may not look . . .
>
> And so the life-blood of this rose
> Puddled with shameful knowledge, flows
> Through leaves no chaste hand may unclose . . .

The point here is not that Fanny equals Jenny in some simple poetic equation, for the poem is not about a particular woman but about prostitution in general. However, it looks very much as if Fanny's advent into Gabriel's life in the years 1858 and 1859 inspired him to treat his theme in this manner, giving it a complex character and enabling him to see the woman, as it were, behind the harlot.[60] This would accord with the fact that his first meeting with her impelled him to return to the long-abandoned *Found*. That picture, however, had been conceived in the earlier Pre-Raphaelite mode of moral idealism, in which the Fallen Woman was inevitably wretched and ashamed and caught in her sin like a calf in a net.

It is my guess that when Gabriel got to know Fanny better, he realized that such an interpretation was neither accurate nor compassionate, and that as his understanding developed, he became dissatisfied with his painting, which remained unfinished for many years and was never wholly completed. 'Jenny' and the pictures of Fanny that began with *Bocca Baciata* represent a more mature, less judging view of women who secured their livelihoods by selling sexual (as distinct from domestic or matrimonial) services. It is interesting to compare the manner in which Fanny's head was drawn in the study for *Found* and its shamed, wincing expression with that drawn *in propria persona* a few months later, head held high and brow raised.[61] In both drawings she is wearing the same earrings and her hair is loosely gathered behind her head but in the first she is pitiable, in the second, proud.

Bocca Baciata was much admired by other artists in the Pre-Raphaelite circle, who seem to have recognized its significance. Spencer Stanhope praised it, as did Arthur Hughes, who told William Allingham that the picture was 'such a superb thing, so awfully lovely' that George Boyce, whom Gabriel had persuaded to buy it, might be tempted 'to kiss the dear thing's lips away'.[62] Swinburne, who was franker, said it was 'more stunning than can be decently expressed',[63] while Holman Hunt complained of its 'gross sensuality of a revolting kind', saying it showed pure animal passion, dressing up the worst vices 'in the garb only deserved by innocence and virtue'.[64] To him, artistic beauty could only represent moral goodness, although as he was on the point of starting a not dissimilar picture perhaps his remark was provoked as much by rivalry as morality. Boyce himself was delighted with his purchase. Two days after seeing it for the first time in October 1858, he called to see Fanny, taking a present of apples and walnuts. Secure for the moment in a stream of admiration, she appears to have given up whoring, perhaps in anticipation of an easier life. She and Boyce had a long gossip, for he had been out of London for the summer, and one of her items of news was that Annie Miller had called on Gabriel, leaving her card like a proper lady.

8

Annie had spent the previous two years continuing her education and quarrelling, in various ways, with her 'guardian'. Details are very unclear but she spent part of 1857 'at school'. She was installed, presumably at Hunt's expense, in lodgings at the house of Mrs Stratford at 11 Bridge Row, in Pimlico. A fellow resident, Miss Prout, was a former teacher and may have represented the 'school' Annie attended. The address was not far from Hunt's own residence and in general he seems to have been pleased with her progress.

In the middle of the year he moved house, choosing a larger and more impressive residence at 1 Tor Villas, Kensington, which was partly shared with his sister Emily, then an art student aged twenty-one and later to be his pupil. Following the death of his father at the end of 1856, Hunt was responsible for his mother and sisters. Annie went to Tor Villas to pose, possibly for the figure of Mary in *The Finding of the Saviour in the Temple*.[1] Mary's head is known to have been drawn from another woman but there exist some figure sketches that may have been made for the purpose of determining the model's pose and for which Annie could have sat. Hunt wrote to Fred on one occasion of putting off another model in order 'to advance the figure from Annie'.[2]

At some stage she fell ill. 'She has not been here the last two days,' Holman told Fred anxiously, 'and her aunt sends a letter to say that [she] has been too poorly. I am afraid it is very serious.'[3] The trouble seems to have been respiratory, perhaps no more than a bad cold or cough, but there was always the possibility that these were the first signs of something fatal. 'I hope she can be saved!' he wrote dramatically, arranging to take her to consult his doctor.

Soon he reported happily that 'Dr Elliotson gave a very favourable verdict of Annie's case – her lungs are weak but not diseased'.[4] She thus avoided the invalid label that stuck so firmly to Lizzie. In September she missed two more days' modelling but this time Holman was only anxious over his lost sittings.

His concern over Annie's health may have been partly in the nature of a premarital check-up, for it was widely believed that weakness and disease were inherited and that the 'unfit' should be discouraged from breeding. This was an additional argument against marrying girls from the slums, which Hunt may have hoped to quash by demonstrating Annie's clean bill of health. He told his friends, the Combes, that when he next visited them he would consult 'seriously upon the subject of matrimony and decide one way or the other for good'.[5] By the beginning of 1858 he had finally decided it was time to marry.

On 21 January he took his friend and pupil Robert Martineau to call on George Boyce. Boyce reported:

> After desultory chat and looking at drawings etc. Hunt introduced the subject which principally brought him. Having in prospect to marry Annie Miller, after that her education both of mind and manners shall have been completed, he wished to destroy as far as was possible all traces of her former occupation, viz. that of sitting to certain artists . . . and as mine was the only direct study of her head, as it was, he would hold it a favour if I would give it him and he in return would give me something of his doing that I might like.

Boyce was fond of Annie and pleased with his drawing, so at first he resisted,

> but finding that it was a serious point with him, and that my refusing would be in some degree an obstacle in the carrying out of his wishes with regard to her (which it would be both selfish and unkind and foolish in the remotest degree to thwart) I at last reluctantly assented . . . He thanked me heartily for my compliance. He gave me real pleasure by telling me that she says I always behaved most kindly to her.[6]

The desire to retrieve her portrait seems somewhat obsessional but as models were generally debarred from becoming ladies and Holman himself was socially insecure, he would not have wished anyone to possess evidence of his prospective wife's inferior origins. A week later, however, Brown recorded that Holman, having been 'all hot' on the subject of marrying Annie, had now 'somehow quite cooled again in a few days and says now that it is never to be'.[7]

It is not clear what the new obstacles were. By April 1858 he was in disgrace with his family, when *Household Words* printed the story 'Calmuck' based on his old relationship with the rustic Emma Watkins. The Hunts' outraged overreaction may have been symptomatic of family pressure against marriage to Annie. Or perhaps she herself objected to his continuing demands and criticisms of her conduct. The epigraph to the relevant chapter of his autobiography contains the following enigmatic lines, from a children's rhyme:

Cock, cock, cock, cock, cock, cockchafer,
If you won't come, I won't have you.

and a quotation from Carlyle to the effect that 'to labour honestly' is the 'everlasting duty of all men'.[8] This was an aspect of bourgeois ethics that he felt Annie did not share.

In June 1858 a minor crisis occurred; Annie appears to have got into trouble with her landlady, Mrs Stratford, over some issue of 'deceit'. Mrs Stratford called the police, whom Annie referred to Fred Stephens and whom he referred to Hunt himself. Meanwhile Mrs Stratford went to Chelsea, to call on Mrs Bramah, who had given Annie her first lessons in ladylike comportment and who had apparently recommended her as a lodger. Annie's 'sustained duplicity' was complained of. Stephens was hurriedly summoned and he reported to Hunt that Mrs Bramah was 'much shocked' at the revelations – so much so, indeed, that the dire 'question' (that is, was she pure?) was asked. Happily Mrs Stratford had answered in the affirmative. Mrs Bramah intimated that her servants had earlier told tales about Annie's deceitful ways but she was 'kind and indulgent as ever' and made 'ready excuses' for Annie's behaviour. Moreover, Annie's virtue, which seems to have been the chief preoccupation, was unsullied, as Stephens and Mrs Bramah agreed: 'I expressed my belief in the purity of the person,' he wrote, 'of which she appeared satisfied from Mrs S's statement.' In fact, Fred was rather more worried about the duplicity *he* was involved in through failing to confirm to Mrs Bramah that Hunt's interest in Annie was matrimonial. Mrs Bramah was 'more than ever convinced that you were interested in a more serious way than she is aware (from either of us)', he reported to Hunt, 'and *said A.M. understood so*'. He backed off this line of conversation, 'for really I felt ashamed to even tacitly leave her so in error . . .' and finished by cautioning his friend against continuing the relationship, apparently aware that Annie's 'misdemeanours' served as spurs rather than warnings; whenever she seemed most at risk, Hunt redoubled his efforts at rescue.[9]

Hunt was fairly unruffled about the whole business. He instructed Stephens to call on Annie and inform her of his advice, which was to keep more careful accounts in future and to watch her spending. Rigorous household book-keeping was a fetish of the time particularly among the lower middle class, who were persuaded that careful accounting would avert disasters, and that an inability to do this was the cause and not the effect of the poverty of the lower orders. Any extra money Annie desired would have to be earned, but not by modelling. Annie's response was proud: 'a steady and stern refusal to receive anything more' from him. She declined to listen and positively rejected the idea that she give up modelling and look for a more respectable occupation. She refused to take £5 offered by Hunt against her future account with Mrs Stratford, saying she did not know how much longer she would be staying there, and accused Miss Prout of 'tale-bearing' and 'neglect of duty'. She angrily asserted that Hunt had also neglected her, saying, as Fred reported to him, 'she firmly believed you had sent her there to be rid of her . . . she throws the whole blame on you, in shortness utterly intractable'.[10]

She was true to her word and refused further communication with both her unacknowledged admirer and his surrogate until September, when Hunt called on her personally; his refusal to deal with her directly must have been a most infuriating aspect of his relationship with Annie. It appears that he was once again determined to wed her: he was both infatuated and unable to believe that she might not do as he wished. He told his sister Emily, who was not pleased, and then called on Annie's sister Harriet, now the wife of a gasfitter, 'a dreadful slut' according to

Hunt, living not far from him in Kensington. But his courage
failed and as he reported to Fred, 'I came away without exposing
more of my design . . . telling her that Annie was quite well . . .
for there were ears and eyes at every chink in the house, not to say
all the other houses in the street.'[11] To announce his forthcoming
engagement in such circumstances would have been humiliating.
His last call was on Annie herself, whom he apparently offered to
marry as soon as *The Saviour in the Temple* was sold.

This offer, a curious echo of Gabriel's to Lizzie some two years
before, may have been meant as a final inducement, to secure her
correct and compliant behaviour by holding out himself as the
prize; or the balance of power may have been on Annie's side and
her silence a statement that she did not want him after all. She
apparently replied that she would give him an answer later. No
announcement followed, however, and it is difficult at this
distance to guess what was happening. It seems to me very
possible that she was now setting her sights rather higher than
Hunt, or perhaps looking in other directions. Hunt's fourteen-
roomed house in Campden Hill and the prices he was now
beginning to obtain for his paintings were by no means negligible,
but it must have been clear to her that their interests were
incompatible. She told Stephens that she had never been interested
in art and Holman was not the sort of person ever to enjoy
dancing at Cremorne. It seems to have been somewhere around
this date that she made the acquaintance of Lord Ranelagh.

The 7th Viscount represented precisely that world of aristocratic libertinism so abhorred by bourgeois moralists, and with a
heroic military career and a father who left several illegitimate
offspring as well as his lawful heir, born four months after his
parents' wedding, he sounds like a true denizen of *Vanity Fair*. But
although described as a 'real swell' and a 'notorious rake',
Ranelagh appears to have been an amiable, attractive fellow. He
was involved with more than one Pre-Raphaelite woman: in the
1860s Marie Spartali, of whom more later, conceived a grand
passion for him that was eventually vetoed by her father. At a
social level, Ranelagh's world was vastly more entertaining than
Hunt's, as far as Annie was concerned.

Rejected by Annie, Holman began to consider alternatives. In
February 1859 he wrote to the Combes in Oxford, setting out his
specifications for a suitable mate, preferably '5 feet 6 or 7 with

rather aquiline nose, long round neck and very beautiful –
complexion either fair or dark if good and not more than 24, you
must first ascertain that she is not engaged and that she could be
content to live on about £500 a year . . . Birth or money rather a
disadvantage than otherwise.'[12] The Combes suggested a Miss
Strong, for whose amiability they had high regard, and it is said
that later in the year Hunt proposed to her and was refused. It is
possible that he then returned to Annie and began a picture of her
entitled *Il Dolce Far Niente*, meaning 'Sweet Doing Nothing' or,
more critically, 'Sweet Indolence', an apparent allusion to her
dislike of the bourgeois work ethic. The dating of this painting is
obscure: the artist later said it was started in 1860 from a
professional model,[13] but as this was at a time when he was
anxious to erase all traces of Annie from his life it need not be
believed, and much about the picture points to it having been
begun from Annie; it was finished, indisputably, from Hunt's
wife Fanny, several years later. Both the hair and the pose suggest
Annie was the original model, and there is a tension between the
sensuous treatment of the figure, who is clad in a sumptuous
Renaissance costume, and the virtuous nature of the subject, a
young engaged woman reading by the fireside. She is fingering
her ring, which, like the absence of the same ring in *The
Awakening Conscience*, draws attention to her condition and
suggests to the spectator that she, or the artist, is thinking of
marriage and sexual fulfilment. Because of the difficulty of
knowing exactly when *Il Dolce Far Niente* was designed or
executed, it is not possible to read firm biographical significance
into it, but it is satisfying to speculate that it contains a good deal
of Hunt's ambiguous feelings towards Annie Miller as their
relationship deteriorated through the months of 1859; and that,
somehow, he used the more tractable medium of paint to create
the image of woman as he desired she should be in life.[14]

By the summer Hunt seems to have been on the edge of an
emotional breakdown. His behaviour towards Annie grew more
erratic, perhaps reflecting the pain it caused him to admit that his
plan had failed. At some stage he learnt, possibly from artists'
gossip at a Hogarth Club meeting, that three years earlier she had
been seen with the 'swell Regent Street whore' and at another
unspecified date 'she was met one day dressed in the extreme of
fashion walking down St James' Street with a live Lord Somebody

– a great rake'.[15] This was, of course, the fate he had always feared – and unconsciously prepared – for her. Rampant suspicion seems to have set in. Annie was asked to hand over 'a certain letter which she received from Brussels', which he was convinced was from another man. She said it was from a woman and offered to let him read it; he declined, and later changing his mind, learnt she had destroyed it. Fred was told to find out if George Boyce had been in Belgium, and if he had been writing to Annie. 'I can scarcely think of anything she ever told me of her position that I have not discovered to be false,' he commented, unwilling to relinquish his sense of superiority but entirely failing to acknowledge the contradiction when he described his own instructions to Stephens as: 'the things to be mentioned are truth although not the whole truth'.[16] The notion that the lower classes were congenital liars was a strong one. In addition, Hunt decided that instead of writing to him she was placing secret messages in *The Times* personal column, which was used extensively to communicate at a time when parents and employers still claimed the right to read all household mail. 'I expect one soon to have my name written in full,' he confided to Fred with more than a touch of paranoia, adding that he had 'directed Miss Prout to keep an eye on all letters received and sent away' by Annie, in the hope that this would 'unravel the mystery'.[17]

More seriously, she seems to have run out of funds. From Hunt's point of view, this was a risky situation, for if left penniless she might be driven on to the streets – the very place he had determined to save her from. If he abandoned her now, he would be pushing her towards prostitution. It was a nasty dilemma for him, but one that Annie does not seem to have exploited. On 19 August Fred passed on from Mrs Stratford the information that Annie seldom went out and was in a 'terrible bad' mood. Her cough had returned and her sister had tried unsuccessfully to borrow money. All Holman's original aspirations revived. 'The fact of her remaining at home now in poverty and difficulties certainly makes it seem she dreads to fall to the lowest,' he wrote; 'if so, she ought to be helped.' Perhaps she was now 'humbled enough to consider some plan of honest industry'.[18] He sent Mrs Stratford £5 to cover her lodger's bills and told Fred to buy Annie a copy of *Mary Barton*, Mrs Gaskell's story of the weaver's pretty daughter who narrowly misses being 'ruined' by the mill-owner's son and whose happy escape is contrasted with that of her aunt, who runs off with an officer and ends her days as a bedraggled whore. Tact was not Holman's strong point. The book was 'of all others most likely to make some impression on her', he wrote, adding that it cost only two shillings. He was, he affirmed, ready to do her 'any friendly service . . . if she would consider what she might be qualified for' and would 'give up her silly pride'.[19] Two weeks later, however, his tone was colder. 'I have nothing further to propose to aid the poor devil,' he told Fred, thanking him for all his efforts to 'save the silly fool'.[20]

It appears he now gave up all intention of marriage and merely wished to discharge his obligation by placing her in suitable employment. But his views did not coincide with Annie's and she proudly resisted his suggestions. By October, when Fanny reported her call at Chatham Place, she had reached the end of her resources. Evidently as part of her gentrification process, she had visiting cards printed, one of which she left at Gabriel's address. Faced with the choice of either obeying Hunt and taking what he regarded as suitable work, or defying him by going back to modelling, it is clear that she determined on the latter course. It is, I think, significant that at this point she turned not to the fashionable Lord Somebodies and swell whores, who might well have helped her towards a lucrative career, but to the painters who had shown her most consideration. On 22 December, Boyce recorded in his diary: 'Miss Annie Miller called on me in the evening in an excited state to ask me to recommend her someone to sit to. She was determined on sitting again in preference to doing anything else. All was broken off between her and Hunt. I pitied the poor girl very much, by reason of the distraction of her mind and heart.'[21]

Boyce had been told off once before for drawing Annie, so he immediately went to call on Hunt to ascertain if it would now be all right to employ her. Hunt replied that 'it seemed now as if she could do nothing else for she rejected all his efforts to find employment through friends'. He offered Boyce an explanation of the whole sorry affair: 'Finding he could not get her to do what he wanted to make her a desirable wife for him, nor to wean herself from old objectionable habits, he had broken off the engagement; but the whole affair had preyed on his mind for years.' Boyce was satisfied and a few days after Christmas, Annie Miller went to model at his Buckingham Street studio. While she was there, Gabriel came and made a quick pencil study of her. 'She looked more beautiful than ever,' Boyce noted.[22]

For a few weeks, Boyce and Gabriel vied for Annie's attentions and Fanny seems to have been quite displaced. Once again, the contest seems to have been won by Gabriel, who was no doubt delighted to escort Hunt's erstwhile intended around town. He drew her on at least five occasions,[23] responding to her regular features and fine wealth of hair; compared with Boyce's 1854 portrait of a meek maiden, she was now shown confidently, as if aware of her appeal. On several occasions, Gabriel 'poached' her when she had been booked by Boyce; a typical note, scrawled on his visiting card, read: 'Dear Boyce, Annie and I have come with 1,000 apologies, but really she must – do let her – sit to me tomorrow, and probably for some days to come. Pray pardon.'[24] On 11 February 1860, when Boyce had just begun an oil portrait, Gabriel came in the afternoon and went off with Annie. On 27 February she again went to sit, but as Gabriel arrived soon afterwards, Boyce himself noted that he 'did scarcely any work'.[25] On 29 March, however, he was able to paint uninterrupted and when the sitting was finished, he lent her a copy of *Wuthering Heights*, perhaps more to her taste than *Mary Barton*, and escorted her to the boat home to Pimlico.

Jane Burden was the first of the Pre-Raphaelite women to reach the goal of marriage after a conventional engagement. A blanket of silence was later laid over the twelve months that followed the formal announcement in the spring of 1858, evidently to conceal the fact that, like Emma and Annie, she was being educated and improved, to fit her for middle-class society. It has been remarked that later in life she displayed a cultural level above that of her class origins and whatever the 'deficiences' of her upbringing, she evidently remedied them well. When she first met the painters, she was perhaps too overawed to say very much and found silence a useful form of camouflage, but she was also intelligent enough to learn new social habits quickly and become familiar with the artistic ideas of the Pre-Raphaelite group. Knowledge of the etiquette of visiting or the running of a household was also necessary and while there was a good deal of advice in Mrs

Beeton's indispensable companion for the newly-wed wife, it is likely that Jane received some direct instruction in manners and servant management from some lady similar in status to Mrs Combe, or Mrs Acland. Curiously, although it is assumed that Jane remained in Oxford during this period, she was not introduced to Georgie and her sister when they stayed for a week in June with Ned's friends the Maclarens.

Sewing also featured largely in the life of an engaged girl, for a bride was expected to 'go well-appointed to her husband's home, well supplied with a store of good household linen, and with abundance of such clothes as are not likely to become useless by being unfashionable', such as underwear and nightdresses. Without such a trousseau, it would be assumed she 'left everything to be purchased with her husband's money', thus proclaiming her poverty to the servants, whose gossip would proceed outwards and upwards until the poor bride's social position was known to all her new neighbours.[26] Even if she did not wish to conceal her background, Jane would have been expected to make a fair number of garments for herself and possibly shirts for her husband; we know she was a good needlewoman, and when every garment was made by hand, one of a woman's main domestic responsibilities was the family linen; only at the top of the social scale were servants employed to make and mend clothing.

Her engagement appears to have gone smoothly, with but one cloud. In August, Morris had a wonderfully male holiday rowing down the Seine with Charley Faulkner and Philip Webb and later he went to Paris 'to buy old manuscripts and armour'. Then, wrote his biographer in a very obscure passage, 'the instability which he found, or thought he found, in his own character, became for a time acute. The overstrain of the crowded years through which he had been passing with all their inward revolutions, their pangs of growth and fevers of imagination had left him, like some lover in his own poems, languid and subject to strange fluctuations of mood.'[27] This seems to be a roundabout way of saying he had a minor breakdown and decided to give up painting, which may be connected in some way with Gabriel's reappearance on the scene. Rossetti was not a cad and would not deliberately have intervened in others' affairs but in June Boyce found him doodling a rough sketch of 'a "stunner" at Oxford, which he tore in fragments but which I rescued from the fire grate'.[28] A few weeks later, while Morris was in France, Gabriel travelled to Oxford, ostensibly to discuss his unfinished murals, and while he was there made a very fine ink drawing of Jane. It was described, in deference to his supposed task, as a study for Guenevere, but it was nothing of the kind; it was, rather, a striking, intense portrait that is often chosen to illustrate both the artist's skill and the sitter's looks.[29] Jane is shown wearing a flounced dress with a sort of cape collar and a loose bow at the neck, but these details are only sketched in. The head has a wealth of glossy dark hair and the large sombre eyes look down with a gaze that might be serene or mournful. The picture is inscribed with the monogram DGR and the date 'Oxford 1858'; it was soon seen in London where, according to Georgie, it was taken by Ned to the Macdonald home in Marylebone 'for us to marvel at'.[30] On 15 December Gabriel showed it to Boyce – and incidentally the same evening took him to Dean Street to meet Fanny for the first time. One wonders if some of Morris's strange fluctuations of mood were caused by the public interest being shown in his bride-to-be; he had perhaps not yet shed all the conventions of his upbringing. Jane's feelings are unknown, but evidently she did not refuse to sit for Gabriel.

More public curiosity was shown in March 1859 when Ned and Boyce, visiting Oxford for the weekend, took a boat with Charley Faulkner and Crom Price and rowed upstream to Godstow where, instead of Miss Lipscombe, they caught a glimpse of the 'stunner' whom Boyce identified in his diary as the future Mrs William Morris. She was not on show in the evening, however, when they dined at Topsy's lodging, together with the excitable Swinburne.[31] The view of Miss Burden was perhaps a distant one, for when Boyce was finally introduced to Mrs Morris a year later, he confessed himself 'surprised at the fine and beautiful character of her face'.[32] As his interest in Fanny and Annie indicated, however, he preferred the lively, blonde type.

Jane's wedding took place in St Michael's Church in Oxford on Tuesday 26 April 1859. Gabriel's absence has often been remarked but others were missing too. No member of the Morris family appears to have attended, no doubt to avert the social difficulties involved in meeting the Burdens, and there were few guests. Morris's college friends supported him, Richard Dixon performing the ceremony and Charles Faulkner acting as best man. Jane's father gave her away and Bessie may have been her bridesmaid; with her father and Faulkner, she was a witness to the marriage. The only other person present appears to have been Ned, who recorded the nervousness that characterized the whole affair: the newly-ordained Dixon, who had travelled from his South London curacy for the occasion, with over-rehearsed anxiety joined 'William and Mary' in holy matrimony.

They left on a honeymoon that took Jane to London and to the sea, which she saw for the first time – 'at Dover on a grey day, extremely disappointing'.[33] They travelled first to Paris and then through northern France and Flanders to Ghent and Bruges to Cologne and thence up the Rhine as far as Basle, before returning by the same route, on a six weeks' tour. It must have been a daunting experience, for Jane had barely been out of Oxford, spoke no language but English and was more used to obeying commands than giving them. Added to that, she was alone with her husband for the first time. Victorian honeymoons, particularly where both partners must be presumed virgins, are awesome to contemplate and it is to be hoped that Jane and William struggled successfully through their mutual initiation in foreign hotel rooms. It is possible that owing to shyness on both sides, it took them some time to get to the point of intercourse, but this speculation is based only on the fact that Jane did not conceive until a year after her wedding, which is hardly conclusive. There is no way of knowing how either experienced the sexual relationship; all one can say is that it seems to have ceased after a relatively short time, and was perhaps never very satisfactory.

They returned to London in the summer of 1859, while Lizzie was still absent. Meanwhile Annie was trying to avoid submitting to Hunt's prescriptions and Fanny was enjoying her success as the painters' new model. Jane was introduced only to Georgie and such was the impression made by her stateliness that Georgie dreamed of her the same night. The Morrises began married life in an apartment in Great Ormond Street; with his friend Philip Webb, Topsy was planning to build himself and his bride a splendid house, in the Kent countryside. His income at this date was somewhere between £600 and £900 a year thanks to his father's shares, a sum which provided for a very high standard of living. The Burden income had probably never reached £50 a year and Janey's new wealth may have been difficult for her to

comprehend. She was never given any responsibility for household finances and was probably, like many wives, kept largely in
ignorance of money matters. So her marriage began.

Georgie Macdonald's engagement threatened to be everlasting,
for Ned Jones had no inheritance and was not yet earning high fees
as an artist. By the beginning of 1859 he was living in a new
apartment at Russell Place in Fitzroy Street, while Georgie was
with her family in Beaumont Street, Marylebone. It may have
been at this period that she took up wood engraving, in place of
the abandoned art lessons, although this fact was virtually
suppressed in her quasi-autobiographical *Memorials* of her husband's life and work. However, her younger sister Louie's
engraving was mentioned, in the context of Ned's encouragement
and his promise that one day 'L.M. and E.J.' would illustrate a
book together; one hopes that he also welcomed and assisted
Georgie in her endeavours. He seems to have felt no urgency to
make her his wife. In September, when the Macdonalds were due
to leave London for the next Methodist posting, there was near
rebellion from the young people and some resistance from
Hannah too. Georgie was despondent, for they were to move to
Manchester where there would be few opportunities to see her
beloved Ned. She might also have felt that this provided an
opportunity to fix a wedding date, despite Ned's lack of money.
But she did not lament his failure to do so, for, in Georgie's eyes,
Ned could do no wrong; reluctantly she accepted her fate. It was
worsened when the few weeks that remained in London were
curtailed by the decision of a 'family council' that she should
accompany her mother on a visit to the seaside. It seems that, as
none of the girls wished to miss any time in London, Georgie was
sent away with Hannah because her future did not depend on
last-minute meetings with eligible men. In fact, although Ned
may well have wished to postpone marriage while he established
himself in the art world, he was genuinely fond of Georgie and
went down to where she and her mother were staying on her
nineteenth birthday and took them to Canterbury to see the
Cathedral.

When the dreaded parting came in September, it was 'lightened'
for Ned, as Georgie put it, by his being invited to Italy. He
returned in October but she does not seem to have seen him until
December, when he paid a short visit to Manchester before going

to see his father at Christmas, and then not again until April 1860, when in response to a generous invitation from Emma Brown, she was able to return to London 'for a happy month in Fortess Terrace, seeing Edward constantly'. The invitation was exceptionally kind, she later acknowledged, for 'besides the proverbial irksomeness of the society of betrothed people', the Browns had little space and 'it must have needed the best will in the world to accommodate even one person beyond their own family', yet she was aware only of 'one continuous stream of hospitality'.[34] No doubt her own cheerful contribution to the household, amusing the children and providing music on the piano, helped to make her stay a happy one, but it appears that there was also a further motive. The Browns hoped that the visit would help to advance Georgie's wedding. When nothing seemed to be happening in this respect, Brown took Ned aside and told him that 'he had better be married without delay'; perhaps he was fearful of a repetition of the long, and finally abandoned, 'engagement' between Gabriel and Lizzie. No arguments of poverty or prudence weighed with Brown, who had himself survived babies in penury and, according to Georgie, the matter was immediately settled. Left to himself, Ned would probably not have made a move so soon. It was arranged that the wedding would take place in Manchester, in June 1860, on the fourth anniversary of their engagement, in the same church where her parents had married. Georgie would be nearly twenty and Ned twenty-seven. At the beginning of May she went home to make her preparations.

Her financial prospects were poor, in comparison with Jane's, but she at least was not entering wholly unknown territory: this was what she had been reared for and she did not doubt her ability to be a cheerful wife, companion and helpmeet to her husband, as advocated in the advice manuals. Reading these one is struck by the truly horrific manner in which women were advised to defer to men on all matters and to refrain from asserting their own needs or demands: their duty, and their delight, was to make life as pleasant as possible for their husbands, for then their own lives would also be happy. Problems were readily acknowledged and a large part of Mrs Ellis's little book, *The Wives of England: Their Relative Duties, Domestic Influence and Social Obligations*, was devoted to the difficulties of dealing with men who were drunken, violent or bad-tempered, or who came home whenever they pleased and demanded instant meals, with everyone in attendance. Wives were instructed to solve such matters by self-sacrifice and a sweet demeanour, taking on themselves the full responsibility for household harmony; a husband with a cold or angry wife would have even more cause for complaint. Even the kindest of men expected deference and obedience from his spouse and this was assumed to be the natural order of things. A few voices, like those of Barbara Smith, Bessie Parkes and John Stuart Mill, were raised against this and it is interesting that even Mrs Ellis, who appears to have upheld largely conventional standards, found some aspects of women's condition insupportable. Men were trained to be selfish, she noted, by indulgent mothers and public schools, 'where the very name of woman is a by-word for contempt', and by sisters who, from early childhood 'are accustomed to fill an inferior place, to give up, to fall back, and to be as nothing in comparison with their brothers'. In this context, males soon learnt 'the dignity of superior power and the triumph of occupying a superior place'; it was only surprising, she said, that men were not more selfish still.[35]

In this respect, Georgie only half filled a 'traditional' role; she expected her marriage to be one of companionship rather than submission. In other respects too she moved into a world of changing values, which demanded adaptation. Even those whose class position was secure had to accept new technology and new ways of thinking. Geographical mobility, especially among the middle classes, involved the separation of families, so that young wives of Georgie's generation did not have the experience of their mothers, aunts and grandparents to call on; the day of expert advice was dawning. Many young middle-class women, married to technicians and professional men, also coped with running a home and rearing children without a great deal of domestic help until later in life, when they could perhaps afford more servants and probably needed fewer. In addition, their husbands were more often away from the home, as it became more common for the workplace to be at a distance from the family residence, and wives were left in charge of domestic affairs for what might be a very long day. Georgie and her generation lived in the transitional era between what is vulgarly called the 'traditional' and the 'modern' woman: still largely bound by archaic laws and social conventions, yet obliged to be resourceful, responsible and innovative.

As studies have shown, women of this period were anxious to improve their own lives and those of the children by advances in hygiene and education: piped water, baths, flush lavatories, medical care, varied diet, space to play and sleep, holidays and excursions, wider knowledge and experience. All these marked a departure from the world of the early nineteenth century when advances in science and industry were only beginning to make themselves felt at the domestic level. Women recognized, as Georgie did, the inadequacies of their own education and strove to improve their knowledge and ensure that their own daughters were better served. They welcomed home improvements and domestic inventions (such as closed ranges, washing tubs and sewing machines) that cut the drudgery of housework.[36] And, since much of their own time might be devoted to nursing the sick, they took a keen interest in medical developments and new theories, in the belief that certain potions or regimens would prevent or alleviate the often distressing and chronic diseases of the time; sadly it was not until later in the century that infant mortality, for example, showed any significant decline and the middle classes were only a little better off than the proletariat in this respect. Working-class fatalism may indeed have made death and disease easier to bear than the desperate middle-class hope, fostered by doctors and scientists, that cures were possible if certain instructions were followed.

In addition to all this, Georgie herself entered an artistic world which she carefully described to her mother as 'not so sheltered' as her own home had been.[37] She had given up her religion when young, as Ned had discovered early in their engagement, although I assume she continued to attend her father's chapel as long as she was living at home. Perhaps she, like her sister Alice, felt that Wesleyanism had been more of a blight than a blessing; it had not visibly lightened her mother's burden.[38] It is significant that neither parent attempted to make her change her mind. It was a family habit not to speak on matters of disagreement and Georgie's mother kept her own counsel on the subject of Georgie's apostasy, only once urging her to send her children to church if she could not take them herself.[39] But Georgie remained adamant and very late in life she joked that a religious servant, whom the family alleged had followed her with a prayerbook in his hand, would have had to walk a long way before he found her entering a church![40] This is not to say that she was an atheist: she had, I suspect, her own very personal and rigorous version of God, and was fiercely opposed only to all manifestations of organized religion.

She was not dismayed by the prospect of poverty. On the eve of her wedding, she assessed their material goods: £30 in cash from Ned's earnings and her own 'small deal table with a drawer in it that held my wood-engraving tools'.[41] This table, which appears to have been her only significant possession, was clearly valued as a solid symbol of her own aspirations. It tells us that, like her husband, Georgie had serious artistic ambitions, although as it turned out, Ned's brushes and pens were to eclipse her engraving tools.

The process began almost immediately. Ned confessed to being afraid of marriage: just as Effie had to sustain and comfort a weeping Millais throughout the ordeal, so Ned warned, 'I shouldn't be surprised if I bolt off the day before and am never heard of again.'[42] On the day of his wedding he developed symptoms of acute stress-induced laryngitis and the following morning Georgie found herself marooned in a hotel room in Chester, where they had planned to stay one night *en route* for France, with Ned a helpless invalid and her own role transformed from blissful bride to sickroom nurse. When her necklace broke on the bedpost and she searched for the beads on the floor, she admitted her disappointment. It was a foretaste of the lifelong role as supportive, self-denying wife she was to play, for Ned's illnesses were recurrent, manifestations of his unconscious emotional selfishness to which Georgie's needs and wishes were subordinated. He cannot exactly be blamed, for such a power role was built into the contemporary ideology of gender: only the romanticism that surrounded weddings suggested otherwise, and it was perhaps the loss of this ideal that made Georgie weep, on her hands and knees in a strange hotel room.

9

Ned and Georgie planned to go to Paris for their honeymoon to meet Gabriel and Lizzie, who, to everyone's surprise, had also got married. 'This sudden news was the first I heard of it,' remarked Bell Scott afterwards, adding that the Rossetti family were taken aback by the announcement.[1] Politeness prevailed however and the idea of a secret, unbroken engagement was allowed to gain currency. But the wedding was clearly unexpected and, for some, unwelcome. Within the Rossetti family, tradition held that the marriage was a calamity.[2]

Our last sight of Lizzie was in Matlock in the spring of 1858. Where or how she was living in the intervening two years is unknown and virtually the only ascertainable fact is that in July 1859, shortly before her thirtieth birthday, her father died. Mrs Siddall was left a widow with four unmarried daughters and two sons under twenty, one of whom was slow-witted. The cutlery business at Kent Place was kept going but it must have been a difficult and anxious time for the family and the financial strain no doubt aggravated Lizzie's unhappiness. There is no sign that she tried to continue her career as an artist after Gabriel's desertion; she was probably too proud to ask Ruskin to renew his allowance. Her prospects were very limited. As her great-niece wrote many years later, apparently recalling Siddall family memories of Lizzie's despair, 'after having his companionship for such a long time one could hardly imagine that she would have married some perhaps ordinary working man and settled down to a humdrum life'.[3] Her sister Lydia was doing just that, at the age of twenty-eight having recently become engaged to nineteen-year-old Joseph Wheeler, a coachbuilder's son working as a junior clerk.

It seems to have been during this 'gap' in her life that, perhaps to block out her misery, Lizzie became seriously addicted to laudanum, displaying many of the symptoms of today's heroin addicts. The drug was, of course, not illegal. Nor, contrary to popular belief, are the opiates lethal in themselves: it is possible to remain permanently on what is now called a maintenance dose without experiencing deterioration or crises; the chief effect is simply one of euphoria, and the myth of the inevitable downward spiral is similar to that ascribed to prostitution, a cultural prophylactic. Nevertheless, Lizzie's intake was high. 'She told me once that she had taken quarts of laudanum in her time,' said the housekeeper's niece at Chatham Place.[4] She was thus at risk of overdosing.

When Lizzie reappeared in Pre-Raphaelite records, she was gravely ill at Hastings with Gabriel. A hurried wedding was planned. Gabriel wrote first to alert his mother, saying as if in justification that, 'like all the important things I ever meant to do', it had been deferred 'almost beyond possibility', and adding rather opaquely, 'I have hardly deserved that Lizzie should still consent to it, but she has done so, and I trust I may still have time to prove my thankfulness to her.'[5] To his brother William Michael, he was candid about Lizzie's condition: she had terrible 'fits of illness' when she vomited everything she took, even water, and which compounded 'her dreadful state of health in other respects'.[6] Altogether it was a very gloomy prospect and he doubted whether she would pull through.

The most likely explanation of this rapid turn of events is that, believing that she was dying, Lizzie or her relatives had urgently appealed to Gabriel, and that he, appalled by her condition, had rushed her off to Hastings where she had once been happy. Just over a month earlier, he and Boyce had been cheerfully squabbling over who should enjoy Annie Miller's company, so there is little doubt that his decision to return to Lizzie was sudden. It is possible that he felt responsible for her deterioration. In the absence of a specific diagnosis of disease, her symptoms are difficult to interpret, but could indicate either a severe case of opium poisoning, possibly the aftermath of an overdose, or the acute effects of withdrawal; this might have been the crisis that led to his being summoned. Something dramatic had occurred, from which he felt he must rescue her. He must either save her life or at least ensure that she died without his being blamed for having heartlessly abandoned her. It seems that the first appeal was made through Ruskin, as Lizzie's former patron; this is the only explanation for Hall Caine's comment, never previously published, that 'Ruskin did R[ossetti] an ill turn with a high intention when he persuaded him to go on with the marriage which he recognized as a duty. A stronger man than R., having done the woman one wrong would not, at any outside appeal, have gone on to do her another. He would have stopped, if necessary, at the church door.'[7] Towards the end of his life Holman Hunt gave an account of Lizzie's relationship with Gabriel which included the claim that having once secured her love, Gabriel appeared to cease caring for her and that they grew

> more and more apart, till she got very ill and was supposed to be dying. Just before her end, Rossetti came to see her . . . she had asked to see him to bid him goodbye, she was really dangerously ill. He was touched and professed love for her, and said if she would but get better, he would marry her. She did get better and he did marry her.[8]

After their arrival at Hastings around 13 April, Gabriel made immediate plans for the wedding to take place in St Clement's Church. The earliest possible date, after banns had been called on three successive Sundays, was the week of 7 May, and Gabriel chose his thirty-second birthday, 11 May, for the ceremony, although he was not sure Lizzie would live so long. If not, he told William Michael, he would have 'so much to grieve for and what is worse so much to reproach myself with that I do not know how it might end for me'.[9] She seemed about to die 'more than once a day', he told Brown, describing Lizzie's vomiting and nausea. But she was subject to sudden improvements and was sometimes able to eat a little. Emma Brown offered to come to Hastings and look after her, a kindness that Gabriel refused, saying he felt he could 'not come away at all unless she seems safe for a time'.[10] In the end the wedding, postponed several times as Lizzie was unable to reach the church, took place on 23 May. No friends or family were present and the otherwise unknown couple Anne and Alfred

Chalfield were witnesses. An element of the snobbery to which
both bride and groom were susceptible was seen in the description
on the marriage register of Charles Siddall as an optician rather
than ironmonger and in the announcement that Gabriel sent to
The Times, where he called himself 'eldest son of the late Gabriel
Rossetti, of Vasto degli Abruzzi, Kingdom of Naples', and his
wife as 'Elizabeth Eleanor, daughter of the late Charles Siddal, of
Sheffield'; neither father had been near his birthplace in thirty
years.

One draft of a poem she wrote may relate to Lizzie's perception
of Gabriel's reappearance in her life:

> Many a mile over land and sea
> Unsummoned my love returned to me;
> I remember not the words he said
> But only the trees moaning overhead.
>
> And he came ready to take and bear
> The cross I had carried for many a year,
> But words came slowly one by one
> From frozen lips shut still and dumb.
>
> How sounded my words so still and slow
> To the great strong heart that loved me so,
> Who came to save me from pain and wrong
> And to comfort me with his love so strong?
>
> I felt the wind strike chill and cold
> And vapours rise from the red-brown mould;
> I felt the spell that held my breath
> Bending me down to a living death.[11]

A similar poem, which seems to express Lizzie's belief that she
was dying, is 'Worn Out':

> Thy strong arms are round me, love,
> My head is on thy breast;
> Low words of comfort come from thee
> Yet my soul has no rest.

For I am but a startled thing
Nor can I ever be
Aught save a bird whose broken wing
Must fly away from thee.

I cannot give to thee the love
I gave so long ago,
The love that turned and struck me down
Amid the blinding snow.

I can but give a failing heart
And weary eyes of pain,
A faded mouth that cannot smile
And may not laugh again.

Yet keep thine arms around me, love,
Until I fall asleep;
Then leave me, saying no goodbye
Lest I might wake, and weep.

Whatever the nature of her illness, Lizzie was well enough to leave Hastings on the afternoon of her wedding and travel to Folkestone, from where the boat left for Boulogne; here she was introduced to Monsieur and Madame Maenza, old friends of the Rossetti family with whom Gabriel had stayed as a youth in 1843 and 1844. They took some local excursions and fantasized about renting an old chateau with a 'wonderful garden and lots of paintable things'[12] before proceeding to Paris, which Lizzie had so enjoyed five years before and where Gabriel had planned they should meet the newly-married Ned and Georgie. When Ned dramatically fell ill, Georgie wrote to cancel the arrangement and apologize. Gabriel replied, making light of the disappointment and saying that Lizzie was anyway too sick to do much sightseeing. Instead, he was reading Pepys with her: 'It is by far the most comic book in the world. We have still got it with us from Mudie's and meant to have yelled over it in company if you had come . . . We are now reading Boswell's Johnson which is almost as rich in parts.'[13] They were also amusing themselves with the English language on foreign menus and he quoted some thirteen examples, including 'Dabs of divers dimensions' and

'Strasbourg's pie of liver'. They stayed at the Hotel Meurice before moving to cheaper lodgings on the rue de Rivoli, and Lizzie was reported to be rather better. 'Paris certainly agrees with her, as it always does,' Gabriel wrote.[14] They thought of settling in France (at one stage Gabriel planned to return to London to collect his painting things) and they acquired two dogs.

In Paris Gabriel completed what he termed his 'bogie' or ghost drawing, *How They Met Themselves*,[15] which in other circumstances would have been a bizarre, doleful way to celebrate a wedding. In a thick forest, two lovers with the features stylistically used by Gabriel to represent himself and Lizzie, encounter their earlier selves, walking in a nimbus and looking with some horror on two later figures. The later woman has her head flung back and her arms outstretched in a gesture of imminent collapse. Gabriel could not counterfeit emotion: this was his artistic expression of the alteration between the lovers' earlier and later relationship, underlined in the double date of the monogram: '1851–1860'. He also began to compose a watercolour of *Bonifazio's Mistress*,[16] which shows a woman dying while having her portrait painted – again a rather macabre subject for a newly-married man, but a recognizable means, perhaps, of handling emotion by indirect expression in art; the woman's head is in the uplifted position familiar in so many of the pictures of Lizzie. Both these works seem to me to indicate that when he married her, Gabriel believed her to be on the edge of death.

Lizzie and Gabriel returned to London on 21 June, and took some rooms in Hampstead while looking for permanent accommodation; the lease on Chatham Place, which was not considered suitable for a married couple, was not up until the autumn and the idea was that Gabriel should go there to paint during the day. He also had to accustom his family and friends to his and Lizzie's new status as a married couple which, given Lizzie's volatile state, was not easy. In fact, they had few friends in common, as Gabriel remarked to Allingham who, together with the Browns, was one of the small number of Gabriel's acquaintances whom Lizzie knew. She had, for example, never met Boyce or Ned Jones or William Morris. The middle-class protocol of 'establishing' a new wife by means of cards announcing the marriage, courtesy calls by friends and relatives, and other such social practices was dispensed with, probably on the grounds that Lizzie could not cope with many visitors; to Bell Scott's inquiry in October, Gabriel simply commented that it was all 'too much trouble, you know'.[17] He seems, however, to have taken some trouble to devise a monogram for Lizzie's new initials – EER – which was similar in construction to his own at this date. There was some gossip about their affairs: Mrs Bell Scott reported a party at which she heard that 'Mrs Gabriel Rossetti has not yet been seem in his mother's house, and has been invisible to everyone.'[18] Emma Brown was said to be with her every day.

A month after her return came Lizzie's first social outing as Mrs Rossetti, when on 26 July she and Gabriel went to meet Ned and Georgie at the Zoo, 'place of meeting The Wombat's Lair', together with Emma, Brown and Lucy.[19] She hoped, too, to get to the Royal Academy exhibition before it closed. On meeting her for the first time, Georgie was struck by her elegance – Lizzie had just come back from Paris – and by her hair; she wrote:

> We went home with them to their rooms at Hampstead and I know that I then received an impression which never wore away, of romance and tragedy between her and her husband. I see her in the little upstairs bedroom with its lattice window, to which she carried me when we arrived and the mass of her beautiful deep-red hair as she took off her bonnet: she wore her hair very loosely fastened up, so that it fell in soft, heavy wings . . . Whilst we were in her room she shewed me a design she had just made, called 'The Woeful Victory'.[20]

The subject of this composition was courtly: 'two knights fight for a Princess – the one she loves is vanquished'.[21] The victorious knight is old in years and dark-haired, dressed in chainmail; the dead one is young, fair and innocent.

Contrary to the impression later given by her brother-in-law, Lizzie did not immediately succumb to invalidism. She was weak but, as Gabriel put it, 'always so obstinately plucky in illness that there is no keeping her down if she can only be up and doing'.[22] On the other hand, she was frequently unwell when it came to irksome duties such as writing a thank-you note to her mother-in-law for a dinner invitation she was sufficiently fit to accept.[23] Several of Gabriel's letters at this date were written on her behalf. From his correspondence it appears that he was fearful of a relapse

and did not know from day to day how she would be. At the end
of July she became pregnant.

For three months they lived quietly at Hampstead and Gabriel
began a 'wedding celebration' picture of Lizzie entitled *Regina
Cordium*,[24] a flat, rather stylized portrait 'with the decorative
qualities of a playing card',[25] her head set against a gold
background covered with a red lattice of hearts and kisses. The
face and hair are broader than he had been used to show her with,
but it was some years since he had drawn her and it is not
surprising that, given his more recent enthusiasms for Ruth
Herbert, Fanny Cornforth and Annie Miller, he should have
brought something of their qualities to his new 'Queen of Hearts'.
In fact, a photograph of Lizzie, apparently dating from the time of
her marriage, showing her with a shawl clasped round her
shoulders[26] suggests that the painting is not a bad likeness. Close
to, however, the flesh is roughly painted with a greenish tinge and
the general effect is rather disagreeable. The sitter's hooded,
almost sightless eyes are prominent and she holds a pansy, symbol
of thought and memory. But it was, at least, an attempt to place
Lizzie among the gallery of gorgeous women his art had now
taken to depicting.

In September she succumbed to another bout of illness which
was sufficiently alarming for Gabriel to summon his mother's
doctor and for the local practitioner to be called while he was
fetching the first. It is possible that the alarm related to the early
stages of pregnancy. She seems to have soon recovered sufficiently
to go to Brighton with Lydia, from where she reported that after
ten days she had gained some weight and felt better, 'although I
am in constant pain and cannot sleep at night for fear of another
illness like the last. But do not feel anxious about it as I would not
fail to let you know in time, and perhaps after all I am better here
with Lyddy than quite alone at Hampstead,' she wrote.[27]

Househunting and money were Gabriel's main preoccupations.
The dealer Gambart offered fifty guineas for a head that may have
been *Regina Cordium*.[28] Lizzie wrote that she would like to see the
finished picture but was resigned to its departure. 'Let me know
its fate as soon as it is sealed,' she wrote, adding, 'and pray do not
worry yourself about it as there is no real cause for doing so. I can
do without money till next Thursday, after which time £3 a week
would be quite enough for all our wants – including rent of

J. M. B.
X mas /48

1   The first portrait of Emma, drawn by Ford Madox Brown in December 1848, shortly
after she became his model

2   Portrait of Emma by candlelight,
drawn by Gabriel Rossetti in May 1853
following Emma's marriage to Ford
Madox Brown

3   Portrait of Emma drawn by Gabriel
Rossetti in 1860

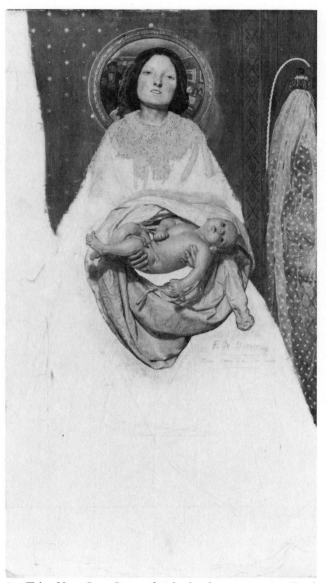

4   Take Your Son, Sir! unfinished oil painting by Ford
Madox Brown. Emma posed for the mother in 1851,
following the birth of her daughter Catherine the previous
year. The baby was painted later, from her second son
Arthur, born in 1856

5   Study for *Twelfth Night* by Walter Deverell, *c.* 1850. Lizzie posed for the figure of
Viola, on the extreme left, presumably in the costume depicted here. This was her
first modelling job

6   Study for the head of *Ophelia*, by John Everett Millais, for which Lizzie posed
in 1852

7 Lizzie drawing Gabriel in the studio at Chatham Place, sketched by Gabriel in September 1853

8 Self-portrait by Lizzie, painted 1853–4

9 Photographic portrait of Lizzie, probably taken in the mid-1850s. After her death, it was stated that no photos of Lizzie survived, but this portrait, evidently posed in an 'artistic' manner, seems to have been handed down within the Sidall family

10   Lizzie seated on an upright chair, drawn by Gabriel Rossetti in 1854

11 Lovers Listening to Egyptian Girls, drawn by Lizzie in 1854–5

12 The Ladies' Lament from Sir Patrick Spens, painted in watercolour by Lizzie and signed E.E.S 1856

13   Head study by Edward Burne-Jones, *c.* 1861, possibly drawn from Lizzie

14   *Regina Cordium* ('*Queen of Hearts*'), painted by Gabriel in 1860 shortly after he and Lizzie were married

15 *The Awakening Conscience*, by W. Holman Hunt, for which Annie posed in 1853

16 Portrait of Annie, aged about nineteen, drawn
by George Boyce in February 1854

17 Detail of *Waiting*, painted by Millais in 1854.
Annie is thought to have sat for the figure

18   Detail from *Dante's Dream on the Anniversary of the Death of Beatrice*, painted by Gabriel Rossetti in 1854. Annie posed for the right-hand attendant shown here, while Lizzie's features are seen on the face of Beatrice, who is being kissed by the figure of Love

19   Photograph of Annie, taken in the early 1860s

20   *Lady in Yellow*, painted by Gabriel, for which Annie posed in 1863

21   Study for *Found,* Rossetti's unfinished painting of a prostitute and a young man with a calf in a cart. Fanny recalled posing for this drawing shortly after she met Gabriel in 1858

22   Fanny Cornforth and George Boyce at the easel, drawn by Gabriel Rossetti in 1858

23 Detail from study for *Thoughts of the Past*, drawn by J. R. Spencer Stanhope in the studio below Rossetti's at Chatham Place by Blackfriars Bridge in December 1858

24 Detail from finished picture *Thoughts of the Past*, by Spencer Stanhope. Fanny posed for the figure of the young prostitute, but later the head was repainted

25   Detail from unfinished painting by Edward Burne-Jones now known as *Medusa* and dating from the early 1860s. Fanny is thought to have been the model

26   Portrait of Fanny, aged about twenty-five, drawn by Gabriel in 1859

27   *Fazio's Mistress*, painted by Gabriel in 1863, with Fanny as the model, shown plaiting
her hair after washing it. Later, Gabriel identified this picture as 'most like' Fanny

28   Photograph of Fanny, probably taken in the mid-
1860s to a pose devised by Gabriel

29   Fanny as an elephant playing cards, sketched by
Gabriel in a letter to Fanny during the 1870s

30 Fanny eating grapes, drawn by Gabriel in 1864

31 Portrait of Jane Burden as a study for
Guenevere, drawn by Gabriel in Oxford in 1858

32 Studio photograph of Jane, taken around
1860

33   *La Belle Iseult*, the only known painting by William Morris, for which Jane posed in
1858

34 Detail of photograph of Jane, posed by Gabriel during a
photographic session in the garden at Cheyne Walk, 1865

35   *Proserpine*, painted by Gabriel in 1874 with Jane as model

36   Photograph of Jane taken in 1879, apparently for
passport purposes

37   *Astarte Syriaca*, painted in 1876. This was the last
of Gabriel's pictures for which Jane modelled directly;
later pictures with her features were painted from
earlier studies

38　Photograph of Jane aged about twenty-five, in a
pose selected by Gabriel in 1865

39　Photograph of Jane in old age, seated in the
garden at Kelmscott Manor

40   The Morris and Burne-Jones families, photographed in 1874 in the garden of the Burne-Jones home in Fulham, London. (From the left): Margaret Burne-Jones, Edward (Ned) Burne-Jones, Philip Burne-Jones, Georgie Burne-Jones, May Morris, William Morris, Jane Morris, Jenny Morris

41   Photograph of Georgie, aged sixteen

42   Portrait of Georgie in 1860, drawn by Gabriel to
commemorate her marriage to Edward Burne-Jones

43   *Clara von Bork*, painted by Burne-Jones in 1860. The figure of Clara
was modelled on Georgie

44 Photograph of Georgie reading, taken in the mid 1870s

45   Photograph of Georgie with her infant son
Phil, taken around 1862

46   Portrait of Georgie, painted in 1870 by
Edward Poynter

47   Portrait of Georgie, with Margaret and Phil in the background, painted by Burne-
Jones in the 1870s

48   Mary as *Cassandra*, drawn by Burne-Jones in 1870

49   Portrait of Mary, drawn in chalks by Rossetti in 1870

course.' Of herself, she wrote, 'I should like to have my watercolours sent down if possible, as I am destitute of all means of keeping myself alive. I have kept myself alive hitherto by going out to sea in the smallest boat I can find. What do you say to my not being sick in the very roughest weather?'[29] She was still away on 4 September when Ruskin called on his return from Europe to offer his congratulations, but on his second visit he was pleased to receive from her 'a bride's kiss so full and queenly kind'.[30] If, as surmised, Ruskin had been instrumental in promoting Lizzie's marriage, such pleasure on his part would be natural; he had otherwise lost interest in her affairs. He told Gabriel that 'Ida should be happy to see how much more beautifully, and tenderly you draw when you are drawing her than when you draw anybody else'[31] – but then his moral disapproval of Fanny was to become well known and he had already declined to help Gabriel publish 'Jenny' because of its indecorous subject matter.

Fanny, it appears, was shattered by Gabriel's marriage. A fortnight after it took place she sent a message to George Boyce through a friend to say she was very ill. He went to call and 'found her so in bed. It appears she frets constantly about R., who is with his wife in Paris, the latter very ill and in a deep decline. Altogether a most melancholy state of affairs. F. was seeing a doctor and was in a very nervous, critical state.'[32]

It is hard to know what to make of this extreme reaction, evidently more emotional than physical. It is surely unlikely that Fanny hoped to marry Gabriel herself, despite my earlier observations on prostitutes' aspirations. Certainly he can have had no such intention, for it would have meant introducing her on terms of equality to Mamma and his sisters Maria and Christina, who were, as it happened, then assisting in the work of the St Mary Magdalene home fo. fallen women at Highgate, with the object of 'reclaiming' women like Fanny. If not marriage, then perhaps she had hopes of one day setting up house with Gabriel as his permanent mistress, and achieving the security she so desired. Or perhaps she was just in love with him and quite unprepared for the sudden reappearance of a 'beloved' of whom she knew little, since Gabriel was adept at keeping his life in separate compartments. It is possible that, consumed with worry over Lizzie,

Gabriel at this date stopped whatever contribution he may have been making to Fanny's rent. Boyce, who was often out of town, was clearly no substitute. So, either out of necessity or on the rebound, Fanny got married herself.

On 11 August 1860, a month after Gabriel and Lizzie moved to Hampstead, she espoused Timothy Hughes, a Liverpool-born mechanic working with a South Bank engineering firm, at St John's Church, Waterloo. She married under the name of Sarah Cox and was in her mid-twenties. She appears to have vacated Tenison Street briefly for another nearby lodging: her husband-to-be was already living at the former address.[33] Marriage conferred respectability of a kind and henceforth she was politely known as 'Mrs Hughes', but the circumstances were not auspicious. As we shall see, Fanny relinquished neither her affection for Gabriel nor her ambition; marriage to a mechanic was a temporary expedient.

She did not stop seeing Gabriel but continued to work for him as a model. The picture evidence indicates that she sat for *Fair Rosamund*[34] and for the Magdalen – her favoured role – in *The Sermon on the Mount*.[35] But the atmosphere in the studio must have been very different from the delightful days when Gabriel had drawn her with her arms about George Boyce's neck. She also modelled a good deal for Ned Jones, presumably in the front room of the apartment in Russell Place, which was made over into a studio. She sat, for example, for Nimue in *Merlin and Nimue*[36] and for *Sidonia von Bork*,[37] the portrait of the witch-heroine in Meinhold's Gothic romance which Ned found so wonderful that he never released himself from the spell it cast over his youth. She also appears to have modelled for another wicked beauty, if the evidence of his unfinished painting known as *Medusa* or *Woman in an Interior* is accepted.[38] In this work, Fanny's face is given a heavier, squarer look than in Gabriel's work, as if Ned perceived her in a harsher light, less luscious than threatening. He was always afraid of women's physical sexuality, as the bloodless, androgynous figures of his later paintings suggest, and towards the end of his life he made 'fat ladies' and Wagnerian heroines into objects of riotous, cruel fun. At around the same time, Fanny also sat, reclining on a sofa in one of her most characteristic poses, for a study of Venus for the first, watercolour version of Ned's *Laus Veneris*, based on the legend of Tannhaüser, the wandering knight who abandons himself to a life of sensual pleasure.[39] She wore a voluminous gown, with huge sleeves that reached almost to the floor.

Fanny was the model for the sorceress Sidonia while Georgie, significantly, sat for the picture of her virtuous counterpart and cousin, *Clara von Bork*,[40] painted at the same time, the images forming a pair of small icons to Ned's two most potent images of Woman. Unlike the scheming, seductive Sidonia whose hair and dress are covered with a tangled, symbolic net, Clara is shown as open, trusting and protective. In her hands she cradles a nest of fledgling doves, keeping them safe from the black cat, Sidonia's familiar, that prowls at her feet.

It was the nurturing role Georgie was to play so well in real life. After the sad start to her marriage, she took to domesticity on a pittance with delight and the first years she was with Ned were perhaps the happiest she knew. To furnish their new home in Russell Place, an oak table and black-stained rush-seated chairs and sofa had been designed by Philip Webb and made at the Euston Road Boys' Home, but because of the cancelled honeymoon, only the table arrived at Russell Place before the young couple and so 'the bride received her first visitors' while sitting on the table.[41] In addition, Ned had decorated a plain sideboard in readiness for their homecoming with pictures of 'kind and cruel ladies', feeding or tormenting animals,[42] and his aunt presented Georgie with her most prized possession, a new piano of unpolished American walnut, on which Ned painted more designs inside the lid and below the keyboard. This item was a luxury few young couples in their position could afford and is an index of their priorities for, if asked, Aunt Catherwood would surely have made a more practical present. But Georgie delighted in making music, and would play for guests late into the evening. On the back of her first household account book, Ned drew two little sketches, one showing her at the piano, and the other with a shopping basket, which in her words portrays 'his impression that I practised housewifery as well as music'.[43] At a party in the summer of 1860 Mrs Bell Scott remarked that Georgie sang some old songs (including 'Greensleeves') 'in loud wild tones quite novel and charming'.[44] Georgie's own family were now nearly all in Manchester and, like Lizzie, she found she knew few of Ned's London friends besides the Browns. 'The first friend I made in my new life,' she later recalled, was William Allingham. Late in July came the deferred meeting with Lizzie and Gabriel at the Zoo, and soon afterwards the Joneses went to stay with the Morrises at their new home, the Red House, at Upton in Kent.

Jane and Topsy had just moved in, their chief concern during the year they lived in Great Ormond Street having been the building, decorating and furnishing of this proposed 'Palace of Art' in the parish of Bexley, then still a rural area but easily accessible by train from London Bridge station. On giving up painting, Morris had transferred his energies to this project, which was designed to his specifications by Philip Webb; it was to be a 'proving piece' for both architect and owner. The location had 'something of the sadness of that common English lowland country of which Morris was so fond . . . fertile, well-wooded and watered, and interspersed with pleasant orchards and coppices'.[45] The house was built in an orchard and was surrounded by apple and cherry trees; it was architecturally ahead of its time, being an early example of the new vernacular style that was to flourish at the end of the century. Built in brick – hence its name Red House – it was somewhat heavy and graceless, as if elegance and comfort were not the chief object of a dwelling. Inside, the severity was the setting for a decorative scheme similar to that at the Oxford Union: mural paintings and patterned ceilings, a secular equivalent of the painted walls whose remains were to be found in old country churches. Webb designed much of the furniture, including massive tables, chairs, cupboards, and such items as firedogs and table glass; a huge settle which Morris had designed and helped to paint at Red Lion Square was installed in the first-floor drawing room, and Ned presented a great wardrobe decorated with scenes from Chaucer's *Prioress's Tale*. Gabriel painted the panels of a cupboard with scenes from Dante, showing Jane as Beatrice, with Fanny and Red Lion Mary as her attendants; part of the elaborate superscription, appropriate for a wedding gift, read 'My Lady carries Love within her eyes',[46] and the central panel carried a schematic image of a Cupid figure entitled *Dantis Amor*.[47]

The decoration of the walls began in the late summer of 1860 when the house was newly finished. All friends and visitors were enlisted to help and these months of joyful sociability enlaced with art were later remembered by Georgie as 'a time to swear by, if human happiness were doubted'.[48] On Lizzie's return from Brighton she joined the party at the Red House, from where she wrote to Gabriel about the painting he had just sold. Her letter read:

> My dear Gabriel,
> I am most sorry to think of your picture going at that low price but of course there was nothing else to be done. I wish you would put aside or send on to me the money for those knives, as I do not wish those people to think I am unable to pay for them. The price of the knives is two shillings each.
>   Your affectionate Lizzie[49]

The tone of this is practical and straightforward, reminiscent of long-married couples. It may have been at this time that Lizzie was working on her own wedding present for Jane, a wooden jewellery box, imitative on a tiny scale of the great wardrobe and settle, painted with pictures of lovers and ladies, which is now at Kelmscott Manor. She also lent a hand with the wall painting, for which Ned designed a large scheme of stories.

Jane, at this period, took an active and equal part in the Red House productions, which deserve to be seen as something rather more substantial than artistic house-decoration; they represent the beginnings of what was later to flower into the Arts and Crafts movement, a characteristic late-Victorian revolt against industrial production, in which women were prominent.[50] Jane Morris's contribution to this should not be overlooked. It is not thought that she was much involved in the architectural design of the Red House, although her one recorded comment, that the coal cellar was too small,[51] suggests that she may have been allocated a sort of 'housewife advisory role' in the planning and execution of her new home. She had no experience of living in such a large house, however, and may have felt a little out of her depth.

Although he entered marriage without much idea of what he wanted from it, her husband was generally egalitarian and companionable, and keen for others to join in his enthusiasms, so Janey was encouraged to participate in the Red House decorations. Together, husband and wife painted the pattern on the drawing-room ceiling, in a spirit of collaboration that recalled Morris's early story in which a medieval brother and sister work together

in a rather unmedieval manner, carving figures and foliage on a
Gothic cathedral.[52] Jane's particular care, however, were the
curtains and hangings planned for the interior of Red House,
whose atmosphere was to be enhanced by tapestry-like fabrics, for
which nothing suitable could be found on the market. Morris had
started experiments in embroidery before he met Jane. 'He got
frames made, had worsted dyed to his taste . . . and began a piece
of work with his own hands. This was the celebrated "If I Can"
bird and tree hanging of which I still have a piece at Kelmscott
Manor,' she later recalled, continuing, 'After I came on the scene,
he taught me the first principles of laying the stitches closely so as
to cover the ground smoothly and radiating them properly.
Afterwards we studied old pieces and by unpicking etc. we learnt
very much but it was uphill work but only carried through by his
enormous energy and perseverance.'[53]

Enthusiasm informs this recollection, half a century after the
events, and suggests that whatever happened later, Jane's marriage
began well. It was she who discovered and bought the fabric for
one of Morris's most famous designs. 'The first stuff I got to
embroider on was a piece of indigo-dyed blue serge I found by
chance in a London shop,' she related. 'I took it home and he was
delighted with it and set to work at once designing flowers.' These
were simple, stylized plants based on daisies, primroses and
campions, similar in effect to the later 'Daisy' wallpaper and tiles.
'These we worked in a simple rough way,' Jane continued. 'The
work went quickly and when finished we covered the walls of the
bedroom at Red House to our great joy.'[54] The stitch was a simple
couched running stitch requiring no great skill with the needle but
producing an immediate and attractive effect. The curtains seem
to have been worked almost entirely by Jane herself, with perhaps
some assistance from visitors and her sister Bessie. It is believed
that the hangings formed part of the 'medieval court' display at the
1862 International Exhibition in London when, it may be noted,
the Morris company received two awards for embroideries. As a
whole, the firm's work was regarded as rough and primitive, as
was its intention. The hangings were later given to the Joneses for
their house at Rottingdean and now, 120 years after they were
made, their faded but serviceable remains are hanging, as Jane left
them, at Kelmscott Manor.

'Another scheme for adorning the house was a series of

tapestries for the dining room,' she wrote, using the term tapestry as it was then commonly employed for all embroidered and appliquéd hangings. This was for 'twelve large figures with a tree between each two, flowers at the feet and a pattern all over the background'. Of the twelve figures, known as the Illustrious Women, only six were completed or nearly so, for it was conceived as a long-term project. 'During the slow progress of this gigantic work,' Jane wrote in explanation, 'we were making experiments in silk and gold, work afterwards to bloom into altar cloths, etc.'[55] This was a reference to the later embroidery work of Morris & Co; the Illustrious Women were not finished by the time the Morrises left Red House to live over the workshop in central London. Bessie worked on some of them.[56]

The identification of the figures has proved difficult. There are several possible literary sources, including Chaucer's *Legend of Good Women*, Boccaccio's *Illustrious Women* and Tennyson's 'Dream of Fair Women', in which tragic victims like Iphigenia and Jephtha's daughter feature along with stouter beauties such as Cleopatra. But to hunt for direct parallels may be misleading, for the Red House embroideries were not illustrations but an original series of heroic women. Similar creations were being undertaken in other art forms, such as the paintings by Gabriel and Ned of legendary women like Fair Rosamund and Sidonia, or the many stained-glass designs for stylized angels and saints, which used the same flat, face-on technique as the tapestries. Ned actually designed a 'Good Women' embroidery series for selected pupils at Winnington Hall school (run by a disciple of Ruskin's) to work on under Georgie's supervision. She had herself previously completed a panel showing a favourite theme of Ned's, with Merlin and Morgan le Fay, enchanter and enchantress mutually attracted and repelled, and she had started another of Arthur and Lancelot.

Why, in the early 1860s, did this small Pre-Raphaelite circle become so heavily involved in representations of legendary women? It was of course a form of homage to the female principle and as such was appropriate to marriage and domesticity, but what is noticeable about the figures produced is their lack of liveliness or individuality. They are often stylized cut-outs pinned up on wall or window. Whether singly or in series they are also isolated, decontextualized, stripped of meaning; the iconographic medieval model on which they are based is frequently insufficient

for identification purposes and compared with earlier Pre-
Raphaelite productions, the accessories are often rudimentary.
The trend to depersonalization is clear in Ned's outline of the
projected Winnington embroideries, where a total of twelve
figures was planned:

> All the ground will be powdered with daisies – only where
> Dido, Hypsipyle and Medea and Ariadne come there will be sea
> instead of grass, and shells instead of daisies. First will come
> Chaucer, looking very frightened according to the poem, and
> inditing the poem with a thrush upon his shoulder – then comes
> Love, a little angry, bringing Alcestis . . . Then a tree and a
> vision of ladies begins, all have scrolls with their name and life
> and death written, above their heads. The ladies are to be in uni-
> forms of blue and white, and red and white, alternately . . .[57]

In this description the poet Chaucer is in fact the most important
figure, closely followed by the (male) representation of Love; the
women are hardly distinguishable from each other. It is not
surprising to find that the leader of the female group is the
self-sacrificial wife Alcestis, who featured largely in Victorian art
as an illustration of True Love. Incidentally, a similar scheme to
the Winnington one is to be seen in the blue-and-white tiles of the
'Dutch Kitchen' designed for the South Kensington Museum[58] by
Edward Poynter, who married Georgie's sister Aggie. Without
the scrolls bearing their names, it would be hard to tell who the
figures are meant to be.

With the womenfolk detailed either to sit for or to embroider
these figures of other women, it is difficult to escape the
conclusion that the artists' preoccupation with illustrious but
long-departed ladies, safely rendered into objects, reflects the
process that was taking place in their lives, as the men's careers,
charged with new responsibilities, pushed ahead while the women
dropped into domesticity, relinquishing their own ambition. The
sadness that is visible in the melancholy faces of most of the
females depicted in the paintings and embroideries is striking: why
should figures intended to celebrate Womanhood possess such a
sombre look? It suggests an unconscious acknowledgement that at
this period in their lives, and in their social scene, their role was
essentially supportive and inactive. Images of women hung on the

walls of houses in celebration of their proper sphere. This is not to blame the painters: social and personal circumstances are more than sufficient explanation and, as we have seen, in many ways the men counteracted the main currents of the time, allowing women a larger place in life. But the tendency to glamourize and at the same time diminish women, displaying their decorative qualities while playing down their creative ones, was strong and seldom evaded. Yet one wonders whether, in planning a frieze of wonderful women for his dining room, William Morris or his friends ever asked how his own wife differed from her embroideries? In doing the work, did Jane or Georgie ever feel themselves to be sewing down their own situation? Their contribution was, of course, essential to the creative scheme, and Jane's stitching in particular has a fine, supple elegance which enhances the design, but in a way it serves only to underline the recurrent contradiction in the Pre-Raphaelite women's position. At the same time as they were encouraged to contribute and participate in the practice of art, which was generally reserved as a serious business for men, they were discouraged, set in a dependent relation, downgraded.

At Red House in the late summer of 1860, Georgie recalled how she and Janey spent their mornings at the embroidery frame or wood engraving while the men were mainly engaged in wall painting. In the afternoons the women sometimes went out for a drive in the Red House wagonnette, 'to explore the country round by the help of a map of Kent', visiting what were then still rural villages like St Mary and St Paul's Cray. It was not a time of great sexual division, for at mealtimes and in the evenings all joined in jokes and boisterous games such as the men had enjoyed among themselves at Oxford. The jokes seem usually to have taken the form of teasing Morris, in order to provoke the manic rages to which he was liable; on one occasion Ned and Charley refused to speak to him during dinner except through Jane. As the decorations were in progress, the first-floor studio was used as living and dining room, 'and a most cheerful place it was, with windows looking three ways and a little horizontal slip of a window over the door' through which birds could be seen hopping on the roof.[59] And after work, they played games. One evening, Georgie remembered, Jane was seeker in hide-and-seek, searching for Ned: 'I see her tall figure and beautiful face as she creeps slowly nearer and nearer to the room where she feels sure he must be, and at last I hear her startled cry and his peal of laughter as he bursts from his hiding place.'[60]

But these weeks of youthful high spirits were drawing to an end. One morning as she and Jane sat sewing, Georgie noted the seeds of change, when she found her friend was not busy with decorative embroidery and 'saw in her basket a strange garment, fine, small and shapeless – a little shirt for him or her'.[61] Jane had in fact become pregnant in April, just before moving to Red House. With Lizzie following suit in July and Georgie to do so at the start of 1861, a new phase was beginning.

10

Jane's first child was born on 17 January 1861; she was named Jane
Alice and known universally as Jenny. Emma Brown came to
assist: this was the first baby to be born in the younger circle of
friends and as their most experienced acquaintance, with three
children and five pregnancies behind her, she was able to offer
advice and support. The proud father wrote laconically to Brown,
a veteran of such events: 'Kid having appeared, Mrs Brown kindly
says she will stay till Monday, when you are to come and fetch
her, please. I send a list of trains . . . Janey and kid (girl) are both
very well.'[1]

A doctor would also have been in attendance and a 'monthly
nurse' hired to care for mother and baby, so Jane was relatively
well provided for. At this date the medical profession had only
just begun to dominate the management of childbirth through
anaesthetics and instruments and reference to male authority, and
most confinements were still purely domestic affairs. The
transition to professionalism was brought about not only by
scientific advances and belief in progress but also by increasing
mobility among the nineteenth-century population of Britain.
Having moved so far from her own place of birth, Jane had no kin
or neighbours to help at this time, and Emma travelled a good
distance from her home in North London in order to fulfil, as it
were, the function of an elder sister. By the end of the century this
role would be entirely undertaken by paid professional obstetri-
cians and midwives.[2] It is perhaps surprising that Mrs Burden was
not present, but there is no record of Jane's mother ever
visiting Red House and it is possible that she was deemed too

old-fashioned and ignorant to be of any use.

From the beginning a nanny or nurse was hired to look after
baby Jenny. With the servants we can see what an alteration had
taken place in Jane's life; she clearly did not personally have to do
any housework or childcare. The 1861 Census shows that at the
age of twenty-one she was mistress of a large establishment
containing herself, husband and infant, and employing four
living-in servants. This was an index of status and probably
represented the summit of achievement for most middle-class
couples. Even the poorest middle-class household expected to
employ at least one servant; while living in Finchley, the Browns
had obtained a girl from the Barnet workhouse, and in Kentish
Town they had two servants. Three was the number held to be
sufficient to prevent wives being turned into 'drabs and drudges'
themselves.[3] In addition, daily or occasional women might be
hired for washing, charring and other heavy work; their rank was
lowest of all in the highly stratified servants' hierarchy. More than
three servants, however, denoted real, perhaps ostentatious
wealth, and a male servant, in the shape of a butler, groom or
coachman, was a sign of true affluence; beyond this lay the upper
reaches of the bourgeoisie and landed gentry.

As enumerated in the 1861 Census, the Morrises employed a
cook, twenty-eight-year-old Charlotte Cooper from Somerset; a
twenty-seven-year-old housemaid named Jane Chapman; nanny
Elizabeth Reynolds, aged thirty-one, from Leyton; and groom
Thomas Reynolds, aged twenty-five, born in Woodford. In view
of their Essex origin and shared name, it seems likely that
Elizabeth and Thomas Reynolds were related and had found
employment at Red House through some connection with
Morris's family at Walthamstow.[4] Servants frequently found
places through a network of recommendations by employers.
Their master entered his occupation as 'Artist Painter BA' on the
Census return and the houseguest who happened to be staying at
Red House on the night of the Census, Algernon Swinburne, was
described as 'Student Oxford'. He had in fact been expelled from
the University the previous year.[5] Jane's sister Bessie was not then
living with her, but with their reunited parents in a Holywell
yard. It is not clear from the available information whether Jane's
husband was making any provision at this time for his indigent
in-laws when he was still well-off, despite his high level of

spending on Red House. Nor is Jane's relationship with her family clear; her children grew up knowing little about their maternal grandparents. The impression given by this lack of contact is that she was not greatly attached to her parents.[6]

It was considered indelicate, or perhaps unpropitious given the dangers that might befall, to mention pregnancy until it was well established and so Lizzie's condition was announced only after Jane's daughter was born. By the end of 1860 she and Gabriel had solved their housing problem by giving up the Hampstead cottage and taking on the adjacent apartment at Chatham Place, thus doubling the living space. The extra rooms provided a parlour, drawing room and bedroom, and seem to have been more or less regarded as Lizzie's area, with the old studio and sitting room for Gabriel to paint in and receive guests. One of the advantages was that, as it was a service apartment, they did not require servants; the housekeeper, Mrs Birrell, and her daughter Catherine performed or arranged the necessary duties. There was no kitchen: hot water was brought up and meals were either eaten out or brought in, and Lizzie was thus relieved of a good deal of domestic responsibility. They did, however, furnish and redecorate the apartment: Lizzie's paintings were hung on the drawing-room walls, Gabriel designed some original wallpaper, a full-length frieze of trees in red and black, to be printed either on brown wrapping-paper or blue sugar-paper, and he wrote proudly to Allingham: 'I should like you to see how nice the rooms are looking, and how many nice things we have got in them.'[7] One of their items of furniture was a small round table on a tripod leg, which Lizzie bought as a present for her husband.[8] The fate of the dogs they had brought back from France is not recorded, but at some stage Lizzie acquired a caged bullfinch, one of the pet songbirds so popular in Victorian London, and she and Gabriel began to buy attractive blue-and-white 'willow pattern' china.

Their housewarming party took place on 11 January 1861; the guests were Georgie, Ned, Ruskin, William Michael and Christina. Gabriel's mother had been ill and his failure to visit her, caused by Lizzie's being 'unusually unwell' had prompted a call from his aunt Charlotte and cousin Henrietta, perhaps also in recognition of their duty towards his new wife. But Lizzie clearly did not get on with her in-laws, nor did she even try, leaving her husband to send their thanks for a Christmas gift – of a wastepaper

basket.[9] Her brother-in-law commented that neither side made
much effort to meet, and recalled Lizzie's behaviour as offhand
and unsympathetic, saying she showed an 'attitude of reserve . . .
alien from approach . . . certainly distant'[10] and that her conversation was flippant and sarcastic in tone.[11] This may have been an
effect of her laudanum addiction, but seems more likely to be her
reaction to the antipathy she felt from her new relatives. Mrs
Rossetti was a formidable person, whose approval was hard to
gain. One has the feeling that few prospective sons- or daughters-
in-law measured up to her high expectations for her children and
Lizzie must have been aware of the Rossettis' surprise and lack of
delight at Gabriel's wedding. By this date, incidentally, William
Michael's engagement had been abandoned, for unclear reasons.

Lizzie got on better with friends like Emma and Georgie. She,
Gabriel, Ned and Georgie made an excursion to Hampton Court,
and over the winter of 1860–1 they often spent evenings together.
On one such occasion Lizzie sent the following note:

> My dear little Georgie,
>   I hope you intend coming over with Ned tomorrow evening
> like a sweetmeat, it seems so long since I saw you dear. Janey
> will be here I hope to meet you.
>   With a willow pattern dish full of love to you and Ned,
>   Lizzie[12]

She was ten years older than Georgie, with a wider range of
experience, and Georgie, who was rather in awe of her, recalled
evenings spent with Lizzie while Ned and Gabriel gossiped in the
studio before joining their wives, remembering that Lizzie 'did
not talk happily when we were alone, but was excited and
melancholy, though with much humour and tenderness'. Her
nervousness subsided when her husband came into the room, for
'Gabriel's presence seemed needed to set her jarring nerves straight
. . . I see them now as he took his place by her on the sofa and her
excitement sank back into peace.'[13] At this point in her recollections, Georgie pondered the question of Lizzie's health, asking
'how it was possible for her to suffer so much without her
developing a specific disease',[14] which suggests she was
unaware of Lizzie's addiction, of which the anxious behaviour she described is characteristic. Instead, she ascribed it to

a kind of artistic overstretching.

Together, the two women planned to illustrate a book of fairy tales. At the beginning of the new year, Gabriel wrote to a friend:

> Indeed and of course my wife *does* draw still. Her last designs would I am sure surprise and delight you, and I hope she is going to do better than ever now. I feel surer every time she works that she has real genius – none of your make-believe – in conception and colour, and if she can only add a little more of the precision in carrying out which it so much needs health and strength to attain, she will I am sure paint such pictures as no woman has painted yet.

Then, as if suddenly conscious of inappropriate hyperbole, he added, 'but it is no use hoping for too much'.[15] Lizzie's drawing of *The Woeful Victory* was a careful piece of work, but seems to have been her last completed composition; it was 'wholly her own invention', according to William Michael.[16] The only example of Georgie's work to have been published shows an unidentified scene with a young princess and two male figures.[17] The older, darker man is wrenching the younger by the hair. The drawing, apparently meant to be engraved, has similarities with *The Woeful Victory* but has more an air of Grimm than of Malory. It is, I believe, the one design Georgie said she completed for the projected book of fairy tales.[18]

The choice of material should not be described as slight, trivial and typically feminine, for a little while later Ned was using similar subjects for his paintings of Cinderella and Bluebeard's Wife, which may have been partly inspired by Georgie's work. She admitted to preferring drawing to housework. 'I remember thinking it quite natural that in the middle of the morning I should ask our only maid – a pretty one – to stand for me that I might try to draw her,' she wrote.[19]

The 1861 Census return for 24 Russell Place shows twenty-year-old Georgiana Jones living with her twenty-seven-year-old husband Edward C.B. Jones and their young London-born servant Annie West. In the same house lived an English-language teacher and his family and servant, and an elderly widow and her daughter, Emily Sarjent, aged twenty-four, described as 'Artist – Portrait Painter'. Ned's entry identified him as 'Painter', and it appears that Georgie was also so entered, by means of ditto marks, until a sense of propriety prompted the addition of the word 'Wife'.[20] 'It is pathetic to think how we women longed to keep pace with the men,' wrote Georgie later of her artistic ambitions, 'and how gladly they kept us by them until their pace quickened and we had to fall behind.' Of herself, she added: 'I stopped, as so many women do, well on this side of tolerable skill, daunted by the path which has to be followed alone if the end is to be reached . . .'[21]

The reasons why women have historically seldom excelled as painters have often been considered and are too complex to be rehearsed here.[22] We have already seen something of Lizzie's attempt to enter the male world of professional picture-making and the patronizing contempt with which her work was and is regarded. Several of her contemporaries fared little better. It is true that there were increasing numbers of women artists, as the exhibitions of the new Society of Lady Artists showed, but the very separatism suggests that, as was indeed the case, they found it hard to achieve equal recognition. Holman's sister Emily Hunt persevered, exhibiting several times at the Royal Academy, but seems to have relinquished her career on marriage. Holman's unkind attitude towards Emily's work – setting her to paint pigeons, for example, with which he himself had great difficulties – and his denigration of her efforts (caused perhaps by family arguments that had nothing to do with art) are examples of the struggles women painters had to face.[23] Lizzie's friend Anna Mary Howitt, who had studied in Germany, was so crushed by 'severe private censure' of one of her paintings by Ruskin that she gave up art altogether.[24] It is possible that the picture in question was her *Castaway*, on the Fallen Woman theme; Ruskin had strong views on 'morality' in art. Joanna Boyce, George's sister, was regarded as a highly talented painter, and her single submission to the 1855 Royal Academy was described by Brown as 'the best head in the rooms'.[25] In 1857, at the age of twenty-five, Joanna married Henry Wells, painter and miniaturist, and they had two daughters. The Tate Gallery possesses her *Gretchen*, a girl whose rosy cheeks express no hint of her seduction,[26] but the artist's career ended with her early death in 1861. Barbara Leigh Smith continued to paint after her marriage to Eugene Bodichon, but appears to have done so somewhat defensively, as if for a hobby rather than a profession, and her work is accorded little recognition.

One reason why the women 'fell behind', however, must surely have been their failure to ask why the men's 'pace quickened' and theirs did not. Georgie blamed herself for being 'daunted' but the truth is that women were rarely encouraged and easily discouraged, lacking the confidence to assert their talent. In practice, of the Pre-Raphaelite circle only Gabriel and Madox Brown gave women much support. Brown took several women as pupils, and trained both his daughters as artists, although in the end both seem to have found the spirit of the age against them, and also against this attempt to re-create a household atelier.

Just as he promoted Lizzie's work, Gabriel tried to help Georgie by recommending her, in the spring of 1861, to Alexander Gilchrist, who needed some of Blake's pictures copied for his forthcoming biography. Gabriel put forward her name, saying she was 'very diffident, but I believe in her capabilities fully, as she really draws heads with feeling . . .';[27] her husband, he added, would be able to help if she got into difficulties. But Georgie either did not get or did not take this commission. She had no place to work: her account of drawing the maid in the middle of her chores points to a contrast with Ned's appropriation of a whole room in what must have been a very small apartment for his exclusive use as a studio, and his access to hired models. She participated in his work, of course, either by posing herself, or by reading aloud to him as he worked. A stylized version of her face and figure, dressed in red robes, occupies many of his paintings of this period. But if he did not consciously discourage her, he certainly did not take her work seriously. Towards the end of Ned's life his studio assistant raised the subject of women artists. 'There aren't any,' said the Master at once. 'Well,' the assistant amended, 'those who profess to be.' 'They don't count,' replied Ned.[28] Another time he claimed, only half humorously, that it was a pity to educate women, as it 'only spoils them, takes away all their charm'.[29] With his own brand of charm and determination, Ned made sure Georgie was a wife and not a competitor. Nor would she have wished otherwise: wives who competed with their husbands were regarded as disgraceful and dangerous. 'If there be any case in which a woman might be forgiven for entertaining an honest pride in the superiority of her own talent,' wrote Mrs Ellis in most censorious style, 'it would be where she regarded it as only a means of doing higher homage to her husband.' Talent was 'a jewel which cannot with propriety be worn' by a married woman and any expression of belief in her own gifts, even where the husband's were equal or greater, was 'fatal to her happiness, peace of mind and conjugal concord'.[30] In any case, as a further obstacle, like the other women, Georgie was now pregnant.

Lizzie's pregnancy seems to have proceeded well until almost the end and there is no indication that her opium addiction caused difficulties or complications. Towards the third week in April 1861, however, something went wrong and the daughter she was carrying died in the womb. This was not immediately evident but she was seen both by her regular doctor and by an eminent obstetrician from the Lying-In Hospital. From the symptoms described, it appears that it was a case of the still unexplained accidental haemorrhage whereby the placenta becomes detached from the mother and the baby dies unless the condition is spotted and birth speedily induced. Lizzie's doctors did not commit themselves to a diagnosis and Gabriel was able to report that she herself had 'too much courage to be in the least downcast herself; and this is one great point, nor is her strength unusually low. So we can but wait and trust for a happy termination'.[31] But on 2 May 1861 the child was born dead.

The main concern was for Lizzie herself. She was looked after by a monthly nurse, whom Georgie described as 'a delightful old countrywoman, whose words and ways were quoted for years afterwards',[32] and the first of her friends to be summoned was Emma, whom Gabriel asked to call the very next day. The message to his mother was contradictory: 'Do not encourage anyone to come just now,' he wrote, 'I mean, of course, except yourselves.'[33] But Mrs Rossetti, as Georgie later discovered, was unhelpful with babies and no reactions to the stillbirth were recorded from that side of the family. It is possible that Lydia and Clara Siddall spent some time with their sister, but there is no record that Lizzie's own mother came or was summoned at this crisis. Gabriel had the sad duty of informing his friends. 'Rossetti called,' reported Boyce. 'His wife has just been confined of a stillborn child and was doing well.'[34] It was the general view that she recovered remarkably quickly, and within ten days her husband was able to write that she was 'progressing very well, all things considered, and has got over her confinement better than we had ventured to hope'.[35] Soon, she was 'getting on all right and would be quite set up I believe were it not for an unfortunate lack of appetite which keeps her mostly fasting and prevents her from gaining much strength'.[36] This was, of course, nothing unusual for Lizzie, and may have been the side-effect of an increased laudanum dose, taken to dull the pain. By July she was well enough to go out daily and to visit the Royal Academy.

Her mental state was not good. When Georgie and Ned called for the first time they found Lizzie 'sitting in a low chair with the childless cradle on the floor beside her'. She looked tragic and abstracted, like Gabriel's drawing of Ophelia when spurned by Hamlet and 'she cried with a kind of soft wildness as we came in, "Hush, Ned, you'll waken it!"'[37] A short while later Lizzie proposed passing on the layette to Georgie, whose baby was due in the autumn. Distressed, Gabriel wrote: 'Lizzie has been talking to me of parting with a certain small wardrobe to you. But don't let her, please. It looks such a bad omen for us . . .'[38] Superstition is a powerful but contradictory force at such moments: Lizzie's instinct to dispose of the dead baby's clothes suggests that she could not bear the constant reminder.

With their shared experience of pregnancy and childbirth, these women in the Pre-Raphaelite world – Emma, Lizzie, Jane and Georgie – were beginning to form a stronger group, and as if in response or rivalry the men conceived and developed the idea of the firm that was later known as Morris & Co. The notion was floated within a week of Jenny Morris's birth. It was conceived as an artistic enterprise, devoted to designing and selling the kind of interior decoration that the group of friends had been busy applying to Red House, as a commercial sideline to their painting and a means of adding to their incomes. Fatherhood brought greater responsibilities and, in addition, Morris's investment income was declining so that he needed a profitable occupation that gave scope to his decorative skills and entrepreneurial talents. The firm was finally set up in April, with eight original partners; the core group was made up of the four husbands, Morris, Rossetti, Jones and Brown, together with Arthur Hughes (who soon dropped out), the architect Philip Webb, a friend of Brown's named Marshall, and Charley Faulkner, the old Birmingham friend of Ned's who had joined in the Oxford Union adventure – he briefly relinquished his college fellowship to train as a draughtsman and keep the firm's books. In concept the business was a masculine enterprise, stressing the qualifications of the 'Artists of Reputation' whose services were offered to discerning patrons. It involved regular meetings, which the partners were paid to attend, and may be said to have represented a new version of the artistic Brotherhood. The original Pre-Raphaelite Brotherhood had been a sort of club for young bachelors, and the abortive 'artists' colony' or college, a common residence for young married men. Now, as the women strengthened their sisterhood and influence, the men regrouped as business partners. Married women had no legal status and were unable to participate in commercial life, as partners, lenders or guarantors; they were thus significantly excluded from taking any formal role in the operations of Morris & Co.

However, the ambivalent nature of much Pre-Raphaelite experience is illustrated by the fact that the women were by no means excluded from the work of the firm in practice. Jane, and later Bessie, had responsibility for embroidery commissions, supervising the outworkers as well as doing some of the stitching. Tile painting was another branch where women were active at the beginning, and Georgie took up her brush again, alongside Charley's sisters, Kate and Lucy Faulkner, to produce hand-painted tiles, although it was Ned who earned 5s a time for the designs. And so the women were able, even encouraged, to take part in the enterprise, which has since been accorded a position of immense significance in the history of European design. But it was a subsidiary, dependent role, which reinforced rather than overthrew the prevailing social and personal gender roles.

They had, of course, other concerns. Janey was soon pregnant again, and Georgie's first baby was born in October 1861. She was the only one of the Pre-Raphaelite women to set down a record of childbirth, from which it appears that she was the least prepared of all. Despite her mother's eleven children, she herself knew little about the matter, for medical details were often kept from young ladies. It was accepted practice for other children to be sent away from home to stay with relatives while new babies were born, and

there were no antenatal classes. She was the first of the Macdonald
sisters to marry, and it is surprising that her mother did not come
to London to be with her at this time. There was, it is true, not
much room to accommodate her. In the early autumn of 1861 the
Neds, as they were familiarly known, moved from Russell Place
to a slightly larger apartment on the first floor of 62 Great Russell
Street, opposite the new British Museum. Again, Ned's studio
occupied the main front room, with a sitting room beyond and
bedroom above. Miss Sampson, however, managed to stay, so it
would not have been impossible for Mrs Macdonald to have done
so, had she wished and had she been invited.

Baby Phil's arrival was one of Georgie's most 'testing times'.
'No one had told us any details connected with it,' she wrote later;
'the doctor and the wise woman were to arrange everything.'
Nurse Wheeler, who had looked after Lizzie, was engaged to take
all in her charge. However, when Georgie went into labour
neither doctor nor midwife was available and quite unexpectedly
she and Ned, who knew even less, had to cope with the birth
process themselves. Ned rose to the occasion, applying intellect as
a 'manageable force applicable to everything', but almost collapsed as a result. When Mrs Wheeler eventually arrived, she
found the new father in a worse condition than either mother or
baby, and Georgie herself recalled 'in the reaction that followed, a
day in which the small stranger within our gates was the most
valiant member of the family'.[39] It is difficult today to reconstruct
the alarm and anxiety of a Victorian confinement. Ned's own
mother had died shortly after his birth, apparently from post-natal
infection or puerperal fever. Midwives were usually unqualified
except for their valuable experience, and brought with them a
variety of 'traditions' that may well be called superstitions.
Doctors might be more scientific, and able to intervene with a
new range of obstetric tools, but their sense of hygiene was
minimal at this date and they frequently spread infection rather
than curbing it. For the rest of the century complications and
puerperal fever continued to cause the deaths of five women
in every thousand, and while chloroform, introduced and
popularized by Queen Victoria in the 1850s, helped to banish
much of the pain of childbirth, the dangers were not so easily
vanquished. A few months before Georgie's harrowing
experience, Joanna Boyce Wells died at the age of twenty-eight

following the birth of her second daughter.[40]

Jane and Lizzie went together to see Georgie and her little son. She remembered them sitting side by side in her room, 'as unlike as possible and quite perfect as a contrast to each other'. Both were in good health and looking well, Janey's 'colourless perfection of feature' being softened by kindness, and Lizzie's wistfulness giving an 'unearthly character to her beauty'. The sceptical opinions earlier expressed on the quality of their respective looks are somewhat undermined by Nurse Wheeler's reported comment, 'Was there ever two such beautiful ladies!' and it is a delightful picture of three friends together, welcoming the new infant.[41]

Ned made a proud, if somewhat reluctant father. Having been reared as a favoured, delicate, only child, he did not like emotional any more than professional competition, and paternity proved 'a fresh drain on his strength', as indeed did anything that threatened his art. Of fatherhood he said, only partly in jest, that 'children and pictures are too important to be produced by one man'.[42] Throughout his life, Ned held firm to the belief that art was his priority; much later, he teased Georgie by saying, 'Nothing matters in this world but pictures,' because he knew she disagreed. But she knew him well and would not be provoked. 'Yes dear, I know you think so, and 'they *are* very important,' was all she would answer.[43]

One wonders if she ever applied the theory of painters and children to herself. She seems to have feared for the loss of her art with her new responsibilities and soon after Phil's birth wrote to tell Ruskin that she was continuing her engraving. Ruskin, who had taken the Joneses under his wing in order to patronize Ned after failing with Gabriel, and who was planning to take them on a trip to Italy, responded with a masterpiece of conventional Victorian thought on the separate sphere of women. It began, 'I'm delighted to hear of the woodcutting. It will not, I believe, interfere with any motherly care or duty and is far more noble and useful work than any other of which feminine fingers are capable without too much disturbance of feminine thought and nature.' With such support, who needed discouragement? Worse followed, for it appears that Georgie had in fact given up all ideas of original work; Ruskin continued, 'I can't imagine anything prettier or more wifely than cutting one's husband's drawings on the wood block – there is just the proper quality of echo in it, and you may put the spirit and affection and fidelity into it, which *no* other person could.' One can almost hear Ruskin's desire for such a marital echo of his own, and appreciate once more Effie's luck in having escaped. Georgie was then told she should not even take her menial copyist's role too seriously; his final words were 'never work hard at it. Keep your rooms tidy and baby happy and then after that as much wood work as you've time and liking for ... .'[44] 'Alas,' was Georgie's own comment, 'time and liking never came together and the pretty scheme dropped through, finding a place, let us hope, among the pieces of porphyry or serpentine with which Edward claimed that good intentions pave the floor of heaven.'[45]

Of course, Ruskin's prescriptions did not cause Georgie to abandon wood engraving; they were rather one reflection of a position that seems to have been gaining ground in mid-century and which he himself articulated most powerfully in his discussion of girls' education, *Of Queens' Gardens*, where he preached that Woman

> must be enduringly, incorruptibly good; instinctively, infallibly wise – wise, not for self-development, but for self-renunciation; wise, not that she may set herself above her husband, but that she may never fail from his side; wise, not with the narrowness of insolent and loveless pride, but with the passionate gentleness of an infinitely variable, because infinitely applicable, modesty of service . . .[46]

and so on, with the infinitely persuasive adjectives masking the essential message that women should serve men. This was the dominant view; the alternative vision of marriage as an equal partnership was making only slow headway as yet, either in theory or practice, and its most conspicuous example, that of the non-marriage of George Eliot and G.H. Lewes,[47] was so outside the pale of correct middle-class society that it served rather to deter than encourage conjugal egalitarianism. Incidentally, Georgie was later to find George Eliot a good and supportive friend.

With the birth of her son, however, Georgie's life entered a new phase. She continued with her music, and successfully set poems by Keats and Gabriel to extracts from Beethoven, being much praised for her skill in both arrangement and performance.[48] But her first duties were now those of wife and mother, and the demands of art began to fade. Drawing seems to have been soon abandoned. When little Phil was two months old, Georgie took him to meet his grandparents and aunts in Manchester, where in deference to their religion he was christened, with Gabriel and Ruskin godparents by proxy. Thence they proceeded to visit Ned's father in Birmingham. Back in London for Christmas, Ned again fell sick, coughing blood dramatically on Christmas Eve. It was not TB as feared, but his recovery took some time and baby Phil was ill too, at the age of four months. Georgie's job was an anxious one. By the spring of 1862 she had come to realize what she had lost: 'I had been used to be much with Edward,' she wrote, 'reading aloud to him while he worked, and in many ways sharing the life of the studio – and I remember the feeling of exile with which I now heard through its closed doors the well-known voices of friends together with Edward's familiar laugh, while I sat with my little son on my knee and dropped selfish tears upon him . . .'[49] It would be anachronistic to suppose that Ned might have opened the studio to his wife and baby, or shared in the childcare to enable Georgie to continue with her own art, but her long-remembered anguish at being shut out is still heart-rending.

II

It is difficult to judge how far Fanny Cornforth's material situation was altered by marriage, but there is some evidence that it suffered a decline. In 1861, a year after her wedding, she was still living in Tenison Street, Waterloo, in a lodging house containing ten separate 'households', and a total of eighteen residents.

The house was run by Mrs Roberts, a young widow with a ten-year-old son, and the tenants included four working men whose occupations were listed in the Census as warehouseman, waiter, colourist and jeweller; two were married but neither had children living with them. Fanny's establishment was the largest in the house, consisting of herself, her husband Timothy, a servant girl, a boarder described as a dressmaker and a young visitor from Brighton who was a stay-maker. In addition, there were five young single women, living independently, one of whom described herself as an actress, one as a milliner and three as dressmakers. It is hard to imagine where all these people slept, but overcrowding was common in Victorian London, and conditions in Tenison Street were not extreme.

Fanny's fellow residents were typical of young working men and women such as the capital absorbed in their thousands, with middle-ranking skills but no security of employment. It is possible, however, that some or all of the young women belonged to Fanny's own profession: they certainly laid claim to occupations from which it was believed that part-time prostitutes were recruited, and it is tempting to speculate that Fanny herself was playing some role here, perhaps by providing accommodation or introducing suitable clients. Her boarder, eighteen-year-old Maria Roberts from Buckinghamshire, and her visitor, twenty-one-

year-old Harriet Young, may also have been on the game: it is
impossible to tell. One hint that all was not as it should have been
is the fact that, quite inexplicably, Fanny and her husband gave
their names to the Census enumerator as Sarah and Timothy
Cornforth. Considering they had married the previous year in the
same parish under the name of Hughes, this was odd. They gave
their ages as twenty-seven and thirty-one respectively. The
irregularity does not prove anything about Fanny's way of life,
least of all that she had set up in business as a madam or bawd, but
it does add an intriguing dimension to our picture of her. As we
have seen, she spent at least part of 1860–2 modelling for Gabriel
and Ned. Curiously, when writing about Ned's models in her
Memorials, Georgie did not mention Fanny. She did recall,
however, 'a handsome German woman' who wished to put her
past behind her and was accordingly offered a job as nursemaid to
baby Phil, only to find that the past, presumably in the shape of
her former clients, would not leave her alone; she soon departed.[1]
Was Fanny perhaps responsible for introducing other prostitutes
into the artists' circle?

At Chatham Place, Lizzie's condition, whether caused by the
loss of her baby or more long-standing distress, was giving rise to
concern by the middle of 1861. When Mrs Wheeler's time as
monthly nurse was up at the end of May, it was arranged that
Lizzie should stay with the Browns in Kentish Town, no doubt so
that Emma, who had lost two babies herself, could provide
sympathetic support. It may have been this period that Brown
later remembered when he recalled her pathetic figure sitting for
hours with her feet inside the fender, staring into the fire.[2] Drug
addicts often find it hard to keep warm. On 10 June, quite without
warning, she left the house and returned alone to Blackfriars. Her
explanation, passed on to the Browns next day, was that she 'felt
unwell . . . and finding the noise rather too much for her, left
before your return lest she should be feeling worse'; Gabriel
apologized for her discourtesy.[3] Such abrupt decisions and
departures are a feature of narcotic addiction, and it seems that
Lizzie was not otherwise ill, for she was soon reputed to have been
'working very hard these past few days', on a 'beautiful
watercolour sketch'.[4] In July she went to stay at Red House, to
continue helping with the mural decorations. Morris's drawing of
Jane in a medieval gown, now known as *Iseult on the Ship*,[5]

is thought to date from this period, perhaps for an uncompleted decorative scheme.

From here Lizzie wrote an affectionate note to Gabriel in response to the news of Joanna Boyce Wells' death:

My dearest Gug,

It is indeed a dreadful thing about poor Mrs Wells. All people who are at all happy or useful seem to be taken away. It will be a fearful blow to her husband for she must have been the head of the firm and most useful to him.

If you can come down here on Saturday evening I shall be very glad indeed. I want you to do something to the figure I have been trying to paint on the wall. But I fear it must all come out for I am too blind and sick to see what I am about.

Hoping you will not allow spontock to be too much worried,

I remain, your affectionate Lizzie[6]

Lizzie seems to have spent the rest of the year quietly, occasionally sitting to Gabriel as in the early days. It is possible that she sat to Spencer Stanhope, whose studio was on the floor below at Chatham Place, and that he used a study of her face for the repainted head of the woman in his *Thoughts of the Past*, which bears a distinct resemblance to her.[7] However, she had lost her former independence and relied heavily on Gabriel's presence. Her sister Lydia was no longer available to keep her company, for on 24 November 1861 she was married to Joseph Wheeler. Family tradition held that Lizzie advised the couple against a long engagement, but in fact Lydia may have used a time-honoured technique to hasten her wedding, for when it took place she was nearly five months pregnant.[8] Many years later the actress Nellie Farren claimed that Lizzie and Gabriel had expressed a desire to adopt her as a child,[9] which is perhaps further evidence of the erratic impulses to which Lizzie was now prone. It was also rumoured that in the autumn Lizzie became pregnant again. In November, when Gabriel went to Yorkshire for a portrait commission, Lizzie went again to Red House. As at the Browns' earlier in the year, she was seized with a sudden desire to escape, and returned abruptly to Chatham Place alone. Gabriel was very worried and wrote urgently to his mother asking her to take some money at once, as Lizzie was without funds. Mrs Rossetti must

have understood the necessity, and certainly the family seem to
have remembered her in this period as sad and melancholy, given
to shallow, sarcastic comments.

But Swinburne, who was frequently at Chatham Place in these
months, later defended Lizzie's gaiety, complaining that in his
memoir William Michael had described her in too miserable a
manner. 'I never knew so brilliant and appreciative a woman,'
wrote Swinburne, recollecting how he 'used to come and read to
her sometimes when she was well enough' and how she laughed
with delight at the comic drama of Fletcher's *The Spanish Curate*
on the archetypal theme of manoeuvring for an inheritance.[10] She
liked wit and humour, satire and strong characterization, and had
'a unique and indescribable personal charm'. The common picture
of a sorrowful and depressive Lizzie is hardly supported by this
testimony. 'Do you remember Gabriel and Lizzie's unwritten
dirge on Plint?' Swinburne asked, recalling the sudden death of a
Pre-Raphaelite patron in July 1861, 'hers was the best line'.[11]
Around the same time, Georgie recorded a lively visit to the
theatre with Swinburne in the party and Lizzie declaring that 'as
she sat at one end of the row we filled and he at the other, a boy
who was selling books of the play looked at Swinburne and took
fright, and then, when he came round to where she was, started
again with terror, muttering to himself, "There's another of
'em!"' in reference to their red hair.[12] Lizzie was also amused by
the satirical limericks Gabriel composed for his friends and
enemies. One got no further than the first couplet:

> There is a poor creature named Lizzie
> Whose aspect is meagre and frizzy . . .

but one was completed, 'to her great satisfaction':

> There is a poor creature named Lizzie
> Whose pictures are dear at a tizzy [sixpence]
> And of this the great proof
> Is that all stand aloof
> From paying that sum unto Lizzie.

Her own verse, however, was very sorrowful. Some was
devised for a male voice, as in 'Gone':

To touch the glove upon her tender hand,
To watch the jewel sparkle in her ring,
Lifted my heart into a sudden song
As when the wild birds sing.

To touch her shadow on the sunny grass,
To break her pathway through the darkened wood,
Filled all my life with trembling and tears
And silence where I stood.

I watch the shadows gather round my heart,
I live to know that she is gone –
Gone gone for ever, like the tender dove
That left the Ark alone.

'The Lust of the Eyes' is a lament for lost love:

I care not for my Lady's soul
Though I worship before her smile;
I care not where be my Lady's goal
When her beauty shall lose its wile.

Low I sit down at my Lady's feet
Gazing through her wild eyes
Smiling to think how my love will fleet
When their starlike beauty dies.

I care not if my Lady pray
To our Father which is in Heaven
But for joy my heart's quick pulses play
For to me her love is given.

Then who shall close my Lady's eyes
And who shall fold her hands?
Will any hearken if she cries
Up to the unknown lands?

Although many of Lizzie's poems seem obsessively to foreshadow
her own death, this was in fact a common theme in Victorian
romanticism. Especially popular in her circle, and encouraged by

the fashion for spiritualism, was the slightly indecent, maudlin subject of young lovers meeting after death. Gabriel had treated this most famously in 'The Blessed Damozel', a poem whose impact was out of all proportion to its merit, and Lizzie introduced the theme several times into her work. In 'Early Death', for example:

> Oh grieve not with thy bitter tears
> The life that passes fast;
> The gates of heaven will open wide
> And take me in at last.
>
> Then sit down meekly at my side
> And watch my young life flee;
> Then solemn peace of holy death
> Come quickly unto thee.
>
> But true love, seek me in the throng
> Of spirits floating past,
> And I will take thee by the hands
> And know thee mine at last.

'He and She and Angels Three' has the same subject:

> Ruthless hands have torn her
> From one that loved her well;
> Angels have upborne her,
> Christ her grief to tell.
>
> She shall stand to listen,
> She shall stand and sing,
> Till three winged angels,
> Her lover's soul shall bring.
>
> He and she and the angels three
> Before God's face shall stand;
> There they shall pray among themselves
> And sing at His right hand.

and so also does 'Lord May I Come?', which ends

How is it in the unknown land?
Do the dead wander hand in hand?
God, give me trust in thee.

Do we clasp dead hands and quiver
With an endless joy for ever?
Do tall white angels gaze and wend
Along the banks where lilies bend?
Lord, we know not how this may be:
Good Lord we put our faith in thee –
O God, remember me.

These poems may be read as expressing the longing for death that Lizzie, in her most miserable moments, is assumed to have felt, as well as her fantasy that the happier days of her love for Gabriel could be recovered. But they also have their place in the genre of what Gabriel called 'bogie' poems. Her friendship with Swinburne is significant here, for her lines in 'Lord May I Come?' may be compared with his invocation of the lovers after death in 'The Triumph of Time', who

. . . it may be, struck through by the dream,
Feel the dust quicken and quiver, and seem
Alive as of old to the lips, and leap
Spirit to spirit as lovers use.

It would be interesting to know if the use of 'quiver' by both poets was coincidental. 'The Triumph of Time' in turn inspired Rupert Brooke, who in the Edwardian era echoed Swinburne in 'The Way that Lovers Use', 'Dust', and 'Sonnet Inspired by the Proceedings of the Society for Psychical Research'.

To place her work in a poetic tradition is not to deny that Lizzie's sadness was real. A drawing of what I believe to be her head in profile, done by Ned in the last weeks or months of her life, shows a rather mournful, helpless face, with pale unseeing eye and straggly hair pulled loosely back.[13] Another picture which strongly conveys her appearance at this period is the famous and largely posthumous *Beata Beatrix*,[14] for which some studies were done before her death. The pose and expression of the figure, who is represented as in a trance at the moment of passing from earth to heaven, strongly suggest those of an addict who is feeling the immediate effects of a fix – for which trance might be an approximate description. This aspect of *Beata Beatrix*, forcibly apparent to those working in the field of narcotic addiction,[15] has never hitherto been remarked, despite the recognized significance of the white poppy, from which opium derives, that is placed in Beatrice's hands by the dove. This is not to say that the painting is simply a picture of an opium addict. In addition to the purely aesthetic and art-historical meanings and significance of the work, the Dantean subject has a further biographical relevance, for it was as the Ideal Beloved that Gabriel had first come to love and paint Lizzie. The sundial that points towards Beatrice's face may be partly phallic[16] but surely also represents the sharp thrust of Time against the artist's early idealism, indicated by the figures of the poet and Love in the sunlit background. The gentle dove was of course Gabriel's favourite image for Lizzie's quiet, meek demeanour when he first knew her. Ten years later, she sat in the shadow of laudanum. As we have seen, Gabriel did his best not to leave her alone, apparently fearful lest she should be taken suddenly ill, either by lack of laudanum or, more probably, by another 'accidental' overdose. It is possible that he made some effort to curb her consumption, for it was known that the drug was inimical to unborn children. Elizabeth Barrett Browning, who was otherwise addicted, successfully gave up laudanum during her pregnancy and if Lizzie's old friend Bessie Parkes, who visited her in the New Year of 1862, was correct,[17] Lizzie was again pregnant, so it is likely that stronger steps were taken to reduce her dosage. To have given it up altogether would have caused withdrawal symptoms, easily mistaken for those of the organic disease she was thought to be suffering from, and for which the laudanum was taken. A reduced dose, or longer intervals, would have had the effect of making her increasingly agitated and anxious. This agitation seems to have been particularly marked on the night of her death.

The inquest heard from Gabriel that on the afternoon of Monday 10 February 1862 Lizzie had seemed 'perfectly well'. Between six and seven in the evening they went to join Swinburne for dinner at the Sablonnière hotel restaurant in Leicester Square, 'but before we started she appeared drowsy and when we got halfway in the cab I proposed going home again'. Lizzie wished to go on, however, and while they had their meal as planned 'she seemed somewhat between flightiness and drowsiness, a little excited'. This alternation sounds like the effect of opium, and was evidently Lizzie's normal condition, for Swinburne told the coroner that he saw 'nothing particular in the deceased except she appeared a little weaker than usual'. They dined quickly and by 8 p.m. Lizzie and Gabriel were on their way back to Blackfriars. Here the housekeeper's niece, Ellen Macintyre, attended to Lizzie at 8.30, when 'she seemed cheerful'. Gabriel went out at about 9 o'clock to visit the Working Men's College, and returned at 11.30 to find Lizzie 'in bed and snoring . . . utterly without consciousness'. He immediately called Mrs Birrell and Ellen upstairs, but nothing roused her, and medical help was summoned. Dr Hutchinson, who had attended her confinement, came at once, and found his patient 'in a comatose state – we tried to rouse her, but without any avail'. She was too deeply unconscious to swallow any antidote and Hutchinson 'then injected several quarts of water into the stomach and washed the stomach out' – all to no effect, although Lizzie was still breathing. During this unpleasant procedure Gabriel called three more doctors and sent a message to the Siddall family. Her sister Clara arrived at 3 a.m. Gabriel set off to fetch Brown, arriving there at 5 a.m. and returning to Blackfriars not long before Lizzie died, at 7.20 on the morning of 11 February 1862. She was thirty-two years old.

Among the first to be notified were the Joneses, who received the news between 9 and 10 a.m. from Red Lion Mary. Georgie at once hurried to Blackfriars; she wrote to her sister the next day: 'I scarcely believe the words as I write them, but yesterday I saw her dead . . . I went down directly I heard it and saw her poor body laid in the very bed where I have seen her lie and laugh in the midst of illness.' Gabriel was not to be seen, and Georgie noted that Brown was in charge of all arrangements. The account she was given tallied with that reported at the inquest: 'The evening before she was in good health (for her) and very good spirits – Gabriel took her home, saw her prepare for bed, went out to the Working Men's College, and on his return found her insensible from the effects of an overdose of laudanum – which she used to take medicinally.'[18] At this time there seem to have been no rumours of suicide, and no suggestion that Gabriel had gone off to visit Fanny. Violet Hunt, who spread the story that Gabriel had not gone to the Working Men's College, knew that this was untrue. Although there were other, persistent tales of angry scenes between Lizzie and Gabriel over Fanny, we do not have evidence of any major quarrels after their marriage.[19]

The inquest established that the fatal dose, taken with brandy and water, must have been, in Dr Hutchinson's words, 'a very large dose . . . the phial found in the room was a 2oz phial'. The smell of laudanum was strong and he estimated that Lizzie had taken about 100 drops, an amount that Gabriel confirmed she was in the habit of taking. It was not, therefore, a massive, deliberate overdose about which there could be no debate. Although there was no standard measure and strengths are thus difficult to compare, Helen Gladstone, sister to the future prime minister, had swallowed and survived a dose of 300 drops a few years earlier.[20] The verdict thus returned was that of accidental death, and so, as Swinburne cryptically reported, 'the worst chance of all was avoided'.[21] By this he presumably meant a verdict of suicide, which at this date still attracted a large degree of social and religious disapproval, hurtful to surviving relatives. Insanity was also a verdict to be feared, stigmatizing families and descendants, who were thought capable of inheriting the affliction. The coroner, however, seems to have been less concerned with suicide than with excluding all possibility of foul play, although doubtless his questions were routine ones, designed to a standard form. Mrs Birrell said stoutly of Lizzie that she 'knew of no hurt to her nor don't suspect any. Her husband and herself lived very comfortable together.' Clara Siddall said, 'I know of no harm to her. I don't suspect any.' Dr Hutchinson agreed she was 'in a very nervous condition' when he had attended her the previous year, but he had in fact only seen her once in the months since the stillbirth. Catherine Birrell said she had often bought a shilling's worth of laudanum for Lizzie, but not during the past half-year, and repeated like the others: 'I know of no hurt to her. I waited upon her and they lived very happily together.' Gabriel echoed these replies; he told the coroner that Lizzie 'had not spoken of wishing to die' and in fact 'contemplated going out of town in a day or two and had bought a new mantle the day before . . . My impression is that she did not do it to injure herself but to quiet her nerves. She could not have lived without laudanum. She could not sleep at times nor take food . . .'[22] He believed she had taken a dose before setting out for the restaurant.

If it were not for the rumours, there would be no reason to doubt the coroner's verdict. Like alcohol, the opiates first act as a stimulant and then as a sedative, so it was possible for Lizzie to take a small dose to make herself cheerful during supper and then a larger dose to make her sleep when she was ready for bed. There was always the danger of an overdose, given the lack of standardization and the addict's uncertain judgement. In 1863, when statistics were first kept, there were in Britain a total of 126 deaths from narcotic poisoning, of which 106 were classified as accidental. Opium poisoning was commonplace, not always regarded as requiring medical attention, and some deaths from opium poisoning were probably not recorded as such. The opiates were also used by suicides, however, and nineteen deaths were so classified in 1863.[23]

The view that Lizzie meant to kill herself is based on the alleged report, handed down within the Brown and Rossetti families, that she left a farewell note, which Gabriel showed to Brown, who at once destroyed it, realizing the significance of a note in relation to an inquest verdict. Hall Caine, Gabriel's companion in his last years, seemed to have been given a similar story, and wrote that Lizzie's note had 'left such a scar on his heart as would never be healed'.[24] Violet Hunt, using either her imagination or gossip from Brown's grandson Ford Madox Ford and others, claimed that the note read: 'My life is so miserable that I wish for no more of it.'[25] This was challenged by Brown's granddaughter, Helen Angeli, who at first dismissed Violet Hunt's account completely,[26] but later asserted that the note read simply, 'Take care of Harry' – Lizzie's youngest, handicapped brother.[27]

From what is known about Lizzie, it is hard to imagine her articulating concern for Harry as she made arrangements to end her life. Although it is true that Gabriel, and later William Michael, made regular payments to both surviving Siddall brothers when they needed assistance, there was nothing unusual in this and it would have been done without instructions from beyond the grave. Violet Hunt's version is even less likely to be accurate, and I believe that if Lizzie left a note at all, its contents were never revealed. But whatever its contents, if there was a note, then Lizzie apparently intended suicide. Even a note, however, does not prove that Lizzie meant to die, for she must have known that Gabriel was due back within a couple of hours, and she may well have trusted to him to save her; suicide attempts are often an expression of despair. It seems to me that her behaviour fits more into the pattern of severe addiction: chronic, increasing and careless drug-taking is indicative of a self-destructive urge and it is often only a matter of time before death occurs, since the individual has lost the will, or the desire, to live. Before he married her, Gabriel had found Lizzie on such a knife-edge and in some senses he had been waiting for it to recur. In this context 'accident' and 'suicide' would be virtually synonymous, although a farewell note would show specific intent.

Several of her poems were explicitly suicidal. As already pointed out, a longing for the release of death is a stock Romantic theme, but in Lizzie's case it sometimes seems to have been a good deal more personal. In 'At Last', the speaker is a young woman, deserted by her lover and on the brink of death:

> O mother, open the window wide
> And let the daylight in;
> The hills grow darker to my sight
> And thoughts begin to swim.

She commends her infant son to her mother's keeping, and prepares for the end:

> And mother, wash my pale pale hands
> And then bind up my feet;
> My body may no longer rest
> Out of its winding sheet.

Within this strict ballad mode, the feeling is expressively pathetic. In 'Lord May I Come?' the death wish is made explicit:

> Life and night are falling from me,
> Death and day are opening on me,
> Wherever my footsteps come and go,
> Life is a stony way of woe.
>   Lord, have I long to go?

Hollow hearts are ever near me,
Soulless eyes have ceased to cheer me,
                    Lord, may I come to thee?

Life and youth and summer weather
To my heart no joy can gather.
                    Lord, lift me from life's stony way!
Loved eyes long closed in death watch for me:
Holy death is waiting for me –
                    Lord, may I come today?

These lines were identified by William Michael, some thirty years later, as having been written under the influence of laudanum, in a straggling, weak hand, shortly before Lizzie's death. If so, they contain a rather pointed reference to the 'hollow heart' and 'soulless eyes' of her loving husband. 'A Year and a Day' seems to convey the effects of narcotic experience and the accompanying desire to float out of life, painlessly:

> I lie among the tall green grass
> That bends above my head
> And covers up my wasted face
> And folds me in its bed
> Tenderly and lovingly
> Like grass above the dead.
>
> Dim phantoms of an unknown ill
> Float through my tired brain;
> The unformed visions of my life
> Pass by in ghostly train;
> Some pause to touch me on the cheek,
> Some scatter tears like rain.
>
> . . .
>
> The river ever running down
> Between its grassy bed
> The voices of a thousand birds
> That clang above my head,
> Shall bring to me a sadder dream
> When this sad dream is dead.

A silence falls upon my heart
And hushes all its pain.
I stretch my hands in the long grass
And fall to sleep again,
There to lie empty of all love
Like beaten corn of grain.

Lizzie's mother and sister Lydia came to see her body in the week it lay at Chatham Place, as did Ruskin, and just before the coffin was closed Gabriel placed in it, in his famous gesture of self-sacrifice, the manuscript notebook into which he had fair-copied his unpublished poems. Brown thought this histrionic, but William Michael felt it was an appropriate expression of grief. The burial was on 17 February in the Rossetti family grave in the new middle-class cemetery at Highgate. Gabriel left Blackfriars, keeping her paintings and drawings but sending her other possessions to her family; the unused baby clothes were packed up and sent, with some money, to Lydia, whose daughter was born the following month, and christened Elizabeth Eleanor.

While some of his friends and family seem to have seen Lizzie's death as a merciful deliverance, Gabriel was genuinely and deeply grieved; he 'never ceased to reproach himself with his wife's death as an event that had been due in some degree to a failure of duty on his part'.[28] This was not a matter of rampant infidelity or neglect, as the Pre-Raphaelite myth has so sensationally hinted and supposed, but 'the far deeper wrong of failure of affection for the one being to whom affection was most due'.[29] Gabriel had married Lizzie because he had once loved her, in the hope that he might save her life. Both knew that the love between them could not be revived. Had she lived and raised a family, perhaps their affection might have matured, but Lizzie's addiction precluded that, making her distant, irresponsible and dependent all at the same time. Her child had died and she was not entirely sane. It is possible that she felt herself a burden to her husband – those who kill themselves sometimes persuade themselves that it is best for their families – and this was something which Gabriel always reproached himself for. If he felt remorse, it was because he had, in the end, failed to save her; perhaps because he was also thankful to be free. She died because he did not love her enough.

It was the perfect ending for a tragic heroine – for Ophelia or maybe Eurydice. For once, life was as romantic as legend. Another way of looking at it is to say that Lizzie was defeated and ultimately destroyed by the forces of Victorian ideology, which, not unlike our own, preferred legendary women to those who in real life tried to challenge the prescriptions of class and gender.

Annie Miller's exit from the Pre-Raphaelite stage was also dramatic, but different: she achieved a happy ending. We last saw her in the early spring of 1860, in the painters' company; her last recorded sitting was for George Boyce on 18 April, when he gave her a small landscape sketch, apparently as a sort of farewell gift, as he was leaving town. With Gabriel in Hastings, preparing to marry Lizzie, Annie seems to have disappeared from the artistic world. Her father, it may be noted, had died unlamented at the end of March in Chelsea Hospital.[30]

She may have found other employment, but towards the end of the year she ran out of money altogether, and although she was now occupying a smaller and cheaper room at Mrs Stratford's she had exhausted all her credit. Eventually Mrs Stratford applied again to Fred Stephens, asking Hunt to resume financial responsibility for Annie. It was a humiliation for her, but Hunt's great success in obtaining £5,500 for *Finding of the Saviour* had been well publicized, and so she may have known he was relatively well off. Hunt replied with some sovereigns in an envelope, delivered by Fred, who was also instructed to obtain a copy of Annie's account with Mrs Stratford, for Hunt to scrutinize. He was willing, he said, to establish Annie in regular employment, to arrange an emigration passage to Australia, but she must first put forward 'her own ideas as to what she is ready to do'. Fred was told what to say:

> . . . urge upon her the necessity of considering in after life whether for the sake of a momentary gratification of ill humour and pride, it is worth while to sacrifice an opportunity that can never occur again . . . Remind her of the importance of making a decision in her affairs – on this occasion as well as others, that may be judicious not merely for the day but for the future . . . Instance her choice of sitting against our urgent advice as an instance of her light-hearted judgement, and if she says

anything about Rossetti's assurance that she would have a great
deal of employment point out how nearly all people talk just to
appear pleasant at the moment . . . Do not omit to say that in
rejecting my advice to avoid going to Rossetti and Boyce to sit
she sacrificed my interest in her welfare to a very great extent.
That her refusal to take my assistance over and over again at last
induced me to employ my money in another way . . .[31]

Annie called on Fred as bidden, but brought no statement of Mrs
Stratford's account, saying that whatever Hunt thought to give
would be welcome, and put forward her own proposal that she
train as a milliner, with Hunt presumably paying the premium. It
was, as we have seen, a favoured occupation offering access to the
world of smart Society, and Fred disapproved, pointing out that
millinery was 'very unpromising, the market being very over-
strained'. He then suggested the emigration scheme. Annie did
not like the idea of being packed off to Australia. 'At first this was
evidently taken as a most suspicious move,' Fred reported to
Holman, 'in effect that you wanted to get rid of her.' This was
true, of course, and Annie may have reflected that gentlemen
often paid off their mistresses by setting them up in business or
sending them to the colonies; she and Hunt were acting out roles
they had only partially played. Stephens spelt out the advantage of
Australia – 'probably matrimony . . . the getting rid of old
associates . . . starting a new life, etc.', and the conversation
became warm. 'Let him only pay Mrs Stratford this once more,'
Annie declared, 'and I will never trouble him any more. I'll go and
be a lady's maid.'

Fred almost laughed, pointing out that this too was an
overcrowded profession and that ladies with husbands would not
wish to employ such an attractive maid as Annie. She countered
by saying that, if she should agree to emigrate, she would need
some training – why not millinery? They then discussed the
process of emigration, Annie objecting strongly to the arrangement whereby single women emigrants were sent out under
supervision of a 'matron', who controlled their behaviour; Fred
replied that 'no captain of a ship would ever take a young woman
except under such control, and that she could not shoot herself out
in Melbourne city except under some decent auspices . . .' At this
Annie changed the subject, inquiring about Hunt's envelope

which Fred had placed prominently on the mantelpiece. When she found it contained money but no letter, she was mortified: 'Is this for me? I'm afraid there is some mistake,' and returned 'in a new bitter way' to the subject of emigration, arguing for millinery training first, 'with Melbourne as a vanishing point a good way into the picture'. Fred repeated his instructions. Finally, after two hours' talking, she agreed to think it over and come back in ten days with a decision; then she 'took your envelope and cash and went'.[32]

Hunt was still susceptible; he told Fred that if Annie was now willing to exert herself industriously, he would have 'a duty to make the greatest possible sacrifice to help her once more', but he continued to take a superior moral line. He scorned 'the ridiculous suspicion' that his offers of help were designed to get her out of the way, and 'the notion she expressed that *I* had taken her out of her original position and the inference that her present one was that of a person of the higher classes'. He remarked on 'the too obvious fact that she can't write two lines of English', and on the tone of Mrs Stratford's note, 'which she is doubtless responsible for'. He gave a fine sententious display of his bourgeois origins, castigating Annie as 'a hopeless, proud, improvident girl – who does not know the value of money because she has never worked for it – and if she at this moment had a hundred pounds in her hands the probability is that it would still more encourage her in the ridiculous idea that she was much too great a person to work'. She had wasted all the opportunities offered her and spent seventeen months in idleness rather than 'learn the simplest business to enable her to earn money to lighten the burden on two people in difficulties who are supporting her' (presumably her aunt and uncle in Chelsea).[33] A week later, having inspected Annie's account, Holman sent Mrs Stratford £5 via Fred. He was shocked to find Annie had been living at the rate of 'something like £1 per week, which no girl of her ignorance could be likely to earn'. He categorically declined to pay for a millinery apprenticeship.

Annie was both penniless and powerless, but she did not submit to this bullying; nor, perhaps out of pride, did she appeal to Gabriel, who was at this moment arranging the little housewarming party at Chatham Place with his bride. On 24 January 1861 Mrs Stratford again applied to Stephens on Annie's behalf, perhaps this time hinting at an action for breach of promise, using the letters Annie had received from Hunt. Calling Annie 'a young vixen', Holman now appears to have taken the offensive, calling on Lord Ranelagh, whose testimony that he had escorted Annie Miller in public would be sufficient to destroy any claim she made to being the injured party. Ranelagh apparently confirmed the gossip, which Annie had airily denied, perhaps not suspecting that Hunt would make a check on it, and Holman was satisfied that his 'name in connection with her conduct will be enough to stamp the character of it as infamous particularly when I prove the length of time for which the intimacy went on, and the manner in which he spoke of her'. This does not imply that Annie's relationship with Ranelagh was improper: it was enough that she had been out with him. Fred was given further instructions on handling Annie. 'You must see how she takes the announcement of Lord R's name,' wrote Holman, '– if she is proud of his noble friendship', but he added cautiously that it would be 'unwise to threaten her with exposure of his connection with her in court', unless it was found that Ranelagh was instigating Annie to 'make use of the letters to annoy me'.[34] A public attack on Ranelagh had its problems, as the Viscount was gaining popularity through his work for the Volunteer movement. This was the raising of a militia in response to fears of an invasion by the French, fresh from their success in liberating Italy from the Austrian yoke. Several members of the Pre-Raphaelite circle, including Hunt, volunteered for the newly-formed Artists Rifles; Morris attended some camps and manoeuvres, but the rest do not seem to have progressed beyond a little drill. Ranelagh was a leading figure, publicly admired.

Fred was told to tell Annie that 'the papers she holds are not worth talking about for immediate purposes' but that he was willing to purchase them from her. If she took Hunt to court he would expose her relationship with Ranelagh and if she held on to the letters he would prepare evidence to show 'how far from cruel or inconsiderate' his conduct towards her had been. He also went to some trouble to assemble evidence against her, in what seems a vindictive manner. He inquired into Annie's background from a former neighbour, learning of her unkempt, nit-infested, motherless years and of her father's low wages. He then outlined the Plot, giving Stephens a verbatim account of what he evidently wanted to say to Annie himself. Fred was told to lay some money on the table, a five-pound note and two sovereigns, point out that she had returned no thanks for the previous payments and tell her that the £7 were now offered for the return of all the letters and books she had received from Hunt. When, as expected, she refused, Fred was to say, 'I should have thought . . . that if you are in a position to scorn such a sum, which alone is as much as your father took ten weeks to earn, you might see it your duty to pay a poor woman like Mrs Stratford the large sum you owe.' If she should plan to use the letters to disclose her relationship to Mr Hunt, he would be 'compelled to make known all about you from the time your father cleaned harness . . . and [you] used to run about with clothes hanging to your back and your head of hair a sight to shudder at'. There was a good deal of self-righteousness besides, along the lines of, 'Mr Hunt gets his money by hard work and he is not foolish enough to throw away what can only be got again by a great deal of self-denial,' and the draft of a disclaimer for Annie to sign, renouncing all claims against Hunt and including too a description of his own 'unselfish kindness and liberality' towards her.[35]

However, Annie did not part with the letters nor sign the disclaimer, and Hunt paid Mrs Stratford's bill again, perhaps for the last time. There matters seem to have rested, in a kind of stalemate, and Annie disappeared from Pre-Raphaelite view. She was briefly glimpsed by George Boyce in June 1862 at the International Exhibition, 'looking as handsome as ever, walking with a young man, rather a swell'.[36]

At the beginning of 1863 she reappeared, again seeking work from Gabriel. Now widowed, he was living in Cheyne Walk, Chelsea, not far from her old home, and he offered her employment. She was the model for *Helen of Troy*[37] and *Woman in Yellow*,[38] where she was shown as a fine-looking pensive woman with a loose gown falling off her shoulder. George Boyce was aware she was sitting again, but did not apparently seek her out. And shortly afterwards Annie introduced Gabriel to her new escort, Captain Thompson, first cousin to Lord Ranelagh and former Infantry officer, who had also been active in the Volunteer movement. Millais also met him, and it is possible that Annie was modelling for him too. It is not known how long she had known Captain Thompson, whom Gabriel described as 'a very good gentlemanly fellow',[39] but she had reason to be pleased with

herself and her refinement, for on 23 July 1863 she married him in
St Pancras church. In one move the girl from a Chelsea slum
entered the aristocracy, for even if Captain Thompson was not
wealthy, he was cousin to a Viscount, a rank which wholly
eclipsed that of Hunt, with his anxious pretensions to gentility and
cruel scorn of Annie's origins. She had obtained, at the age of
twenty-eight, the security he had repeatedly denied her, and she
had done it largely by her own efforts. It may be hard to believe
that she could have succeeded without the judicious use of sexual
favours – to Hunt, Rossetti, Ranelagh, Thompson and maybe
others – but there is no evidence to prove that she did and much,
from her relationship with Hunt, to suggest that she was reluctant
to become 'gay'. It seems to me quite possible that she remained
'pure'. Even if she did not, she was a striking example of a woman
who had not fallen but risen.

She was undoubtedly lively, attractive, even flirtatious, and
since she lacked an ingrained sense of what was correct or
improper, it was not surprising that gossip attached itself to her
and to Hunt, as he became a famous and highly regarded painter,
with an established place in society and a wife from his own social
class. In 1862–3, after he had finally disentangled himself from
Annie, Holman paid court to Julia Jackson, niece to Sarah Prinsep
and cousin of Val, whom he met at Little Holland House. Julia
was young, with large round eyes and straight hair; she turned
him down.[40] Hunt spent some months contemplating perpetual
celibacy, fearful lest his passions, 'having no lawful hope – should
burst out by contact with unlawful tinder into an unholy flame'[41]
but reluctant to put up with the conventions of a bourgeois
courtship, like that which his Pre-Raphaelite Brother Thomas
Woolner was experiencing. Woolner complained that all his
movements were determined by the family of his bride-to-be,
Alice Waugh. She was the daughter of a retail pharmacist who had
so prospered that he was able to provide good marriage
settlements for his eight daughters, all of whom had been brought
up in the most correct manner. They seem to have been anxious
for husbands, and by August 1865 Alice's elder sister Fanny had
accepted Holman's proposal. By a 'curious chance' he was obliged
to explain his connection with Annie Miller to her mother, who
was 'shocked beyond measure' and thought it 'incredibly perverse
and shameful'; as a result Hunt anticipated a full investigation and

asked Fred to alert Mrs Bramah to possible inquiries as to his motives and conduct. Of course, he concluded, 'Fanny doesn't yet know of this dreadful history!'[42]

Fred Stephens had also recently married. His wife was Mrs Clara Charles, a widow of little education who, like Annie, had been sent to learn to read and write and whose existence was known to very few of his acquaintance.

Fanny Waugh and Holman Hunt were married on 28 December 1865. It was a large and splendid affair, and Holman asked William Michael Rossetti, an original Pre-Raphaelite Brother and still unmarried, to be his best man. The happy couple were due to set off for the Middle East, where the painter was to resume his biblical scenes. However, gossip surfaced in February, when it appears that Gabriel, living in Chelsea, heard Francis Moody's daughter spreading scandal about Annie Miller and improper goings-on at Mrs Stratford's boarding house. 'Isn't the whole thing a dodge to get cash?' wrote Fred, apparently seeing Annie's unscrupulous hand behind the affair. Not long before, Hunt had asked him to take charge of papers and a portrait relating to Annie, the object being to have the evidence to hand should any 'devilry', as Fred put it, be attempted while he was abroad. The alternative was to destroy the letters and thus destroy the evidence.[43] Gabriel informed him of Annie's marriage, at which he had expressed surprise and doubt, until Millais wrote in support, telling him that Thompson was a 'decent fellow'.[44] It seems that at this time, perhaps in order to squash the possibility of scandal for ever, Hunt successfully negotiated for the return of his letters and presents to Annie. He claimed that his departure for Palestine was delayed by the collapse of a bank in which he had investments, but as his descendants have remarked, this is unlikely to have accounted for the large sum of £1,000 which had to be realized from elsewhere. Part of this may well have gone to purchase the letters;[45] they have not survived, and Hunt no doubt burnt them with relief.

During the first years of her marriage, Annie lived in Hampstead. Here her daughter, Annie Helen, and her son, Thomas James, were born, in 1866 and 1867. By an odd coincidence, Holman's first child, Cyril, was born in the same month as Annie's daughter, in Italy, where he and Fanny were delayed owing to cholera in the Mediterranean region. Six weeks later Fanny died, of puerperal fever. Ten years later, he married her youngest sister Edith, outraging both the Hunt and the Waugh families, for such marriages were illegal in Britain and theirs took place, after a kind of elopement, in Switzerland.

Until Diana Holman-Hunt published the biography of her grandfather in 1969, Annie's existence, and certainly her relationship with Hunt, remained relatively shadowy. She never recorded her own version of her entanglement with the Pre-Raphaelite Brothers so that even now her thoughts and feelings are obscure and difficult to reconstruct. Late in life, when he was rich and famous and more mature, Hunt entertained an all-male gathering with his version of the story, the tale of an unnamed 'pretty girl of humble class' whom he had engaged as his model:

> There was the making of an intelligent woman in her and, good-hearted to the core, he had arranged to have her educated, possibly, so he hinted, with a view to marrying her. But Rossetti, whose principles were exceedingly lax, beguiled the girl away from him. Years afterwards Holman Hunt met her by chance, a buxom matron with a carriage full of children, on Richmond Hill, and learned that she had married happily.[46]

The story grew in the telling: it began in the afternoon, 'went on through dinner to bedtime, and was finished the next morning', with the painter's 'wonderful memory supplying the actual conversations between artist and model and between him and Rossetti', holding his listeners spellbound. One guest remarked that it would make a marvellous novel – and he was right, for Hunt was telling the story with a purpose. Annie may have found Gabriel attractive but there is no evidence that he 'beguiled' her affections away from Hunt. Rather than admit that Annie herself made the choice, the masculine viewpoint blamed another man. In my view, Annie deserves all the credit; to marry happily and so well was no mean achievement, and it was all by her own efforts.

PART THREE

Maturity

12

With Lizzie's death and Annie's departure to a higher world, this tale continues with the lives of Jane, Georgie and Fanny. All were now married women, but as if in refutation of the romantic view of marriage as a haven and the bohemian view of it as banal, the years that followed were among the most turbulent of their lives.

In 1861, Fanny was living with Timothy Hughes on the South Bank. Her relationship with Gabriel was said to have 'lasted until his marriage and then after an interval came on again',[1] but she never really lost touch with him, and modelled for a number of figure drawings during 1861–2. Her own marriage did not last, and indeed it seems that she decided to leave Timothy almost as soon as Lizzie's death was announced. The only clue to the date of their separation is Fanny's later, quite erroneous claim that Timothy died 'within a year or two after their marriage',[2] apparently in reference to the date they parted. The legend is that he drank, but this was true of many working men, and it seems to me plausible that Fanny deliberately sought out Gabriel once he was widowed, in the hope of re-establishing her former relationship with him; she was, after all, extremely fond of him. The earliest sign of Fanny's re-entry into his life was a pencil drawing of her reclining dated July 1862,[3] which was later given to George Boyce. Gabriel did not return to Chatham Place after Lizzie's death, but spent the spring and summer staying with his family or in temporary lodgings while arranging a lease on Tudor House in Cheyne Walk, Chelsea. This he planned to share with his brother, and with Swinburne and the novelist George Meredith, as a bachelor establishment for four single men. But soon after Gabriel moved in, Fanny was installed as his almost-resident mistress: he

took possession on 22 October and on 13 November Boyce called
and 'found Fanny there'.[4] If the number of Gabriel's drawings of
her at this period is an index of emotional intensity, their
relationship flourished over the winter months. On 7 December
Boyce was given another pencil portrait of her 'as she lay on a
couch, hair outspread',[5] and there are several more pictures of
Fanny that belong to this period,[6] mostly of her lying back with
loose hair. There is also a small circular oil portrait, dated 1862,
which shows her as a handsome rather than sensuous woman, and
which may have been meant as a gift.[7]

Strong as the pictorial evidence is, Fanny's frequent presence at
Cheyne Walk was not widely known. As a widower, Gabriel's
social life was restricted for up to two years following his
bereavement and he was not expected to accept or issue
invitations. Only a few of his close male friends were welcome to
call on him casually and to stay when Fanny was expected: Boyce,
Bell Scott, Whistler, Allingham, 'old Brown' and faithful William
Michael, who disapproved of the situation but did not dislike
Fanny. Her presence may have been one reason why Gabriel's
nominal co-tenant Meredith was so seldom to be found at Tudor
House, while Swinburne, whose alcoholism also kept Meredith
away, had been a great friend and admirer of Lizzie and disliked
Fanny. This was ironic, for Swinburne was developing a career as
a decadent amoralist and writing verses about tempting, dangerous women who, like 'Faustine', seem to resemble Fanny:

> Lean back and get some minutes' peace;
> Let your head lean
> Back to the shoulder with its fleece
> Of locks, Faustine.
>
> You could do all things but be good
> Or chaste of mien;
> And that you would not if you could,
> We know, Faustine . . .

In practice, one suspects, he did not enjoy the company of
straightforwardly fleshly women and he certainly became hostile
to Fanny, later referring to her as a 'bitch'.[8] By the summer of
1863, therefore, she and Gabriel were virtually in sole possession

of the house; as he told Allingham: 'Swinburne is away, Meredith has evaporated for good and my brother is seldom here. There is only one more to unite with me in good wishes to you.'[9] Fanny's status as mistress in the sexual if not housekeeping sense is clear from a glimpse of the domestic scene earlier in the year, in Gabriel's letter to Red Lion Mary about some needlework for the new house. After apologizing for not paying her, he wrote: 'Fanny says she would like to know what I am saying to you as I am writing such a lot, so I had better leave off before I am scratched about the nose and eyes.'[10] This was an affectionate joke, for the two women were friends, and Fanny added her sympathies to Gabriel's when she heard Mary had been ill, and promised to write herself, but it was also a signal that she claimed Gabriel as her man. Mary sent a picture, apparently of herself, for Gabriel added a postscript to say: 'The portrait is very nice and Fanny is delighted with it, but nothing short of the idea of Topsy seems capable of accounting for the clenched fist.'[11] It is clear that the two women kept in touch, and at the beginning of 1864 a short note from Gabriel to Mary carried the postscript, 'Fanny wishes you not to forget the photographs.'[12]

Fanny's image dominated Gabriel's art in 1863–5 and this was indeed her finest Pre-Raphaelite hour. She sat for the paintings *Fazio's Mistress*,[13] *Lady Combing Her Hair*,[14] *Lady Lilith*[15] and *The Blue Bower*.[16] The first of these was one of the earliest of Gabriel's 'Venetian' portraits, remarkable chiefly for colour and flesh texture; it shows a woman in a loose gown plaiting her hair before a mirror, an intimate view reinforced by the title, which referred to an Italian poem Gabriel had translated and published which includes the lines:

> I look at the crisp golden-threaded hair,
> Whereof, to thrall my heart, Love twists a net.

The other pictures show Fanny in similarly seductive guise, dressing her hair or just gazing out of the canvas, wearing clothes that look as if they are soon to be removed. Their impression on contemporaries was well conveyed in the first comprehensive account of Rossetti's work, published in 1899, where the author wrote of *Lilith*: 'She herself has a serpent fist and knows the gift of fascination. Bowered in roses, robed in white flowing draperies that slip and reveal the swelling contour of her bust and shoulders, no painter has ever idealized like this the elemental power of carnal loveliness.'[17] Gabriel wrote two poems on the theme: 'Lilith' (later 'Body's Beauty') and 'Eden Bower' in which Lilith, Adam's first wife, revenges herself on him for preferring Eve through the serpent and apple of the Fall: the sexual qualities of her nature are barely concealed beneath the insistent Freudian imagery:

> What great joys had Adam and Lilith!
>   (And O the bower and the hour!)
> Sweet close rings of the serpent's twining
> As heart in heart lay sighing and pining.
>
>   . . .
>
> O bright snake, the death-worm of Adam!
>   (Eden bower's in flower!)
> Wreathe thy neck with my hair's bright tether
> And wear my gold and thy gold together!

The 'Eden Bower' may be read as a fairly transparent rendering of Fanny's loss and repossession of Gabriel. This too was the period when he exorcized his feeling for Lizzie with the ghastly, ghostly painting *Beata Beatrix*. Aside from its narcotic allusions, this was and is regarded as a conjugal memorial imbued with sorrow and sentiment, and partly related to the figures of weeping angels and broken columns so popular in Victorian cemeteries. It refers back, too, to Gabriel's earliest presentation of Lizzie as Delia, with her eyes closed and her hair loose, and despite the vulgarity there is genuine sadness in the picture.

Gabriel's main energies, however, were devoted to images of carnal beauty and loveliness. Some of his friends strongly disapproved, and their aesthetic judgements intermingled with the moral and were applied to the model as well as the work. Fanny was blamed for 'degrading' Gabriel's art. Ruskin was most outspoken. Of the flowers in *Venus Verticordia* (for which, in fact, Fanny was not the model although it conveyed a similar message) he commented:

> They are wonderful to me in their realism; awful – I can use no other word – in their coarseness, showing enormous power,

showing certain conditions of non-sentiment which underlie all
you are doing now, and which make your work, compared to
what it used to be – what Fannie's [*sic*] face is to Lizzie's . . . In
your interest only – and judging from no other person's saying
but from my own sight – I tell you the people you associate
with are ruining you . . .[18]

Ruskin's own repressed sexuality accounts for his inability to
relate to Fanny, but others also believed that she was responsible
for driving away friends. The truth is more complex and it was
not until much later that Gabriel became unvisited and reclusive as
a result of his own behaviour rather than hers. However, there
were difficulties in the early years at Cheyne Walk, since married
couples could not with propriety visit a household that included
Fanny, whose social position, background in prostitution and
relationship with Gabriel were all extremely irregular.

It has often been assumed that Fanny was resident at Cheyne
Walk in the mid-1860s, and that her status was that of 'housekeeper'. This notion seems to have arisen from the fact that she was so
indexed in the published version of Allingham's diary issued by
his widow in 1907. In the text she is called only 'F', and the index
entry seems to derive from a desire to quell speculation as to her
precise role in the Tudor House menage. Sophisticated readers
would be aware that 'housekeeper' was often a synonym for a
live-in mistress of a lower social class, while the innocent would
be neither shocked nor puzzled. There is, in fact, very little
evidence that Fanny assumed the role of housekeeper, and indeed
Gabriel employed the normal range of servants to look after
domestic affairs, one of whom was generally described as
housekeeper. And Fanny had her own establishment at 36 Royal
Avenue, Chelsea, just a few blocks away; this was rented and
furnished for her by Gabriel in what amounts to formal
recognition of her status as mistress. But she also had the key to
Tudor House.

Those friends of Gabriel she met were likely to be those who
ignored strict bourgeois conventions, and indeed in the 1860s
there were signs that an 'alternative', quasi-bohemian lifestyle was
developing, mainly among artists and in Chelsea. William Bell
Scott, now a teacher at the South Kensington School of Design,
lived in a stable but scandalous *ménage à trois* with his wife Letitia

and his mistress Alice Boyd, spending the winters in London and the summers at Alice Boyd's ancestral home in Ayrshire.[19] Charles Howell, the half-Portuguese artistic adventurer who became successively Ruskin's secretary, Burne-Jones's close friend and Rossetti's agent and whose nefarious dealings are too varied to be summarized here, also led a 'loose' private life, although his wife and mistress lived in separate houses.[20] James Whistler, a neighbour of Gabriel's in Chelsea, shared his life with Joanna Heffernan, the model for his *White Girl*, and as early as 1862 she was present when Whistler entertained his male friends, including Gabriel, Swinburne and Boyce, who described Jo as 'a handsome girl with red hair and altogether fine colour'.[21] In November 1866 Gabriel escorted Fanny to dinner with Whistler and Jo at their new house in Walham Grove.[22] Fanny herself was regularly to be found at Tudor House; in 1865, for example, Boyce recorded in his diary five occasions when he called casually and was invited to stay and dine with her and Gabriel. Sometimes other friends like Swinburne or William Michael or Allingham were present, and the atmosphere was comfortably different from that prevailing in more conventional homes and more akin, one suspects, to the male clubs that flourished at this period.

Fanny's attractions were not merely sexual. She had a strong sense of humour, liked a good joke and provided many laughs herself. She never acquired the polite habits of speech demanded by middle-class society and in which Emma, Annie and Jane had all been instructed; instead she retained an unrefined cockney accent, such as was regarded throughout the nineteenth century as a source of comedy in itself.[23] Some of her sayings were recorded: when on a visit in 1867, Allingham noted her forceful objection to Gabriel's bad language: 'Rizetty, I shall leave the room!' – an indignant but ineffective complaint, followed by: 'I shall put you out in the scullery!'[24] She seems to have been the first person to refer – unintentionally – to Charles Howell as 'Owl', a nickname taken up and used affectionately by Ned and Gabriel; on one occasion when she went on a short holiday to Brighton and Shoreham where Howell was also staying, she reported that she 'never seed no owl'.[25] And on one of his visits to Cheyne Walk, Allingham recorded her comments on Bell Scott's altered appearance following an illness which caused hair loss: ' "O my, Mr Scott *is* changed!" she exclaimed. "He ain't got a hye-brow or a hye-lash – not an 'air on his 'ead!" At this Gabriel laughed immoderately, so that poor F., good-natured as she is, pouted at last: "Well, I know I don't say it right." '[26] The following day, Allingham breakfasted at Cheyne Walk and then lay in the garden 'eating strawberries and looking at the peacock' while Fanny, dressed in white, 'went to look at the "chicking", her plural of chicken'.[27] Apart from her dialect, and her presence at such an early hour, the point to notice here is Allingham's use of the term 'good-natured'. Fanny was easy to be with, easygoing, easy to please; she behaved unpretentiously, with an artless vulgarity that was one of her chief charms. Her needs were relatively uncomplicated: she liked attention, presents, being taken to Cremorne, good food and leisure. Her conversation was lively but unintellectual and refreshingly free from the conventional pieties that increasingly made up the bourgeois woman's social vocabulary. She did not take offence when teased, and the affectionate names Gabriel bestowed on her at this period – Lumpses, Chump-Wump and Elephant – reflect her good nature as well as her expanding girth. She did not worry about her soul or her conscience, and she and Gabriel evidently enjoyed each other's company. The fact that she measured affection, as the emotionally insecure often do, in terms of gifts, meant that most of her demands on him were material ones, and although this was later interpreted as predatory by Gabriel's family and friends, there is every indication that he acknowledged his debt to Fanny as fully as if they had been married. Indeed their later relationship took a mercenary form partly because they could not marry. Of course it is unlikely that Gabriel would have married her had she been free, but their later correspondence shows that he regarded her as a dependant, and made appropriate provision. Partly because of the direct, unmystified nature of their relationship, and partly because she has received a bad press, I am disposed to think better of Fanny than most commentators, although it would be unwise to elevate her affair with Gabriel into a *grande passion*. He partly shared the moral attitudes of his redoubtable mother and sisters, and he was also conditioned to confuse love with worship of an ideal figure; Fanny belonged to a lower order. But it was love of a kind, and it is clear that some sort of loyalty or fidelity, admittedly rather elastic, existed between them until the end. All her life Fanny kept an early token of their affection, a small *carte de visite* photograph, inscribed 'to Fanny, DGR, 1863';[28] and also the funny drawings and presents he gave her in the shape of little elephant figures.

In the autumn of 1864 they spent three weeks in Paris together. Gabriel used the trip professionally in the sense of visiting galleries and assessing current developments in painting, but the visit must have been mainly for Fanny's benefit. Her presence was concealed from all but a few friends – to his mother Gabriel wrote most insistently in the first person,[29] and about the only thing Fanny is recorded as doing in Paris was buying a tin of medicinal water costing 100 francs. Some years later, Gabriel sent Swinburne the address of the shop, adding, 'Fanny says the water did her no good, but I know a case where it did much.'[30] This may have been an oblique reference to Lizzie, who had been ill in Paris four years before.

At the beginning of 1864 Gabriel came out of mourning and seemed to many to have recovered from his grief. In February, Boyce entertained a crowd of male friends to dinner at the Arts Club and afterwards took them back to the studio at Chatham Place, which he had taken over from Gabriel and where the conviviality continued. 'The evening went off comfortably,' he noted in his diary, 'though Mrs Birrell told me afterwards that on this very evening 3 years ago Mrs Gabriel Rossetti was taken so ill and died here.'[31]

Gabriel gave his first party at Cheyne Walk in April 1865; Georgie's sister, Aggie, who was then staying with the Joneses sharing their social life in the artistic circle – she eventually married the painter Edward Poynter – sent home a detailed account. This was the famous occasion when the Browns spent two and a half hours travelling circuitously by train from Ker.tish Town to Chelsea via Kew and Clapham rather than incur a cab-fare. Aggie's other comments were equally interesting: poor 'washed-out' Mrs Arthur Hughes was pregnant, 'on the way again, blest if she ain't', and

Mrs Brown, who was otherwise very nice, spilled a cup of coffee down Georgie's chinese blue silk dress like our bonnets, and for this we don't thank her, for time can ne'er restore that dress or another like it. You wouldn't think that Providence, while Georgie was leaving the room to dabble her dress, permitted a waiter to upset a milk jug on her, but so it did. I was a good part of the time with Janey, with whom I get on very well. Madox Brown was very jolly, but so grey that it made me sad to see his wife is one mass of fat . . .[32]

This rather irrational comment may have been an effect of concealing the fact that Emma Brown had, in the phrase of the time, 'taken to drink'. This was confidentially recorded by several of her contemporaries[33] and cryptically mentioned in Brown's diary for 1865, when he resumed entries after a seven-year gap. On 1 October, he wrote, 'E. finished b-sherry', and on 2 October, 'E. tried to get cherry Brandy at pastry cook's, I just in time. E. very unhappy because failed.'[34] Arguments followed, and entries such as 'E.D. [Emma Drunk] eve. stormy in consequence'[35] and 'Evening to dinner with Scotts. E.D. there. Marshalls home with us. E. talked nonsense to Mrs M about ill-treatment and separate maintenance.' This last was followed by a whole day spent in 'only espostulations and waste of time'.[36] It is possible that Emma spilt coffee over Georgie's dress because she was drunk. Significantly, the large number of guests at Cheyne Walk, listed by Aggie as comprising 'William Rossetti, Mr, Mrs, Lucy and Katey Brown, Janey and Morris, our three selves [i.e. Aggie, Georgie and Ned] Bell Scott, Munro the sculptor and his wife, F. G. Stephens, Mr and Mrs Arthur Hughes, Mr and Mrs Taylor, M. Legros and his pretty English wife, Webb and Swinburne . . .'[37] did not include Fanny. It did, however, include Jane, who was soon to replace Fanny in Gabriel's affections.

It is virtually impossible now to say precisely why, in the mid-1860s, Jane Morris unilaterally undid her marriage. Many guesses and explanations have been proffered in the books about her husband, usually based on little more than the writers' own views of her personality, for there is no real evidence, apart from the already-quoted remark that she had 'never loved' him, as to why Jane withdrew affection from Morris. As so often in this story, the protagonist is silent, described only through others' words. Jane was indeed the chief actor in the drama. It was she who took steps to conclude her side of the marriage and to open a new relationship. This is, admittedly, a difficult claim to 'prove' but it offers, I believe, the only convincing explanation of the curious triangle comprising herself, Morris and Gabriel, which has been so often described and analysed.[38] It is less easy, however, to understand why she did it. Her position was, to say the least, comfortable. She lived in a fine large house with several servants, her two lively daughters and a loving husband. She may have wished to avoid endless pregnancies and Emma Brown's experience in this respect may have served as a warning, but it was already recognized in the progressive circle to which the Morrises belonged that frequent pregnancies were bad for women. Aggie Macdonald's pity for poor Mrs Hughes, who was 'on the way again', indicates that this was a fairly widespread view. Various contraceptive methods were available and, although the subject is shrouded in mystery, it is clear that they were being used since, from the middle of the century, the size of middle-class families showed a marked decline, which must be attributed to the use of contraceptives.[39]

It seems probable that the Morrises used some form of contraception after May's birth in March 1862, if their sex life resumed, which there is no particular reason to doubt. The following Christmas Charley Faulkner remarked that Morris's temper was greatly improved: he was happy and cheerful and 'has only kicked one panel out of a door for this twelvemonth past'.[40] It is possible, in view of her later history of backache, that Jane suffered from a gynaecological disorder that prevented conception; many women endured chronic conditions such as prolapse, fibroids, fistula and other complaints, incurable at this time. It is also possible that at some stage she suffered a miscarriage and was advised not to have any more children. The only record of her being ill during the Red House days was in the early weeks of 1865, when she was convalescing at Hastings. In April she was still, according to Aggie Macdonald, 'so weak and delicate as to make one uneasy'.[41] But she was well enough to attend Gabriel's party the same month. Robert Burden had died in February at the age of fifty-five so Jane was in mourning: black made her look exceptionally pallid, according to Aggie. From this date Bessie Burden came to live with her sister. Jane's feelings towards her are not recorded but other members of the Morris family seem to have regarded Miss Burden as the embodiment of her name. She never married.[42]

Later in the year the Morrises left Red House, and from this time on their relationship began to deteriorate. The causes of their removal were mainly financial, as the income from Morris's mining shares dropped steadily and that from the firm did not appreciably rise. Plans to establish workshops at Upton and build a new wing to Red House for Ned and Georgie and their family were made and abandoned, and Morris began selling some of his possessions, such as the chivalric watercolours he had purchased from Gabriel in the mid-1850s. The eventual solution, which caused such heartache that neither Morris nor Jane ever revisited Red House, was to move both home and workshop to Queen Square, in Bloomsbury, in the centre of London, where, from midsummer 1865, they leased a large house. When the Morris family moved there in November, they shared the premises with the firm, living above the workshop, office and showroom. It was undeniably a descent in terms of status. The neighbourhood was crowded and socially 'mixed' with working-class families and tradesmen living in close proximity to bourgeois households, and businesses next to residential areas. At Queen Square there was no garden, no carriage and much less space for entertaining. Georgie noted that for a while Topsy tried to maintain the Red House conviviality by sending out invitations every week but that these soon ceased, owing to Jane's 'ill-health'. Jane seems to have missed the countryside, and to have disliked her new surroundings. Although the Faulkner family – widowed mother and adult children Charley, Kate and Lucy – already lived in Queen Square, and Philip Webb had his home and architectural practice close by in Grays Inn, most of their other friends were moving away from the centre of London, towards the fashionable suburbs in the west. At the end of 1864 Ned and Georgie settled in Kensington, where Holman Hunt and a number of other painters were already established and, as we have seen, Gabriel was part of another cluster in Chelsea. However, all these friends were still accessible, and there seems to have been an increase in entertaining in Pre-Raphaelite circles in the 1860s, perhaps as their prosperity and fame increased; in 1865, for example, the Browns moved from Kentish Town to a fine large house in Fitzroy Square, and soon became well-known for large, regular 'At Home' gatherings. If Jane disliked Queen Square, it may have been from a mixture of disappointment and snobbery. Certainly, from this date, as Georgie noted, she withdrew from the role of hostess, although this perhaps reflected marital as well as social dissatisfaction.

It seems to me that another, hitherto unremarked factor in Janey's withdrawal from her husband was Gabriel's renewed availabilty. If we accept, as Jane seems to have done, that he first aroused her feelings in Oxford in 1857, we must also surmise that this mutual attraction was neutralized, or suppressed, by their respective marriages, and by Gabriel's mourning for Lizzie. By the beginning of 1865, however, he was emerging from the social purdah of widowhood and his charm and magnetism were again to be felt. The pictorial evidence shows that it was about this time that he began to draw Jane again. Since her marriage she had sat for only one portrait, done during the festive gathering at Red House at Christmas 1860, and some studies for a triptych commissioned for Llandaff cathedral. As a new mother in 1861, Jane was an obvious choice for the Virgin in the triptych Adoration scene, although Ruskin (whose taste in holy women was for the frail and infantile) described the result as 'a Madonna with black hair in ringlets like a George II wig and a black complexion like a mulatto'.[43] Morris modelled for the head of King David.[44] Thereafter, for three years, there was no image of Janey from Gabriel's hand. In 1865, however, in what must have been her last weeks at Red House, she sat for at least five portrait drawings, in chalk and pencil. Then there was a further gap, until 1867, before her face reappeared. In the intervening period Gabriel was occupied with his picture of luscious ladies: first Fanny, in *The Blue Bower* and then Marie Ford in *The Beloved*, and Alexa Wilding in *Monna Vanna*. The 1865 drawings were important to Jane; forty years later she wrote a label for one, which read: 'I consider this portrait one of the very best D. G. Rossetti ever did of me (about 1865) June 1, 1908: Jane Morris.'[45] Drawn in black chalk, this portrait is less mannered than those in ink or pencil, done at various other times, and makes Janey look less of a sorceress and more like an ordinary young woman, but otherwise it is hard to tell what particularly pleased her about it. Around this date, too, she posed for a series of photographs, arranged by Gabriel apparently in a kind of tent in the garden of Cheyne Walk. These construct an image rather than a portrait of Jane, and represent an artist's impression. Caught at the correct camera angle, she has the familiar inflected grace and intense, abstracted expression that are seen in Gabriel's famous paintings of her. In less flattering poses, her heavy features and frizzy hair are revealed, and we see a plainer side. The general effect, however, is decidedly glamorous, whether she is sitting or standing, wearing a voluminous silk gown, the pose and gaze expressing the same intriguing melancholy as *La Belle Iseult*, married to one man and in love with another. They are key images in the promotion of Janey as a silent, enigmatic, beautiful woman, the role that was in some sense her career.

Despite these attentions from Gabriel, which may have encouraged Jane in her marital withdrawal, her husband was unaware of any alteration in his position. During 1863–4 Morris conceived and wrote a number of verse tales based on classical love stories such as those of Atalanta, Cupid and Psyche, Alcestis and Admetus, Pygmalion and Galatea. The subjects were loosely related to those of the embroidered Illustrious Women, which also celebrated love and marriage.[46] By 1865 Topsy and Ned were laying plans for a superb illustrated book, to be called *The Earthly Paradise*. This was to contain Morris's verse and Ned's illustrations, cut on to woodblocks by Morris. It seems unlikely that Morris could have conceived and executed a book of love stories dedicated to his wife if he had been aware that his marriage was crumbling. The work proceeded throughout 1866 and was abruptly abandoned some time in 1867, when Morris suddenly decided to issue the first part, unillustrated. This decision is normally said to be due to the difficulty of making an illuminated manuscript with text and decorations in visual harmony with contemporary printing founts;[47] it is also true that Morris's celebration of love was suddenly undermined emotionally. He continued with the verse scheme, but its direction altered course.

The later *Earthly Paradise* tales and the month-poems that separate them are rather melancholy, even despairing. They reflect the writer's unhappiness so clearly that Georgie and her son-in-law, preparing Morris's official biography, felt that the subject could not be avoided. Hence Mackail's masterly sentence that hints so tactfully at the Morrises' failed marriage. 'In the verses that frame the stories,' he wrote of *The Earthly Paradise*, 'there is an autobiography so delicate and outspoken that it must needs be left to speak for itself.'[48] In fact the poems do not speak for themselves; they reveal a poet pining for a lost love. 'Come back, past years,' cries 'April'. 'May' records the passing of Love:

A little while I sighed to find him gone,
A little while the dawning was alone.

'Can we regain what we have lost?' asks 'July' rhetorically, while
'September' is perhaps the most explicit:

Look long, O longing eyes, and look in vain!
Strain idly, aching heart, and yet be wise
And hope no more for things to come again
That thou beholdest once with careless eyes!
Like a new-wakened man thou art, who tries
To dream again the dream that made him glad
When in his arms his loving love he had.

The evidence, sparse though it is, suggests that some time during
1866 or 1867 Jane completed her emotional withdrawal from her
husband and told him explicitly that she did not and could not
love him. Possibly at the same time, but probably earlier, their
sexual relationship ceased. It was a severe blow and disappointment to Morris and he took a long time to adjust; a good deal of
the emotional fortitude he later displayed no doubt originated in
his need to cope with this rejection. A lot has been written,
however, about Morris's life, internal and external, and rather
than add to that speculation, I would like to guess at Jane's feelings
and actions. My conjecture is that from 1865, when Gabriel
re-emerged in society and again drew her portrait, she was
sending out silent but unmistakable signals. Since she left no
record of her life, this can only be deduced from a curious cluster
of paintings which occupied Gabriel in 1865 and which seem to
foreshadow later events. At one level, they could offer an indirect
comment on what Janey and he were about to do. The first picture
of this kind is *The Merciless Lady*,[49] in which a male figure sits
between two women, gazing at the fair-haired girl to his left who
is playing a musical instrument and in more than one way recalls
the painter's first love; her head is thrown back in an Ophelia/
Beatrice pose characteristic of representations of Lizzie. The man's
free hand, however, is held by a dark-haired girl who is trying to
attract his attention from the other side. On the ground are three
glasses of wine, signifying life. The dark girl's glass is full and
untasted, the fair girl's is drained and that of the man is

half-finished. The message is transparent, even overstated: the man is being pulled away from the woman to whom he is bound by the intense regard and tenacious grip of another; as yet, he is held in tension between them.[50]

Washing Hands[51] was a rather different picture, one of Gabriel's few costume genre pieces, set in the eighteenth century with a narrative content that in his own words 'represents the last stage of an unhappy love affair . . . when both of the parties have come to see in reality that it will never do, but when the lady I think is generally the first to have the strength to act on that knowledge. It is all over, in my picture, and she is washing her hands of it.'[52] Because neither of the Morrises modelled for the figures in *Washing Hands*, the inference that the choice of subject relates to what is known of their relationship is less self-evident than the parallels that have so frequently been drawn between the position of Jane, shackled to an unloved husband, and that of the Pias and Proserpines for whom she later sat, but it seems to me that intentionally or not, the picture offers an oblique comment on the Morris marriage rift, which Jane may well have conveyed to Gabriel. It may thus provide a tentative clue to the date at which she had decided that it was 'all over' between her and Topsy. It was followed by one of Gabriel's oddest pictures, developed from a juvenile sketch and entitled *A Fight for a Woman*.[53] Two shadowy figures wrestle as a woman looks on: the emotional significance needs no explication.

It is important to recognize that these paintings do not represent actual events; rather they express emotional tensions and subconscious feelings. By 1865 Gabriel's affair with Fanny had settled down; she was becoming fat and was a comfortable rather than a stimulating companion. His feelings were aroused anew by Jane, who presented herself as emotionally detached, but was still another man's wife. Briefly, Gabriel's feelings expressed themselves in paint, and seem to have been thereby exorcized, for in the following two years his art returned more to the sensuous beauties for which he was famed: *Regina Cordium, Monna Vanna, Fiametta, Jolie Coeur, Monna Rosa*. These were painted from models whose looks he admired, but with whom he was neither romantically nor sexually involved.

Ellen Smith, for example, sat for a number of these female figures; she has been described as a 'laundress of uncertain virtue'[54] who was a popular model for a while, sitting to several painters. The story is that her proletarian admirer objected to this and beat her up, cutting her face and thus ending her modelling career. Later she married a cabman, and at this time she approached George Boyce asking for 'some laundry work on her own account, as her husband's earnings are small'.[55] Alexa Wilding, who became Gabriel's most frequent model, was seen by him in the street in 1865 and was asked to sit: she had strong, regular features and an expressionless face that made her ideal for his purposes. Fearing indecorum, she failed to turn up, and it was not until he saw her again by chance and assured her mother of his respectability that she agreed to pose. She was otherwise a dressmaker with dreams of the stage; her real name was Alice. But although he liked Alexa and paid her a regular retainer of 30s a week so as to be sure of her services, Gabriel found her dull company.[56]

The first hint that Jane was seeing Gabriel comes in the summer of 1866 in a note from Gabriel to Charles Howell, who was always available for slightly dubious errands, asking him to book seats for *Don Giovanni* – 'the best box available, of course, as before' – and to send the tickets and libretto to Jane at Queen Square.[57] Jane liked music and was a keen concert- and opera-goer; her husband did not. He loathed opera as 'the most rococo and degraded of all forms of art' with 'sandy-haired German tenors tweedledeeing' over great passions[58] and so there was nothing untoward in Gabriel obtaining tickets and escorting her. It was not until the start of 1868 that she began to sit to him again, and thus see him regularly, under rather different conditions.

This was a turbulent year for several members of the Pre-Raphaelite circle and seems definitely to have marked the beginning of Jane's affair with Gabriel. That something was stirring is suggested by the fact that the previous October he produced a watercolour showing *Tristram and Yseult Drinking the Love Potion*,[59] whose subject looks back to the Arthurian days of 1857 and depicts the overpowering love that binds Tristram and Yseult despite their respective marriages. This seems to me to constitute a clear allusion to the onset of an overwhelming romantic passion, although like the earlier pictures, it relates more to semi-conscious feelings than to an overt or mutual declaration. The first subject for which Gabriel asked Jane to pose in January

1868 was a relatively formal one, now known as *Mrs William Morris in a Blue Silk Dress*.[60] This had been suggested earlier and belongs, at least in part, to the tradition of portraits of patrons' wives to which Gabriel had already contributed with his second *Regina Cordium* of 1861, for Mr and Mrs Aldam Heaton. In *The Blue Silk Dress*, Jane is shown resting her elbows on a table, and the ring on her wedding finger is prominently visible. Across the top of the picture runs a Latin rubric that stresses her marital state: 'Jane Morris AD 1868 D. G. Rossetti pinxit. Famous for her poet husband and surpassingly famous for her beauty, now may she be famous for my painting.' It was a bold but not scandalous statement, and the surviving evidence suggests that no one read anything into it, for indeed it said more about the painter than his sitter. Gabriel's letters to Jane at this period reveal no hidden agenda: they are all about dates and times for sittings, and how Morris and maybe Bessie will accompany her. Indeed, the formality of the arrangements, finalized on 6 March, is something of a surprise when set against the now popular notions of their passionate love affair. Since the work would take more than one day, the Morrises were invited to stay at Cheyne Walk. Gabriel wrote:

My dear Janey,
    Next Wednesday was the day I hoped to see you, but I think perhaps to secure my finishing something I am about before-hand, I had better say Friday – i.e. 2 days later. On Friday next then I will expect your kind visit, and if you can come early enough to sit that day – i.e. about one o'clock, my gratitude will commence at that hour.

He promised that the pose was easy; that the drawing of her head would take two days, 'then straight to the picture'; and,

If you find it more convenient to come only in time for dinner on Friday, and so have a rest after the journey that night before you sit, that plan will of course do perfectly for me, but if I do not hear to the contrary, I will expect you in time to sit on Friday, and Morris at dinner time. It strikes me as probable that you and Bessie might like to come together, as otherwise she would be left very dull at home, unless she thinks it necessary for the safety of the establishment to stay behind. If she can come, it would give me much pleasure, and there will be no difficulty as to an extra bed-room, as there are several in the house.[61]

This does not read like a clandestine assignation.

The Morrises stayed at Cheyne Walk for a week while the work was completed, and when they returned to Queen Square Jane established the pattern that she followed over the whole spring and summer of modelling regularly for Gabriel. The result was a series of paintings and drawings whose chronology is not definitively established but which together add up to a creative partnership between artist and model. *The Blue Silk Dress* was one of Janey's favourites, perhaps because it was the first to link her fame with Gabriel's skill; it was accompanied by a chalk drawing now entitled *Reverie*[62] which Gabriel hung in a place of honour over his mantelpiece until the end of his life, when it was bequeathed to Jane, and by two other chalk studies, identified as drawings for the oil painting of *Mariana*,[63] also produced in this year. This seems to have started as a portrait of Jane wearing the same blue silk dress, and to have been transformed into a picture to meet the requirements of an earlier commission which Gabriel had yet to carry out.

The subject chosen was that of the sad heroine Mariana. Originally a minor character in Shakespeare's *Measure for Measure*, she had been taken up by Tennyson, from whom Millais had taken the inspiration for his *Mariana* in the early days of the Pre-Raphaelite Brotherhood.[64] Gabriel returned to Shakespeare, depicting the heroine listening to a song, played and sung by a boy with a lute, whose face was an idealized portrait of the patron's son. His Mariana sits at her embroidery frame in the moated grange to which she has been banished on a false accusation of infidelity. The lines of the song, inscribed on the frame, may have an oblique biographical significance:

> Take, O take those lips away
> That so sweetly were forsworn;
> And those eyes, the break of day,
> Lights that do mislead the morn;
> But my kisses bring again,
> Seals of love, but sealed in vain.

But the picture gives no suggestion of the eventual outcome of Mariana's imprisonment, when she is reunited with her lover by the adventurous and improper means of joining him in bed in disguise. Alas for Jane's reputation as a pioneer of art embroidery, her stitching in the picture looks suspiciously like Berlin work! The frame was borrowed[65] and was apparently meant also for inclusion in a third picture, *La Pia de' Tolomei*.

Here the subject had direct and unmistakable biographical relevance, and it is hard to believe that Jane and Gabriel were unaware of how it would be interpreted, at least by Morris and the small circle of friends who knew of or guessed at the hole at the heart of his marriage. To the outside world, of course, it was a subject from Dante. La Pia is a character in *Purgatorio*, imprisoned by a cruel husband in a fortress, where she dies either from malaria or murder; her most famous line is 'Siena made me, Maremma unmade me'. In the painting a melancholy figure of Jane is sitting on a tower surrounded by ivy and sycamore leaves; black crows circle in the stormy sky. Her head is bent forward so as to accentuate the length of her neck and she is pointedly fingering the ring on her wedding finger. In the study for this, the ring is a plain gold band, evidently Jane's actual wedding ring. She is shown wearing a blue dress with gold embroidery at neck and wrist similar to that in the other two pictures, and over this a light, cream-coloured gown that may be the one Gabriel referred to on 17 June when he asked Aglaia Coronio for some Indian muslin 'for a dress which Janey Morris is making up for one of the pictures I am doing from her'.[66] Jane thus made an active contribution by creating the costumes. Probably in relation to the same picture, Gabriel wrote to her on 5 May:

> About the blue silk dress it occurs to me that I think the sleeves should be as full at the top as is consistent with simplicity of outline, and perhaps would gain by being lined with some soft material, but of this you will be the best judge. The pieces of gold embroidery in front might (if you have time to make it) be something like this [sketch] unless as is very possible a better idea strikes you.[67]

The work was thus collaborative; she was a participant rather than the soulful, passive model of Pre-Raphaelite legend. Gabriel's productivity in this period may indeed have derived in part from her enthusiasm.

It is hard to judge the exact nature of their relationship. At the time of the letter just quoted, Jane was with her husband on a visit to her mother-in-law in Essex, and not long before Gabriel had sent her daughters a present of a pair of dormice; now he also told her of the reappearance of one that had escaped at Cheyne Walk, perhaps while she was modelling. Jane inquired about the state of the captured dormouse, whom Gabriel reported was 'quite plumped out and sleek again – only a place he had worn bare on his nose by gnawing at the trap does not fill up yet'. She also made a suggestion for accessories in the next painting. 'The silk is just the thing, and the idea delightful,' he responded. 'I re-enclose the pattern in case you should need it. I suppose, in order to be thoroughly useful, it ought to be as much as 20 inches square, in which case it could be slipped over one of my sofa cushions but only one side of the cushion-case need be embroidered.' He concluded, 'Between this and the dress I shall be giving you an awful lot of work'[68] – but it is clear that Jane was as keen as he. With these paintings, she had found an outlet for her embroidery talents, within the art produced by the man she loved. When his work went on display, so would hers. It is clear from his responses that Gabriel valued Jane's contributions and suggestions, not merely because of romantic infatuation but because of their worth; he respected her judgement.

Their social position was ambiguous below the polite surface. Some of the tensions may be inferred from entries in George Boyce's diary for 1868. On 27 March, for example, he called on Gabriel and Fanny at Cheyne Walk, and saw some 'beautiful studies', presumably for *La Pia*, drawn from Jane and Alexa. On 2 April he joined a full-dress party given by Gabriel, in honour of Jane, attended by her husband and sister, Georgie and Ned, Ford, Lucy and Cathy Madox Brown, William Michael, Faulkner, Philip Webb and Charles and Kitty Howell. Then on 20 April, when he again called at the studio, he found Jane sitting.[69] On 27 May, Morris gave a large party to celebrate the publication of the first volume of *The Earthly Paradise*, and although some of the guests must have been aware of the irony, it was an elaborate and successful occasion. At Allingham's suggestion, Ned wrote 'Earthly Paradise' on the menu card, in commemoration of the gathering.[70] Outwardly, there were no signs of discord, and Jane had evidently not entirely abandoned her role as hostess. When the summer holidays came, however, the Morrises did not go on holiday with the Joneses as usual, but with Charles and Kitty Howell.

13

They went to Southwold in Suffolk, which Gabriel described as 'deadly-lively (or very quiet)'.[1] Howell acted as go-between for Gabriel and Jane; on 20 August Gabriel wrote asking him to 'tell Janey that I hope she will be able to sit to me very soon . . .'[2] and the next day he enclosed a note for her, with the anxious injunction that Howell was not to 'trouble about the enclosed what I send unless it is convenient'.[3] Jane replied by the same means, although her letters do not survive.

The hitherto unnoticed fact that Jane and Gabriel were exchanging clandestine letters in the summer of 1868 indicates that their affair was well under way, but that they were still keen to keep it secret. The part played by Howell, who enjoyed intrigues, should not be underestimated: he may well have encouraged the correspondence. But Jane and Gabriel continued to use his services as a 'pillar-post' in October and November, when Gabriel took his own holiday at the home of Alice Boyd, Penkill Castle in Ayrshire, where she was spending the summer with her lover and his wife. On 9 October Gabriel thanked Howell for his postal delivery, 'the results of which have just appeared in a reply'. Some obstacle, however, nearly prevented Howell from delivering Gabriel's letter to Jane, in a manner described as 'enough to frighten one certainly'; it seems they were afraid of discovery.[4] Two weeks later Gabriel 'can't resist sending another enclosure, which you will manage I know if possible. . .the enclosed ought to reach at once if it is to secure a result which is my only solace out here. . .'[5]

Another factor which suggests that their relationship had reached a critical point was the sudden deterioration in Gabriel's eyesight, which strongly suggests a psychological or emotional cause. Certainly no organic complaint was ever diagnosed for the trouble, which began in September, when Janey resumed her sittings. Their relationship must have become more ardent, even if it was not yet sexual, and it is very tempting to connect Gabriel's afflicted vision with his illicit passion. Its onset effectively prevented him from painting and sent him out of London, almost as if his conscience were working on his body to separate him from a temptation he did not fully wish to succumb to. As I have already argued, Gabriel had a deep sense of morality and a need to worship an ideal beloved who was an image of goodness and purity; like Beatrice, she was a source of moral, emotional and aesthetic inspiration. To regard him, as some commentators have done, as a 'latin' sensualist who bedded all women who came his way is to misread his personality, even after his relationship with Fanny had somewhat loosened his inhibitions. He faced a good deal of internal conflict, not so much in suppressing his sexual desires as in reconciling his intense feelings of adoration with the social demands of the middle-class world in which he moved and where he most seriously wished to be well thought of. An overwhelming passion for another man's wife could be permissible in the world of bohemia, particularly if she returned the love, but in the bourgeois world it was both immoral and socially awkward: open adulterous affairs were the subject of suggestive gossip and disapproval, sometimes amounting to ostracism. A possible solution was recourse to the fiction of Chivalry, which allowed a Victorian gentleman to worship another man's wife in the guise of courtly love, but this too was difficult for Gabriel, whose public face was one of discreet, remorseful grief for Lizzie. Indeed, he still felt genuine private grief over the manner of her death, and the 'unfinished business' between them; many times during the seance and table-tapping craze in the mid-1860s he tried to contact her beyond the grave and ascertain that she was not unhappy.[6] Despite the less than perfect nature of their marriage, to admit a new woman to the position of Ideal Beloved meant, inevitably, one more betrayal. It is not surprising that Gabriel had problems adjusting to his love for Jane, nor that this expressed itself in disturbed vision.

Janey, on the other hand, had already cleared the decks. In any case, she did not share his imperative religious upbringing and she had never loved her husband. This must have been how she represented her situation for Gabriel to depict her as Mariana and La Pia: two women incarcerated by unpleasant men. In a letter to Brown, written from Penkill in October 1868, Gabriel outlined a satirical drama set in Queen Square in which Morris was presented as exhibiting extreme greed and uncouthness:

BROWN   How are you Morris? Have you heard how Gabriel is?

MORRIS   (*dancing*) I wish to God Gabriel – no I mean the cook – was in Hell! Don't you Janey dear? Damn blast etc. etc. Oh ah! Don't you know? Gabriel's all right again. Damn blast etc. etc. – of course you'll stay to dinner Old Chap. I don't know though if we have any. Janey dear it's all your fault. Damn blast etc. etc. –

   (*Dinner brought in.*)

JANEY   (*carving*) Haven't you heard from Gabriel, Mr Brown?

MORRIS   (*nudging her, in a whining tone*) Why Janey dear, that's the bit I always have. You know Brown doesn't like it.

JANEY   O I'm very sorry dear. Here it is. Will you have the other too? What were you saying Mr Brown?

BROWN   I thought Morris might have heard from Gabriel.

MORRIS   (*who has been helped*)

   O ah! Gabri–obble obble Gabri–uuch – uuch –
   Gabri–obble obble obble obble obble –
   (*Morris eats. Tableau.*)[7]

The domestic details in this rather obscure burlesque may well have been supplied by Jane. And when Gabriel returned to London in mid-November, he sent Alice Boyd an equally unsympathetic report of Morris, seen at a party complaining of deafness:

. . . but on a large plug of string being taken out of his ear, he revived a good deal and even scratched himself in places apparently inaccessible. When I left, he was being prepared for departure. The whisky cork had already been got out of his nose, and Janey had nearly succeeded in fishing the paper-knife up from the base of his spine.[8]

He also claimed to have called at Queen Square at the moment when Morris was 'howling and threatening to throw a new piano of his wife's out of the window' because its arrival coincided with his dinner. Morris's rages were legendary and these jokes were of course in the long-established tradition of which Topsy had always been the butt; but they were also coming from a rival for Jane's affection, and have an edge that suggests the situation was worsening.

Morris reacted with stoicism. He continued his verses for *The Earthly Paradise* but turned more and more to Nordic tales with turbulent, unhappy endings. The poem 'October'[9] recalled the time at Southwold and expressed hope for reconciliation if not renewal of love. But thereafter he seems to have resigned himself and tried to blunt his sense of loss by reading and studying Icelandic and Norse sagas, an activity which has always been read as a search for emotional fortitude. In the middle of January 1869 he set out suddenly for Italy with Ned, whose affairs were also in turmoil, and although the two friends got no further than Dover, Morris had left instructions to his wife. 'Janey has stopped her sittings by order during foreign service,' Gabriel told Howell, 'just as I supposed.'[10] And Jane evidently did not defy the ban, which suggests that she was concerned neither to risk her public reputation nor further to anger or humiliate her husband. Under the stress of emotion, Gabriel turned again to poetry. His early work, before the tedious repetitions of the *House of Life* series, was inventively original, and this was true of 'Troy Town', written in the early weeks of 1869. It opens with a soft pornographic account of Helen's votive offering of a chalice shaped like her breast and ends with the awakening of Paris's love for her.

> See my breast, how like it is;
> > *O Troy Town!*
> See it bare for the air to kiss!
> Is the cup to thy heart's desire?
> O for the breast, O make it his!
> > *O Troy's down,*
> > *Tall Troy's on fire!*

> . . .

> Paris turned upon his bed,
>   *O Troy Town!*
> Turned upon his bed and said,
> Dead at heart with the heart's desire –
> 'O to clasp her golden head!'
>   *O Troy's down,*
>   *Tall Troy's on fire!*

Georgie recalled Gabriel reading the poem aloud 'like a challenge to the world'.[11] The personal significance was oblique, yet it clearly spelt the reawakening of love. And it was soon to be unambiguously related to Jane.

The resurgence of poetry that accompanied his ardour led Gabriel to think once again of publishing a volume of work, spurred on too by a sense of being outpaced. His two poetic juniors, Morris and Swinburne, had growing reputations; with the publication of the first *Earthly Paradise* Morris had three published volumes to his credit. And in this literary field which was the source of so much pride to their mother, Gabriel's sisters were also rivalling him. Christina published *Goblin Market* in 1862 and *The Prince's Progress* in 1866 while even the earnest Maria was an author with a textbook of idiomatic Italian issued in 1867. Gabriel had published one book of translations, *Early Italian Poets*, in 1861. Most of his own poems were in the manuscript notebook buried with Lizzie. It was probable, as various people later pointed out, that he could remember them verbatim, but he believed them to be irretrievably lost; that, after all, was the meaning of the sacrificial gesture. The idea of digging up the coffin and rescuing the poems was first raised at the end of 1868, and lodged itself in Gabriel's mind, expressing itself almost palpably the following March when he wrote to his mother describing new sonnets as 'bogies' or ghosts, who 'will keep their shrouds down tolerably close, and creak enough themselves to render a piano unnecessary. As their own vacated graves serve them to dance on, there is no danger of their disturbing the lodgers beneath. . .'[12] The idea was pursued. 'Howell of his own accord entered on the matter,' wrote Gabriel to his brother afterwards, 'and offered to take all the execution of it on himself. This for some time I still hung back from accepting; but eventually I yielded, and the thing was done.'[13] After some bureaucratic delays, since the grave had to be opened without the consent of the owner, Mrs Rossetti, Lizzie's coffin was exhumed by undertakers in the presence of Howell, a lawyer and a doctor, and the sodden, stained, damaged notebook removed. Whether to lessen the guilt and disgust such a proceeding inevitably aroused or to heighten the Gothic qualities of the story, the facts of decomposition were ignored, and the legend launched that Lizzie's hair retained all its brightness even in death.

A more likely state of affairs can be guessed from what Gabriel told William Michael about the book as he began transcribing. 'The poem of "Jenny" . . . has got a great worm-hole right through every page of it,' he wrote. 'It has a dreadful smell – partly no doubt the disinfectants – but the doctor says there is nothing dangerous.'[14]

Gabriel concealed the nasty business from his mother and sisters and told only a few people: his brother, his assistant Treffry Dunn, his close friends Brown, Swinburne and Bell Scott, and Jane. All were likely to think the desecration less deplorable than the loss of his poems. Within a week, however, Howell, who loved secrets, told Morris, Ned and G. F. Watts, and then there was no concealing it. 'I have begged Howell to hold his tongue for the future', Gabriel wrote, 'but if he does not I cannot help it . . . I suppose the truth must ooze out in time.'[15] It was an unfortunate choice of phrase, but accurate: it was not a secret to be easily kept. To Swinburne, Lizzie's passionate supporter, Gabriel justified his action:

> The truth is, no one so much as herself would have approved of my doing this. Art was the only thing for which she felt seriously. Had it been possible to her, I should have found the book on my pillow the night she was buried; and could she have opened the grave no other hand would have been needed.[16]

Swinburne agreed, saying he had often wondered what Lizzie's 'own hope and desire in the matter would have been'.[17]

But there are times when signification outweighs this type of reasoning. A good deal has been written about the exhumation of Rossetti's poems, which is one of the best-known elements of the Pre-Raphaelite story and still has power to evoke an emotional response to what seems a final, ghoulish betrayal of Lizzie. But it had, in my view, less to do with Lizzie than with Jane: the poems buried in 1862, however misguidedly, as a tribute and symbol of lost love were in 1869 dug up to be published in a volume celebrating a new beloved. The dead Lizzie had been replaced by the live Jane. Exhumation was thus symbolic of Love's death and rebirth, and its semiotic purpose should be understood. Gabriel, whose emotional responses were tuned to personification and myth, was not unaware of how the action would be understood and to some degree acknowledged that it was indeed a manifest sign: his adoration of Lizzie had been transferred to Jane. But I am less concerned here with his psychology, which has received a great deal of attention, than with hers: it is clear that she knew about and sanctioned the exhumation. Had he thought she would disapprove, Gabriel would hardly have gone ahead; she was among the few people he told directly. To this extent she encouraged the opening of the coffin.

There is some evidence that during 1869 Jane began to feel that her relationship with Gabriel was getting into deeper water than she had anticipated. In the early months of the year they had continued the series of paintings, with Janey posing for Pandora and Beatrice, both figures of legendary significance but whose real subject was the sitter: Gabriel called them his 'Janey pictures'.[18] There was still no public admission of their feeling for each other and on many occasions when Jane went to Cheyne Walk to pose she was accompanied by her husband. By the middle of the year she was very unwell; the last time the Morrises stayed with Gabriel, she was 'not strong enough to sit'. No letters from this period survive and there remains only one dated drawing, showing Jane reclining on a sofa on 14 July.[19] This was the artist's farewell, for it preceded her departure for the spa of Bad Ems in Germany. Her illness had exhausted available medical treatment, and she had 'been told to go and drink the waters and take baths'.[20] From the obscurity that surrounds all mention of her ailment, it must be assumed that its origin was either gynaecological or emotional. The only specific symptoms described were general debility and backache, but no diagnosis was published and though Jane was to suffer from these complaints for the rest of her life, they did not get much worse. A woman suffering from an organic disorder in her late twenties might well have become permanently crippled by middle age. The causes of Jane's illness, therefore, were probably as much psychological as physical and were perhaps intensified by the stress of her developing love affair, which was tending towards a crisis: she could not indefinitely occupy an ambiguous position between husband and lover. There is evidence that the 'water-cures' available at spas were often designed to treat functional nervous disorders among upper-middle-class women and that despite the utter quackery of most of the 'medical' treatment, they provided a sympathetic environment that might provide an opportunity to work through mental conflicts.[21]

However, it was in some ways a perverse malady that sent Jane abroad for two months, separating her from her beloved and forcing her into the company of a husband she disliked, for Morris accompanied her to Ems as escort and interpreter, much against his natural inclination; he was extremely bored by the visit. On the other hand, it proved a sure way of maintaining Gabriel's affection, for he responded to illness, as Lizzie had found, with renewed devotion. It may, too, have incidentally had the effect of deferring the sexual consummation towards which their emotions were leading them, a moment which Jane may have both desired and feared. An additional aspect is what may be termed the social benefit of the treatment at Bad Ems. From what has already been outlined of Victorian invalidism it is clear that illness was an unbeatable means of asserting ladylike status and of obtaining general sympathy. In view of her behaviour with Gabriel, Jane was in danger of forfeiting both, and her sickness may have been an unconscious means of securing the public support she needed at this point. In this she was successful, for not only did Morris, who might otherwise have been regarded as more deserving of sympathy than his wife, make heroic efforts to endure the boredom of the spa, but it is also true that the legend of Janey's weakness and debility served and still serves to protect her from criticism: the invalid who languished on the sofa most of her life is not generally felt to have been capable of decisive action, and all the responsibility for her extra-marital affair has been ascribed to Gabriel. In the terms used by the old-fashioned divorce courts, he is seen as the culpable figure, whereas in my view that role was largely taken by Jane.

On the journey to Ems the Morrises were accompanied by

Bessie and by Lucy Faulkner, who apparently provided extra care for Jane and returned immediately. The treatment consisted of regular baths and doses of spa water; it lasted some six weeks and Jane and Gabriel maintained an intensive correspondence. One of his early letters gives the best available account of the state of their relationship:

> All that concerns you is the all absorbing question with me, as dear Top will not mind my telling you at this anxious time. The more he loves you, the more he knows that you are too noble and lovely not to be loved: and dear Janey, there are too few things that seem worth expressing as life goes on for one friend to deny another the poor expression of what is most at his heart. But he is before me in granting this, and there is no need for me to say it. I can never tell you how much I am with you at all times. Absence from your sight is what I have long been used to and no absence can ever make me so far from you again as your presence did for years. For this long inconceivable change, you know now what my thanks must be.[22]

This less than lucid account is, oddly, addressed more to Morris than to Jane, as if Gabriel were most concerned to avoid the accusation of coveting another man's wife – a major offence in male eyes. It also strongly suggests that, in order to legitimize the relationship it was being recast within the mock-chivalric code of courtly adoration of a 'noble and lovely' lady. This was, as we have seen, part of the Victorian medieval revival. It was closely linked to the artistic and ideological worship of beauty in female form. Life sometimes consciously copied art and several high-born married women retained knightly admirers whose passion was never meant to prevail, but who were acknowledged socially. A well-known example was Oliver Montague's worship of the Princess of Wales, and there were many other cases. In the upper reaches of society this style of courtly love formed a sort of game that compensated for the virtual impossibility of divorce, enabling married women to receive attentions from other men without public censure. In theory, and often in practice, the adoration was platonic and its chief effect was the elevation of the woman on to an improbably high pedestal. This, it seems to me, is the model on which Gabriel's letter, with its protestations of devotion, was based. Of course, not all such courtly relationships were pure; as Girouard noted: 'if an affair could be embellished with talk of Art and Love, seen in terms of medieval romance or Pre-Raphaelite art and sublimated as a "passion of the soul" in which sex played only a subordinate part, scruples became that much easier to overcome'.[23] A careful study of attitudes within marriage in the second half of the nineteenth century might reveal the date at which adulterous affairs became acceptable among the middle class, for it was a general trend although often ascribed to bohemia alone. Wilfrid Scawen Blunt, who successfully exploited the mood in pursuit of endless sexual conquests, argued that it became common on the fringes of the artistic world with women who were hungry for 'the poetic romance of a neo-pagan kind then beginning to be popular with our fine London ladies, whose bible was Morris's *Earthly Paradise* and book of hours the Pre-Raphaelite art revival as preached by Rossetti'.[24] While Morris would probably not have liked being cast as the inspiration of such behaviour, it is clear that in the pursuit of passionate high-minded love, blending bourgeois propriety with romantic impulses, Jane was something of a pioneer.

To all intents and purposes, she and Gabriel were in love. Gabriel sent affectionate cartoons depicting Jane's imagined situation at Ems and building on the accounts her letters contained. *The Morrises at Ems*[25] shows Jane in a shower bath, with seven large glassfuls of spa water to drink, and Morris reading seven volumes of *The Earthly Paradise*, with whose composition he was proceeding. Later Gabriel wrote, 'I must study donkeys that I may be able to make a cartoon of your first expedition. . .'[26] referring to the fact that those taking the waters were permitted tame excursions by donkey cart. More significantly, he was having his poems set in proof in preparation for publication, in a volume that was largely conceived and executed as an offering to Jane. It contains some fifty newly written sonnets celebrating Love; beneath a welter of sub-romantic wordage they seem obliquely to allude to her, as in the following extracts from 'Bridal Birth' and 'Supreme Surrender':

> As when desire, long darkling, dawns, and first
> The mother looks upon the newborn child,
> Even so my Lady stood at gaze and smiled

When her soul knew at length the Love it nursed.

First touched, the hand now warm around my neck,
Taught memory long to mock desire: and lo!
Across my breast the abandoned hair doth flow,
Where one shorn tress long stirred the longing ache:
And next the heart that trembled for its sake
Lies the queen-heart in sovereign overthrow.

This is not biographical evidence in itself, of course, and all that
can be read into the sonnets of this period is that the poet was
describing in very general and 'poetic' terms feelings of worship-
ful love towards an idealized woman. Only 'The Portrait' offers a
more personal meaning, largely because it complements the
content of the *Blue Silk Dress* painting:

O Lord of all compassionate control,
O Love! Let this my lady's picture glow
Under my hand to praise her name, and show
Even of her inner self the perfect whole:
That he who seeks her beauty's furthest goal,
Beyond the light that the sweet glances throw
And refluent wave of the sweet smile, may know
The very sky and sea-line of her soul.
Lo! it is done. Above the long lithe throat
The mouth's mould testifies of voice and kiss,
The shadowed eyes remember and foresee.
Her face is made her shrine. Let all men note
That in all years (O Love, thy gift is this!)
They that would look on her must come to me.

Concrete evidence that the poems were meant as a tribute to Jane
exists in the form of the proof sheets which Gabriel gave to her
and which she kept, like his letters, for the rest of her life.[27] Some
of the proof versions were specially amended for her, heightening
their meaning and emotional charge. Since Gabriel was given to
constant revision, it would be dangerous to read too much into
this, except that Jane did preserve the sheets for their sentimental
significance. In 'The Stream's Secret', which Gabriel wrote while
Jane was at Ems and revised after her return, the successive

alterations clearly indicate not just different choices of words but a progression in the relationship between the poet and his lady.[28] One stanza thus ran through three stages – the first version and its amendments (succeeding versions bracketed):

> For (scarce till now) we spoke
>   (not till then)
> What (eyes have so long told to eyes,)
>   (confluent thought might ill disguise,)
> Only our lingering glances and half-sighs
> Full oft the buried secret broke,
> Which with snatched hands and lips' reverberate stroke
> Then from the heart (shall) rise
>   (did)

The final published version of the poem was set firmly in the past:

> For then at last we spoke
> What eyes so oft had told to eyes,
> Through that long-lingered silence whose half-sighs
> Alone the buried secret broke,
> Which with snatched hands and lips' reverberate stroke,
> Then from the heart did rise.

The evolution of 'The Stream's Secret' certainly chronicles a recognition and declaration of love. It has been claimed that the sonnets Gabriel published in 1870 celebrate the consummation of his love for Jane;[29] although the evidence of the poems is inconclusive on this point, it was certainly very close.

Georgie was also receiving poems – from Jane's husband. Early in 1870 she was presented with the manuscript of 'The Lovers of Gudrun', one of the later *Earthly Paradise* tales, bearing the inscription 'Georgie from W. M. April 15th 1870. This is the first copy of the poem with some alterations inserted: I wrote it in June 1869. William Morris.'[30] Morris had handbound the book himself in leather with a pomegranate design, and Georgie kept it, as she did all his gifts, until the end of her life. More significantly, the rubric to 'The Lovers of Gudrun' runs: 'This story shows how

two friends loved a fair woman and how he who loved her best
had her to wife, though she loved him little or not at all. . .' A full
account of Morris's emotional life would surely see in the
misfortunes of Gudrun and her lovers Kiartan and Bodli not only
the shadows of Jane, Gabriel and Topsy (as Gabriel believed)[31] but
also those of Georgie, Ned and Topsy. And Georgie may also
have received Morris's version of 'The Death of Paris', which
expressed his sympathy for the erosion of her marriage. For
Georgie was suffering great distress.

We last saw Georgie with her baby son Phil, born in 1861, and
for the next few years motherhood and housewifery occupied her
life. In May 1862 she and Ned were taken to Italy by Ruskin, who
commented that Georgie had left her son with a sister but
nevertheless 'seemed to see everything through a mist of baby',
which was unfair in view of his instructions on her womanly role.
Taken to see a spectacular ravine in Switzerland, 'nothing would
serve her but her husband must draw her baby for her on the sand
of the stream . . .'[32] Georgie's own letters, including a long,
entertaining account of a visit to Murano, suggest an observant
and energetic tourist.[33] She maintained a keen interest in Ned's
work, reporting to Ruskin later in the year that he

had touched up Cupid and Psyche to good purpose (do you
remember speaking slightingly of that young person's face?)
and taken out the sky and put it in again and a few trifles of that
nature, which have wrought wonders. . .in the evenings he sits
in the midst of a select circle of friends, designing stained glass
for the firm of Morris & Co (yea, though you bade me urge him
not) but he draws the figures more carefully and really has done
some most lovely ones, especially one of Iseult and King Mark
her husband where he catches her just about to kill herself and
prevents it. This is not for a church, as you will perceive, but
some highly sensible person is going to have his house
decorated with the history of Tristram and Iseult. There is fun
in store for him in the way of tiles, as another clear-sighted
gentleman is going to have his fireplace tiled with the history of
Cinderella and Ned is going to design the tiles. But this you say
is mere trifling – child's play. Is it? I didn't know and it does not
interfere with any of his other work. . .[34]

Her own sphere was undoubtedly narrowing. A few weeks later she was writing that she was poorly, having worn herself out 'by fidgets and anxieties about my boys',[35] and she was frequently anxious sick-nurse to both husband and son. Early in 1864 she became pregnant again. A number of family visits to the Morrises at Red House by herself, Ned, Phil and her sisters Aggie and Louie, which inspired Ned's lovely little painting *Green Summer*[36] showing a group of girls sitting on the grass listening to one – based on Georgie – reading aloud, paved the way for the scheme to build a new wing for the Joneses. Plans were drawn up by Philip Webb and never thrown away; looking at them forty years later Georgie remarked wistfully, 'How different all our lives would have gone if this scheme had been carried out.'[37] It fell through, partly no doubt because of Jane's estrangement from her husband, but more because of financial anxieties. The firm was still struggling to make a profit; Morris's unearned income was dropping; and Ned had a sudden and frightening experience of artist's insecurity. After a happy family holiday in 1864 with the Morrises and the Faulkners, three-year-old Phil caught scarlet fever. 'Then Georgie was prematurely confined,' Ned told Allingham, 'and immediately seized with the ʻfever so that for eight days their life was in danger, then when she rallied a fortnight ago her own little child died – for these three months I have done no work, but lived most anxiously from day to day.'[38]

The loss of little Christopher, as he was named, changed Georgie; her complexion paled and she felt she had left youth and joy behind, at the age of twenty-five. Instead of joining the Morrises at Red House, she and Ned moved to fashionable Kensington, where their social circle enlarged and rose: Georgie's account of 1865–6 contains a long list of new acquaintances, neighbours and patrons, including the artists Birket Foster and Henry Holiday, the MP William Graham, and George and Rosalind Howard, later Earl and Countess of Carlisle. Ned worked hard to establish himself and he enjoyed the prestige that came with success; the experience of upward mobility and early insecurity was an important element in Ned's career. With her nonconformist background, Georgie was firmer in despising wordly things, by which she felt Ned was beguiled, but by her own admission she took no financial responsibility. 'I know now that Edward had more anxiety about money in those early days than I realized,' she wrote later, 'for it was not a subject he talked much about, and it never occurred to me that we should not have our wants supplied.'[39] She was, however, very pleased when G. F. Watts made her a belated but much welcomed present of a sewing machine, thus enabling her to produce the family's clothing and linen a great deal more efficiently; Ned wrote delightedly that the little machine almost made the garments by itself![40]

Growing prosperity, if not luxury, is visible in the account book the Joneses kept with the firm[41] which enabled them to order goods like furnishing fabric and wine through Morris & Co, while the cost was set against the amounts earned for stained-glass designs and tiles. And their new home in Kensington Square, if not large, was warm and welcoming. Allingham, who was briefly engaged to Georgie's older sister Alice, came to stay regularly: on 31 July 1866, after spending the evening with Gabriel and Swinburne and arriving back at 3 a.m., he slept 'not comfortably' on the sofa. The previous day it may be noted that Ned and Charley had attended a large 'Reform meeting' at Islington Agricultural Hall, part of the public campaign for a wider franchise, and it is evident that at this date Ned was politically in advance of Morris. As early as 1862 he had produced a painting for a good cause, *The Backgammon Players*, which was his contribution to a fund for the 'starving people' in the Lancashire cotton districts as a result of the American civil war.[42] This act of charity may be compared with the time when Emma Brown set up a soup kitchen in her front room, to feed the families of the unemployed at a time of distress. 'She was quite poor then,' wrote her granddaughter, 'and had to go without all sorts of things to get the money.'[43]

Presumably Allingham slept on the sofa at the Joneses' house because Georgie had, in June 1866, given birth to her third child, a much-loved daughter named Margaret. As cholera was reported in London, Allingham invited the whole family to the New Forest, and on 15 August the four Joneses travelled down to the lodgings he had found for them. Extracts from Allingham's diary show the young couple and their friends on holiday:

18 August . . . Ned, Georgie and I to Brockenhurst. Field path, stiles, Ober Green, heather: Queen's Bower. Sit by the little bridge. Oakenshaw, big oak, brook, insects, big beech. Ned sketches. I read aloud Robin Hood and the Monk. . .

30 August. . .Rail to Winchester, with N., G., and Webb – meet Morris there. All walk by the Close and meadows to St Cross. . .

31 August. . .Carriage from Nag's Head takes N., G., M., Phil and me to sea at Milford. . .Hurst shingle. M. and N. sprawl, won't walk. We bury Morris up to the neck in shingle. . .

5 September. . . The Joneses packing up. Baby Margaret, asleep on large bed, her father has made into a grotesque giantess, by means of gloves and shoes peeping out at immense distances. . .[44]

In contrast to this innocent family atmosphere, when in London Ned was seeing too much of certain people whom Georgie came to distrust and even hate. It was a mark of the strongest feeling when she later described Charles Howell as 'one who had come amongst us in friend's clothing, but inwardly he was a stranger to all that our life meant'.[45] In the late 1860s, however, Howell was Ned's closest friend besides Topsy, addressed in affectionate terms as 'My Sweet Owl' or 'Pretty Little Owl'.[46] Ned later broke with Howell completely, for reasons he never fully spelled out, but which seem to have been linked to another of Ned's new friends, who posed an even greater threat to Georgie and to whom she could, thirty years later, still only refer to obliquely as 'A very noticeable introduction of those days. . .to a part of what may be called the Greek colony in London'. She professed to have forgotten exactly how they became acquainted,[47] so deeply had she been hurt.

The sorceress to Ned's Merlin was Mary Zambaco, born Cassavetti, granddaughter of Constantine Ionides, the head of a remarkable Greek immigrant clan of successful businessmen, artistic patrons and attractive, independent and well-off individuals. Mary inherited a fortune from her father, who died in 1858 when she was fifteen. In 1860, when George du Maurier was tentatively looking for an heiress to replace his fiancée Emma Wightwick, whose family had lost their money, he made advances to Mary at her uncle's house in Tulse Hill. But she proved too independent and assertive, and after she had pursued him without a chaperone in Kensington Gardens, du Maurier took fright, and

wrote of her as 'rude and unapproachable but of great talent and
really wonderful beauty';[48] more to the point, she was reputed to
be worth £80,000. A study of the Ionides family group, its internal
relations and its impact on London society remains to be written,
so it is not clear how, with her background, Mary Cassavetti was
able to flout the conventions of behaviour, but she and other
young women in the clan evidently enjoyed a great deal of
personal freedom. Shocked but delighted, du Maurier reported
that at the Ionides' house, the 'girls would sometimes take one's
hands in talking to one, or put their arm round the back of one's
chair at dinner'. And he added, lest the wrong impression be
conveyed, 'with all this ease and *tutoiement*, or perhaps on account
of it, they are I believe the most thoroughly well bred and perfect
gentlefolks in all England'.[49] Unconventionally, the women
claimed the right to their own social life; Mary's cousin Aglaia
Coronio, for example, although married, developed a friendship
with Rossetti, and later turned her attentions to Morris, somewhat
to his embarrassment. But the Greek damsels' emancipation had
its limits, and in the early 1860s Marie Spartali's romance with
Lord Ranelagh was vetoed by her father. She was, however,
allowed to pursue her ambition to be a painter and for several
years from 1864 she was a regular pupil of Ford Madox Brown's,
working in his studio alongside Lucy, Cathy and Oliver.

It is now not possible to establish the reasons for Mary falling in
love with Ned. Apparently she had an impetuous nature and, after
the end of her flirtation with du Maurier, she rejected the English
marriage market entirely and announced her intention of marrying Demetrius Zambaco, a Greek-born medical doctor 'of low
birth', as du Maurier noted, who was working in Paris. They had
a son and a daughter born in 1864 and 1865, but the marriage was
not a success. Dr Zambaco has been described as kindly but dull[50]
and very little else is known of him. He attended the Greek
community in Paris and published a series of medical papers on
esoteric, not to say spicy subjects such as syphilis, leprosy and
'eunuchs past and present'.[51] Mary was pretty, artistic and (so it is
said) used to having her own way. Her mother, Euphrosyne
Cassavetti, known as 'The Duchess', was a remarkable woman,
who sympathized with and supported her daughter, and in 1866
Mary left Demetrius and returned to London with her children, to
live with her mother in Kensington. She had ambitions to become

a sculptor and indeed later had some success as a portrait medallist; it seems to have been through this and through her friendship with Marie Spartali that she came into contact with the Pre-Raphaelite circle. Together, Mary, Marie and Aglaia were known as 'The Three Graces' on account of their beauty and brilliance, and they too contributed to the image of the Pre-Raphaelite Woman whose face is an amalgam of elements. While Jane was at Ems, Gabriel used Marie Spartali as a substitute model for heads and hands; it may be noted, incidentally, that she was accompanied to the sittings by a chaperone who was abused by Gabriel's parrot, an event which caused much mirth, as Gabriel wrote to tell Jane.[52] Later, Jane and Marie became great friends.

In London, Mary Zambaco occupied an awkward position as a married woman without a husband, but her mother was wealthy and protective. As a patron of the arts, Mrs Cassavetti decided to commission a portrait of her daughter from the up-and-coming young painter Edward Jones. Then in the midst of his *Earthly Paradise* illustrations, Ned chose the theme of Cupid finding Psyche, and in the process of painting found himself in love with Mary. All his life Ned depended on female attention, and by 1867 may have been feeling more than usually in need, for the previous year his young sisters-in-law Aggie and Louie Macdonald, to whom he was much attached, had both married, and Georgie had her new baby. Mary had a mop of dark-red hair, a magnetic quality and an air of reckless tragedy that proved immensely appealing, although it would not be accurate to portray Ned as a helpless victim to her bewitching power, for he was as much responsible as she for their developing passion. Later, Georgie wrote carefully, to excuse him from blame, of how beauty and misfortune had power over Ned and of how 'his impulse to comfort those in trouble was so strong that while the trouble lasted the sufferer took precedence over everyone else'.[53] Mary's power over his heart grew steadily during 1867 and 1868 and one can only guess at the depth of Georgie's injury when she realized what was happening. The summer holiday the Joneses and Morrises spent together at Oxford in 1867 was the last they shared and was not a success: Ned was forever anxious to be back in town and complained, unusually, about the children's noise.[54] In November 1867 Georgie and Ned moved again, to the Grange, a large old house in North End Lane, Fulham where, Georgie remarked, 'we finally put away childish things and had our share of sorrow'.[55]

Mary returned Ned's overwhelming passion and soon they were planning to run away together. As Ned later wrote to Gabriel in explanation, he believed her 'to be all my future life'. [56] But here Mary was perhaps deceived, for it is not certain that Ned ever really meant to run off with her, leaving his wife and family; it may have been merely a romantic expression of desire. He could not so easily desert Georgie and face his friends. Gabriel, it may be noted, had little sympathy with Ned's behaviour.

Georgie had other problems as well. For a year the Grange was shared with Ned's old school companion Wilfrid Heeley and his second wife Josephine, who put an additional strain on the household by producing an unplanned baby. In the summer of 1868 Georgie assisted at another confinement, that of her sister Alice Kipling, who came back from India to have her second baby, and remained for half a year. Soon afterwards Georgie's long-lost brother Harry turned up with his wife on a visit from the United States, which also brought her mother Hannah to the Grange; Georgie's father had died the previous year, having been long bed-ridden. Finally, when the indigent painter J. W. Inchbold billeted himself unasked on the Joneses in the midst of this stressful period, Georgie's housekeeping and hospitality must have been strained to the limit.

Ned's attentions were more and more given to Mary. He completed *The Wine of Circe*,[57] which Gabriel described as 'the greatest picture of the year'.[58] This had been several years in progress but now seems to have combined a potent sense of being caught in a spell with an intense formalism, producing a magnificent painting. Circe's face has a distinct look of Mary. Hitherto, Ned's female figures had been largely based on Georgie: small, round-faced, demure. The *Girl by the Goldfish Pool* and the sisters in *Green Summer* were typical. The stylistic change of the 1860s, seen in the work of other artists also, appears in Ned's case to have been accompanied by emotional events. From the late 1860s an image – not a portrait – of Mary pervaded his work: lithe, with tangled hair, a distinctive profile and intense, tragic eyes. In 1869 he began a series of Seasons, using Mary's features for *Summer*, a pensive, nearly naked figure clad in chiffon drapery, with lines from Morris's poem 'The Lapse of the Year':[59]

Summer looked for long am I
Much shall change or ere I die;
Prythee take it not amiss
Though I weary thee with bliss.

The contrasting figure of *Winter* is a Georgie-type woman, clad in fur-trimmed gown and cloak, reading a missal. She is an attractive figure, but exudes pious frigidity by contrast with the figure of *Summer*. The comparison could not be more telling.[60]

Mary's affair with Ned first reached a crisis around the beginning of 1869 when the planned elopement was called off. Ned confessed that however tumultuous his feeling for Mary, he could not leave his wife. Betrayed and distraught, Mary threatened to kill herself in what Gabriel described to Brown in a confidential letter as 'the most dreadful to-do' in Lord Holland's Lane. She had enough laudanum 'for two at least' and also tried to drown herself in the canal 'in front of Browning's house' at Little Venice. Ned struggled with her on the ground, and the police were called. It was all rather sensational. In a panic it was decided that Morris should take Ned off to Rome, in order to remove him from Mary, who was left in London 'beating up the quarters of all his friends for him and howling like Cassandra'.[61] This was the occasion on which Morris forbade Jane to sit to Gabriel during his absence abroad. But in the event, 'Top and Ned got no further than Dover', when Ned became so ill that they were obliged to return to London, where his presence was concealed from Mary. 'The dodge will be not to let a single hint of their movements become known to anybody,' explained Gabriel to Brown, 'or the Greek (whom I believe he is really bent on cutting) will catch him again.'[62] Not surprisingly, Ned's friends rallied to make sure he did not abandon Georgie and, inevitably, Mary was cast in the role of seductress. Gabriel composed a limerick that was widely remembered;[63] it ran:

There is a young artist named Jones
Whose conduct no genius atones:
　　His behaviour in life
　　Is a pang to the wife
And a plague to the neighbours of Jones.

It must have been small consolation to Georgie to know that her husband had failed to run off with his mistress, for he had not broken with Mary entirely. For the next few years they remained friends and Ned continued to draw and paint Mary regularly. In her *Memorials* Georgie chose the epigraph 'Heart, thou and I are here sad and alone' for the years 1868 to 1871, and this was often her position. She received a good deal of support from two new women friends, Marian Evans (George Eliot) and Rosalind Howard, but she opened her heart to none, drawing on the same stoicism that had enabled her to eat the mouse-pie; she told Rosalind that if she dropped her reserve she would break down completely. Writing in February 1869 she disclaimed heroism and heroically refused to apportion blame: 'May we all come well through it at last,' she prayed. 'I know one thing and that is that there is enough love between Edward and me to last out a long life if it is given to us.'[64] If she meant that *she* had enough love she was probably right; her experience was that Ned depended on her stability and moral integrity, to say nothing of her household management, to underpin his work as a painter. Henceforth, she must have known he would never leave.

But it was none the less a painful time. Georgie wrote a sad New Year letter to her sister Louie on an evening when she was by herself, enjoying only 'a lonely peck at my supper', and describing Christmas as very quiet, with no merrymaking. Her resolution was schooled: 'I wish I might never say another harsh thing again, or an uncharitable', she wrote, adding that she hoped that she might have another baby 'but am not too sanguine'.[65] By this stage she and Ned were in separate bedrooms, for when she wrote to invite her sister to stay she explained that Inchbold was in the spare room, but 'my Louie won't mind sharing with me'.[66] Later in the year Georgie went away, taking the children to Oxford to stay in a student's vacant lodging, perhaps secured for her by Charley Faulkner, where she was lonely and miserable. There were more than the usual number of hours in the day, she told Rosalind bleakly.[67] It may be that she also visited Crom Price at his eccentric holiday home Broadway Tower in the Cotswolds, for in August Ned was in correspondence with Crom about his own arrival, in rather curious terms. 'Will next Friday be convenient and will the coast be clear?' he wrote. 'You know what I mean by the coast being clear – assure me of this – and I will really come to you.'[68] Who was it Ned wished to avoid?

Georgie helped look after the Morris girls while their parents were at Bad Ems. Back in London, Ned continued to see and draw Mary. Gabriel told Jane that he expected to see him with 'the Greeks', and that Ned was working on 'a most beautiful single female in profile with some smaller figures by a door in the background'.[69] This was a new picture commissioned by Mrs Cassavetti for a subject of his choice, based on Mary. Ned called it 'Woman in a Red Dress' (symbolic of love's colour) although it has always been known as *Beatrice*. The main figure has Mary's features, but at least one of the subsidiary women standing sadly in the doorway behind has a look of Georgie.

Morris's sympathy was aroused by Georgie's self-command and while abroad he often thought of the Grange. 'Tell me how things go on there,' he wrote to Philip Webb from Ghent, referring not only to his daughters;[70] in the same city he celebrated Georgie's birthday by buying her a pair of Delft cruet bottles. He sent these to Webb with instructions to have them fitted with new silver lids and then presented; 'give them to her with my love when what is necessary is alone', he wrote. But Webb had more tact and handed them over in public; the cruets were a great success and he wrote, 'I've no doubt you will hear so from Georgie.'[71] None of her correspondence survives; Georgie claimed later to have only begun keeping Morris's letters in 1876 and it appears that early letters were destroyed.[72] Morris's sympathy and growing love for Georgie were expressed in poems as well as letters and gifts. On reaching Ems, he completed *The Death of Paris*, told largely through the voice of Oenone, Paris's abandoned wife. Oenone can do little but weep, and she reproaches her husband thus:

> Hearken the while I tell about my life
> The life I led while 'mid the steely gleam
> Thou wert made happy with the joyous strife,
> Or in the soft arms of the Greek king's wife. . .
>
> Yea, Paris, have I not been kind to thee?
> Did I not live thy wishes to fulfil?
> Wert thou not happy when thou lovedst me?
> What dreams then did we have of change or ill?

Paris needs her cure for a mortal wound, but she knows he is still
thinking of Helen, and she cries out in distress:

> Lo, if I heal thee and thou goest again. . .
> E'en then the Greekish flame shall sear your eyes
> The clatter of the Greeks fill all the place
> While she, my woe, the ruin of thy race. . .

It is hard to believe that a personal reference to Mary was not
meant or taken. Morris felt acute distress at what appeared to be
the end of his friends' marriage, following so hard upon his own.
Drafts of manuscript poems in his hand express what seem to be
his view of Ned's betrayal:

> . . .shall I count the hours
> That bring my friend to me with hungry eyes
> Watch him as his feet the staircase mount
> Then face to face we sit? a wall of lies
> Made hard by fear and faint anxieties
> Is drawn between us and he goes away
> And leaves me wishing it were yesterday. . .

In the opening line of these verses, the poet is sitting 'Alone,
unhappy, by the fire' thinking of 'change and folly', and silently
addressing a third person:

> And in mine ears there range some piteous tale
> And but for manhood I was like to wail
> To think of thine; I cannot bridge the space
> 'Twixt what may be and thy sad weary face. . .

He went on:

> Ah do you lift your eyebrows in disdain
> Because I dare to pity or come nigh to your great sorrow –
> . . .for you alone unchanged now seem to be
> A real thing left of the days sweet to me.

On this page a marginal note indicates that Georgie was the person
being addressed. 'Poets' unrealities,' it reads, 'tears can come with

verse, we two are in the same box and need conceal nothing – don't cast me away – scold me but pardon me. What is all this to me (say you) shame in confessing one's real feelings.'[73] This conforms with what we know of Georgie's stiff upper lip and Morris's struggle for self-control. Brought together by a common situation, they found and shared an emotional response that refused to indulge in displays of grief or recrimination against their wandering spouses and which helped them to endure the pain. This sharing grew into a mutual affection that was to last the rest of their days.

14

There are indications that during the 1860s and 1870s there was growing concern among middle-class women about the conditions of married life – the problems of maturity rather than those of youth. As young women gained more autonomy, in such matters as the choice of husband and the right to a career of their own, the issues of courtship and marriageability became less pressing and those of middle life more so.

This was due in part to the steady separation of work and home which was now virtually complete: few middle-class wives played an active part in their husbands' businesses. Another factor was that more and more children were being sent out and away to school rather than being educated at home, thus reducing the middle-class mother's role. And the general prosperity and technological improvements of the nineteenth century raised bourgeois living standards and brought increased leisure, particularly to the women. As yet the world outside the home was not open to them and with the drudgery removed from their lives, middle-class women had more space in which to reflect, and to socialize. Hence what often seems to be the extraordinarily empty nature of Victorian ladies' days, filled with polishing ornaments, embroidering night-caps and paying and receiving calls. Many occupied their time in the great explosion of philanthropy that took place in the second half of the century, this being one area where women were permitted active roles outside the home. At the same time, however, they also demanded higher standards of satisfaction within the family, seeking greater companionship from their husbands. They had been reared on romantic love and were disillusioned by the loss of emotional ardour. So, for a variety of reasons, the problems and difficulties of marriage came under scrutiny.

This more critical approach was aided by the divorce reform introduced in 1857. Before this, divorce was restricted to exceptional cases mainly from among the upper strata of society and was simply not an option for the majority of couples. Even informal divorce or separation was a difficulty among the middle class. It might be common enough in working-class areas, where women traditionally earned money and supported themselves, but bourgeois women had no alternative means of support. In addition, a strong social stigma attached to irregular situations and formed a means of social control upheld by women themselves at least partly to coerce men into assuming their responsibilities. The new legislation, permitting civil divorce where there was proven adultery, in the case of women, or adultery and cruelty in the case of men, was less sympathetic towards wives than husbands. Nor did it bring about instant change. Indeed, for at least a generation, divorce remained as unthinkable as before, owing to the scandal and sensation that accompanied the legal proceedings. Divorced persons were more or less automatically excluded from polite society, and social ostracism obliged many to settle abroad. There were problems too, regarding the children of a divorced couple, for the guilty partner was denied custody and this could be a powerful disincentive. Women were further discouraged from seeking divorce by lack of income, and Mrs Howitt's wry observation that the 'result' of the campaign for a Married Women's Property Act had been the 1857 Divorce Act was a way of pointing out that the law now made it possible in theory for a woman to end an insupportable marriage but still denied her the practical means to do so.

Nevertheless, divorce reform does seem to have had an impact on attitudes within marriage. We have already seen Emma talking noisily, under the influence of drink, about 'ill-treatment and separate maintenance'[1] in pursuit of some apparent grievance. The theoretical availability of divorce encouraged a more questioning view of marriage: rising expectations applied to more than economic affairs. Nor was this purely a female phenomenon: men also looked to their wives for partnership and there was among both sexes a strong surge of middle-class indignation against differential sexual standards. Wives began to expect mutual

fidelity and care from their spouses. At the same time, they sought
the freedoms hitherto enjoyed only by men. These developments
were of course very uneven, and in general women were caught in
the tangles of changing customs rather than simply benefiting
from them; their behaviour helped to shape the patterns of the age.
One result was that many women found they had to face, and
solve, crises of middle age which had seldom occurred in their
parents' generation.

When Georgie found her marriage on the verge of breaking up,
and at the same time received an offer of love and companionship
from an old friend whose wife had long since disengaged herself,
she did not automatically see divorce and remarriage as a solution.
She had been brought up to regard marriage in terms of life-long
devotion: divorce was not considered. Nor, by the same token
(which was not religious, as Georgie had given up all spiritual
sanction beyond that of her own conscience) was adultery, and she
seems to have declined Morris's offer of physical love, an event
which may have been the basis of the following lines:[2]

> She wavered, stopped and turned, methought her eyes,
> The deep grey windows of her heart, were wet;
> Methought they softened with a new regret
> To note in mine unspoken miseries,
> And as a prayer from out my heart did rise
> And struggled on my lips in shame's strong net,
> She stayed me, and cried 'Brother!' Our lips met,
> Her dear hands drew me into paradise.
>
> Sweet seemed that kiss till thence her feet were gone,
> Sweet seemed the word she spake, while it might be
> As wordless music – But truth fell on me
> And kiss and word I knew and, left alone,
> Face to face seemed I to a wall of stone.

Instead of having what is vulgarly known as an affair, Georgie and
Morris established a long and loving relationship of mutual esteem
and support which helped to heal the wounds. 'Hark, how the
tune swells, that erewhile did wane!' says the poem 'October',
sent to Georgie on the back of a letter signed 'your loving friend
W. M.'.[3] As this signature suggests, a certain formality persisted

between them, and to everyone outside her immediate circle Georgie always referred to him as 'Mr Morris', although Ned once caught and rebuked her for using the affectionate 'Topsy' in front of others. How she addressed him directly is unknown. If their affection was largely unspoken, it was none the less deep, and probably only Georgie knew how much she owed to Morris for his love and support in the difficult middle years, as Ned continued to see and paint Mary.

Mary had left one husband and failed to gain another, but still Ned's behaviour was far from unequivocal. He drew many pencil portraits of her, studies for Venus, Galatea and the like, which have an exquisite tenderness and are described by his biographer as those of a lover – 'searching by instinct and by the exact pressure of the pencil for the secret of her unhappiness'.[4] He also wanted other images of her, and early in 1870 he asked Gabriel if he too would draw Mary's portrait, for Ned to possess. Gabriel obliged, and in an incoherent letter of thanks Ned described how the whole idea 'excited and exhilarated me and made me silly – I was so glad to have such a portrait . . . I can't say how the least kindness from any of you goes to my heart.'[5] He wrote of wanting the drawing to be put in a locked frame, for his eyes only, which does not suggest he was yet trying to break off the affair. Owing to the scarcity of documentary evidence, commentators have often assumed that the struggle by the canal in January 1869 marked the effective end of their relationship, but the pictorial evidence shows that this was not the case. He seems, however, to have forsworn elopement, and one can only sympathize with Mary's plight, as she received contradictory messages from the man she loved. Drawing Mary enabled Gabriel to know and understand her better. 'I like her very much,' he told Janey in March 1870, 'and am sure her love is all in all to her.'[6] He praised her beauty and suggested it had increased in the past year, 'with all her love and trouble'. But, he added, 'rainy walks and constant lowness are I fear beginning to break up her health'. Unfortunately Gabriel's pictures of Mary are not very informative, perhaps because he was motivated more by friendship than by a real desire to draw her. A chalk portrait of her in the Victoria and Albert Museum is a good example of his glamourizing ability; the face is in soft focus with cupid's bow lips and the general look of a classic beauty queen.[7] The features show little individuality or expression and although the handling is polite, the portrait as a whole has a superficial quality that is almost vulgar. In the same collection is a chalk drawing by Ned which is not a portrait, but shows a woman with sunken eyes and wild hair, her head held at an angle of distress, her mouth open in an unheard cry. It is a haunting picture of a tragic face, the unhappiness of an individual representing a larger truth. It is Mary as Cassandra.[8]

In the same month that Gabriel completed her portrait, Mary and Ned were together invited to a supper party at the equivalent of a nightclub, to celebrate the engagement of her cousin Alecco Ionides.[9] The following month saw the exhibition at the Old Water Colour Society of Ned's *Beatrice* and his *Phyllis and Demophoon*, for both of which Mary had modelled. In the source legend Phyllis was deserted by her lover and killed herself, turning into an almond tree. When Demophoon returned, he embraced the tree in remorse, causing it to blossom and bear fruit. In the picture the woman, with Mary's face and hair, leans out of the tree, her arms clasped round the body of a young man, who pulls away, looking piteously towards her. Parts of her drapery entangle his ankle and thigh, preventing his escape, yet he does not surrender, and the painting's chief impression is one of perpetual tension, the figures forever clasping and forever breaking away. The lovers' heads touch but their gaze does not meet. In some respects Demophoon has a rather hunted look, and the picture's epigraph was taken from Ovid, where Phyllis reproaches her lover with the words: 'Tell me what have I done except to love unwisely?' *Phyllis and Demophoon* caused a scandal at the Old Water Colour Society, ostensibly on account of Demophoon's nudity but I suspect really on account of its unavoidable allusion to the painter's private life and the pain its exhibition in public must have caused his wife. Georgie herself, incidentally, was represented at the same show in *Love Disguised as Reason*, which depicts a figure in academic gown lecturing two women.[10] Ned's withdrawal of *Phyllis and Demophoon* and his subsequent resignation from the Old Water Colour Society are generally interpreted in terms of artistic integrity, and this must have been part of his motive. But, given the gossipy nature of the London art scene, and the public conventions that still surrounded marriage, he may well have realized that he had gone too far: art and life had been too transparently brought together for display.

It seems unlikely that he was trying to extricate himself from the affair since soon after this exhibition he began his most overt declaration of love for Mary. This was a large gouache portrait, painted for her mother and entitled *An Allegorical Portrait*. This can have misled few, for although Mary's yearning face is surrounded by a whole cupboard of accessories representing Love she is plainly identified by the inscription on the paper wrapped round Cupid's arrow, which reads: 'Mary Aetat XXVI August 7th 1870 EBJ pinxit'.[11] Cupid draws the curtain to reveal her, and she holds flowers representing 'passion' and 'message'. Under her hand is an illuminated book, open at a miniature picture of the artist's own *Chant d'Amour*, which happened to be the subject of the first picture Ned painted for Euphrosyne Cassavetti, and may therefore represent a symbolic connection with his first meeting with her daughter. In my view, this portrait of Mary is somewhat crude, both in its assortment of popular symbols and its rather coarse handling. The overall effect is that of a high–class valentine card, which may say something about the quality of Ned's feeling for Mary.

Georgie also had her portrait painted in 1870, but not by her lover. Commissioned, perhaps in honour of her thirtieth birthday, by Rosalind and George Howard from her brother-in-law Edward Poynter (an Academician with a taste for the classically grandiose and sexually suggestive, who later became President of the Royal Academy), this presented Georgie in a most uncharacteristic manner. She was painted wearing a fashionable muslin gown, with a sash, lace at the neck and several strands of necklace, from one of which hangs a large jewelled heart. Her hair is neatly dressed, and she has a prettily curled fringe, which is seen in no other pictures or photos, for her hair was normally drawn plainly back; she sits daintily in a drawing room, holding up a bowl and saucer of tea. The impression is quite at odds with other contemporary accounts of both her looks and character, and yet the presentation cannot be ascribed to Poynter's impercipience, for his portraits of his wife Aggie and her other sister Louie, done at about the same time as that of Georgie, are quite different in execution. Both Aggie, holding flowers, and Louie, with a fan, display a soulful, Pre-Raphaelite quality not unlike Rossetti's portrait of Jane in a blue dress: the presentation suggests interesting, artistic women. Georgie on the other hand appears to be a society lady taking tea in Mayfair. Her expression, however, is one that gives nothing away, and it is possible that she presented Poynter with such a barrier of reserve, at this most difficult, unhappy time of her life, that he was more or less obliged to depict a superficial image, bringing the accoutrements of middle-class living to the fore. Resolutely, she would not admit her distress. It could not have been more different from what appears to have been Mary's undisguised emotionalism.

More to Georgie's liking than a formal portrait, one imagines, was Topsy's gift for her birthday on 23 July 1870, which also honoured her fortitude. This was an illuminated copy of his shorter poems, made with his own hands, entitled *A Book of Verse*.[12] This was not a private gesture, for Ned himself contributed the first picture, showing a youth and a maiden stretching out their hands vainly from opposite sides of a river, and George Wardle and Fairfax Murray assisted with other parts of the decoration; Morris, however, was responsible for the calligraphy and the design. This resembles his wallpapers with dense, swirling foliage that at times threatens to overrun the words. The book contains twenty-five poems, two translated from Icelandic, mostly dealing with love, death, grief and hope; its personal significance lay not in its content but in its making. Compared with Ned's portrait of Mary – and the dates inscribed on painting and book are but three weeks apart – it is a decorous, dignified love token.

And so, with Topsy's ever-faithful love and support, Georgie survived, maintaining a steady exterior while attempting to repossess her life. In the summer of 1870 she took the children to Whitby by herself since she and Ned did not holiday together after Mary's advent into their life. Marian Evans and George Lewes were at Whitby and she received 'advice and warning' from her friend.[13] Marian knew at first hand, and bitterly, the ostracism suffered by women obliged to live in unmarried union with those they loved, since Lewes could not, for complicated reasons, obtain a divorce from his unfaithful wife, who was living with another man. Marian's position was not unlike that of Georgie and Morris; was her 'warning' on the social consequences of irregularity? Or was Ned urging Georgie towards a decisive break, to free him to be with Mary, perhaps on the grounds that an acknowledgement of her relationship with Topsy would enable Jane and Gabriel to come together openly? In some respects, it must be regretted that divorce was not available to untangle their affairs.

While Georgie and the children were at Whitby, Ned was at the Grange, finishing his portrait of Mary. Jane, who had spent some weeks with Gabriel in Sussex earlier in the year, went to Torquay for the summer with her daughters and sister Bessie. Morris stayed in London, where the Queen Square house was being redecorated, and so did Gabriel, who was painting a large version of *Dante's Dream*. This was, it may be noted, the year of the Franco-Prussian war and the siege of Paris, events to which only Ned is recorded as responding, finding his sympathies pulled in different directions. Socially, he was beginning to suffer the consequences of his infatuation with Mary and its semi-public display. Ruskin, who had been the Joneses' patron and was fond of them both, called Ned to Denmark Hill to deliver a lecture on 'carnality' in painting and in life that was thinly disguised as a paper on Michelangelo. Madox Brown's friendship began to diminish, too, for unspecified reasons. Although Brown was always touchy and difficult, the estrangement may have begun because of his disapproval of Ned's behaviour. But Ned continued to see Mary. In October 1870 his account book with the firm shows that he paid 9s, plus one shilling bus fare, for some work to be carried out 'at Mrs Zambaco's'.[14] Some of his finest drawings of her date from 1871, as does the study for Cassandra described above, and another picture of Mary as Ariadne, both commissioned by her mother.

She also modelled for *Venus Epithalamia*,[15] a gift for Marie Spartali, in celebration of her wedding. After her disappointment over Lord Ranelagh, Marie had fallen in love with W. J. Stillman, a widowed American journalist whose wife had committed suicide and who had three children and no money. Her parents disapproved, but permitted the marriage to go ahead. Ned's painting, which echoes the composition of his *Beatrice*, is a far from cheerful wedding present, with its mournful full-length nude figure bearing Mary's features, and a group of shrouded females seen through a distant door coming down some stairs. A naked figure up a ladder gloomily hanging up garlands hardly enlivens the atmosphere, and altogether marriage looks a most melancholy affair.

There are strong signs that by this date Ned's love for Mary had cooled. Early in 1871 he broke with his 'sweet Owl', thereafter showing great and unremitting hostility. The reasons for this were never made explicit, but there was no shortage. Howell was, to say the least, duplicitous and unscrupulous with regard to money and a compulsive liar. A note in Georgie's hand in Ned's notebook list of paintings refers to a lost *Danae* with the comment: 'Howell said it was burnt; therefore it was not or if it was destroyed then it was by drowning.'[16] To his mortification, Ned had recommended Howell as Ruskin's secretary, until some unnamed misdemeanour led to his dismissal, and in another incident Howell embarrassed Ned in relation to his friend and patron, Luke Ionides. Howell persuaded Ionides to 'buy' some work of Ned's, on the grounds that Ned was hard up, while persuading Ned to make it a gift, on the grounds that Ionides was temporarily out of funds. The gentlemanly reticence of both prevented their discovering that Howell had simply pocketed the money himself until many years later.[17] Ned himself told Gabriel that his decision to break off with Howell was not due to this well-known 'shiftiness in money matters', nor to his equally notorious 'looseness of tongue'[18] and it is thought that its immediate cause had something to do with Mary. Much later Whistler spread the tale that Howell had tried to bring Mary and Georgie together in a spirit of reconciliation, causing Ned such a shock that he fainted, splitting his forehead on the mantelpiece as he fell,[19] but this story came from Howell himself, and is not to be believed. I suspect that the implacable enmity displayed towards him by both Ned and Georgie meant that his offence involved disrespect or embarrassment to her in some way. Ned may have been misbehaving, but he had not lost his sense of the honour due to his wife. He broke with Howell on 8 February 1871, writing abruptly to ask for repayment of a £200 debt, and thereafter urged all his acquaintance to stop seeing Howell. Howell was bitter at the success of Ned's campaign against him: five years later he told Gabriel that Ned had worshipped him 'as long as I rowed with him', and then been a 'most cowardly enemy' when he went on strike, 'trying night and day to ruin me, and doing all that whores do'.[20]

Georgie, as usual, kept her own counsel. Like many under-educated women, in middle life she sought to extend the boundaries of her limited schooling, setting herself to study German, Latin and music. She learnt to play an organ which was later installed in Ned's studio so she could play while he painted; she also took lessons in French from an exiled member of the Paris Commune, one-eyed Jules Andrieu, who, alongside a number of artists' models looking for employment, had found refuge in Britain. She continued in her role of Ned's faithful helpmate, managing his household and servants so as to provide a stable base for his work; never was he bothered by domestic responsibilities. Georgie always read aloud to him in the evenings, for amusement and to save his eyes from strain, and did all his correspondence from dictation until he employed a secretary at the end of his career; there is no doubt that the prolific Burne-Jones output of art was in large measure due to his wife's work – his achievement was facilitated by her support. From today's perspective it appears that he was indulged like a spoilt child, but both were aware of this. In one of the conversations recorded towards the end of his life by his studio assistant there was the following exchange:

EBJ . . .I'd like to have everything I'd like, and for only as long as I'd like it.

GBJ And throw it away when you got tired of it, and have it back again when you wanted it back.

EBJ Just so, Georgie, in fact I'd like to be a baby.[21]

There are indications, too, that Ned fully appreciated Georgie's fidelity and support and understood what he had risked losing. Slowly he disengaged himself from Mary. In 1872 he portrayed her as *Temperance*, pouring water 'with a fine sweeping gesture, on to the last fires of love'[22] and in the autumn she suffered some kind of physical and mental breakdown that seems to have signalled the end of her hopes for their relationship. Morris dined with Mrs Cassavetti in October and reported finding Mary 'looking very well'[23] but at the end of November he wrote to her cousin Aglaia saying, 'I suppose you will have heard before this reaches you all about poor Mary's illness and how very ill she has been; though I hope it will all come right now.'[24] Ned disappeared for a fortnight owing to the crisis. When she recovered, Mary left her children with her mother and went to Paris, hoping to resume her sculpture, and at Easter in 1873 Ned visited her while he was *en route* for Italy with Morris.[25] His last major tribute to her was *The Beguiling of Merlin*, begun in the same year. He modelled the

face and figure of the enchantress Nimue on Mary, later
explaining that the head and the action were very like 'the same
poor traitor . . . the name of her was Mary . . . she was born at
the foot of Olympus [i.e. in Greece] and looked and was
primaeval, and that's the head and the way of standing and turning
and I was being turned into a hawthorn bush in the forest of
Broceliande . . .'[26] But he had escaped from her spell and he could
be cruel; another of his later remarks was: 'A woman at her best,
self-denying and devoted, is pathetic and lovely beyond words;
but once she gets the upper hand and flaunts, she's the devil.'[27]

So Mary has passed into legend as a beautiful, wayward
temptress, when a more sober assessment might look more
critically on Ned as one who promised to love her only to draw
back when his own security was threatened; she undoubtedly
suffered more than he as a result of their affair. From the safety of
later success he maintained a sentimental memory of their
turbulent affair, describing Mary as 'hurricanes and tempests and
billows of the sea – it's no use blaming them . . . only it didn't do
in English suburban surroundings . . .'[28] On the day before his
death he told a young visitor that his favourite name was Mary.[29]
However, he was perhaps guilty of self-preservation rather than of
betrayal. In later life, he transferred his romantic feelings to other
women, or rather girls, for as he grew older he became, like
Ruskin, attracted to younger and younger women, some of
whom were his daughter's age. He was careful never again to get
seriously involved, however, and his romances took on a ritual
quality, appropriate to the 'English suburban surroundings' he
inhabited. He wrote effusive and indeed embarrassing epistles, as a
substitute. With Frances Graham, his patron's daughter, he
evolved a long-running fantasy that they would one day elope and
live together in poverty, just as he had led Mary to believe. To
Georgie he maintained the teasing fiction that men were naturally
polygamous. In the 1890s he claimed to have read a newspaper
report of 60,000 'superfluous' (that is, unmarried) women in
Kensington alone, and remarked, 'That points to polygamy,
Georgie.' She replied, 'No, Ned dear, that points to young men
being unwilling to marry.'[30]

In this manner the need for divorce was averted and an even
tenor returned to the household at the Grange. To the outside
world, perhaps, very little had been visible, for Georgie succeeded

in maintaining a stable image in all but the most distressful times, an image of domestic normality that one suspects was also necessary to her. Thus her outward life, giving no hint of the troubles beneath, was depicted in the following selections from the typed summary of her diary for 1871:[31]

29 Feb   lunched with Edward at the Lewes' to meet Tourge-nieff.
19 Mar   went to Gabriel's with Edward.
14 Apr   Edward and I dined at Denmark Hill.
28 Apr   Edward, Morris & I went to the Sloane Square Theatre.
11 May   to International Exhibition with Edward.
12 May   Edward and I went to the RA.
12 Jun   Edward and I called on Allingham in the evening. He was out.
26 Jun   Hollyer the photographer here all day.

The insistent recording of all the engagements she and Ned carried out together seems to reflect anxiety. But there were other aspects to her life, as the diary record shows:

28 Jun   Phil at home because Morris & Charley Faulkner and Jennie and May came in the morning and pitched the Icelandic tent.
30 Jun   Morris to breakfast and fetched the children to go to Leyton. Edward & I joined the children at Leyton to dinner. I stayed all night.
1 Jul   Morris, Charley, Magnusson and Mr Evans dined with us.
3 Jul   Morris dined or rather supped here on his return from taking Janey and the children to Kelmscott.
5 Jul   Morris slept here.
6 Jul   Morris after breakfast said 'goodbye' and started for Iceland.

Georgie extended her love and support, in an almost polygamous style, to Morris as well as Ned. Henceforth she may be said to have had two husbands.

Morris went to Iceland partly to escape what he later called the
'horrors' of his own domestic situation. Jane had returned with
him from Ems in September 1869 feeling considerably better;
whatever the doubtful medicinal properties of the water, Philip
Webb was instructed to build a shower at Queen Square to enable
her to continue the beneficial baths. She objected to proposals to
stay abroad longer, Topsy told Webb, listing her reasons as:
foreign food, boredom, missing the children, tiringness of travel –
'*summa*, she refuses to think of anything but going straight
home'.[32] By return post, Webb sketched a shower arrangement
and a caricature of a buxom Janey to indicate her improved
health.[33]

But she had other things to go back to. When she reached
London, Gabriel was still at Penkill with Alice Boyd and Bell
Scott, making arrangements to exhume his notebook and publish
his poems. He had originally planned to dedicate the volume to his
brother and commented that he would still do so, 'failing only one
possibility', which was 'out of the question',[34] a dedication to
Jane. He was also planning to resume painting her and described a
fanciful scheme to depict her as Fortune 'seated full face dealing
cards on which will be visible symbols of life, death etc. Behind
her will be her wheel. The spokes wound with festive and fatal
growths and on either side of it will be seated a dove (or a white
peacock) and a raven.'[35] On his return to London, however, he
found their affair the subject of much gossip in the Pre-Raphaelite
circle. Mrs Bell Scott called at Queen Square about an altar cloth
and told Jane that Gabriel was back; he himself refrained from
calling 'as he understands they are watched'. Bell Scott referred to
Jane as Gabriel's 'sweet Lucretia Borgia' and commented that 'the
greatest disturbance in his health and temper . . . is caused by an
uncontrollable desire for the possession of the said L.B.'. And the
gossip was spreading: Mrs Street had spoken to Mrs Bell Scott
'about Gabriel being so fond of Mrs Top'.[36] On 25 November the
Bell Scotts gave a dinner party; they invited the Morrises, Bessie
Burden, Gabriel, the Leweses and various others. Jane and Gabriel
sat next to each other, Scott reported, commenting that Gabriel, 'I
must say acts like a perfect fool if he wants to conceal his
attachment, doing nothing but attend to her, sitting sideways
towards her, that sort of thing. Mrs Linton sat opposite and I shall
be surprised if she did not see anything interesting.' Gabriel tried

to take Jane down to dinner, with Morris 'looking at him all the time'. As for Jane, Scott found her conduct remarkable. 'Of course a woman under such circumstances, before people, is a sealed book,' he commented. 'Still I think she is cool.'[37]

As these remarks show, the relationship was becoming openly known, which marks a further stage in its development. Over the winter months it deepened, feeding on whatever opportunities Jane obtained to pose. One of Gabriel's chief attractions must have been the flattering adoration he offered in both paint and prose. 'How nice it would be if I could feel sure I had painted you once for all so as to let the world know what you were,' he wrote, 'but every new thing I do from you is a disappointment, and it is only at some odd moment when I cannot set about it that I see by a flash the way it ought to be done.'[38] If she had not married Morris, things might have been different:

> If I had you always with me through life, it would somehow have got accomplished . . . For the last 2 years I have felt distinctly the clearing away of the chilling numbness that surrounds me in the utter want of you – but since the other obstacles have kept steadily on the increase, and it comes too late . . .[39]

His flattery could be excessive:

> Places that are empty of you are empty of all life . . . more than all for me, dear Janey, is the fact that you exist, that I can yet look forward to seeing you and speaking to you again . . . You are the noblest and dearest thing that the world has had to show me; and if no lesser loss than the loss of you could have brought me so much bitterness, I would still rather have had this to endure than have missed the fulness of wonder and worship which nothing else could have made known to me . . .[40]

It is small wonder that Jane kept these letters for the rest of her life.

In March 1870 she went to stay at Hastings, apparently wishing to escape from Queen Square; her ill-health provided useful reasons for leaving London. Gabriel promptly borrowed Barbara Bodichon's cottage on the Leigh-Smith estate at Scalands near Robertsbridge, which he and Lizzie had visited nearly sixteen years before. The cottage was at first shared with W. J. Stillman, Marie Spartali's husband-to-be, but eventually Gabriel was on his own, resting his still-troubled eyes and sampling the extensive Leigh-Smith cellar. On 26 March, Jane came for a day visit with Morris and then, around 12 April, in a manoeuvre that must have required some preparation, she returned to stay, on her own. 'Janey Morris is here,' wrote Gabriel casually to his mother on 18 April, 'and benefiting greatly. Top comes from time to time.'[41] They were together for nearly a month, during which time his long-awaited *Poems* were published; he went to town for a day, to sign presentation copies and meet Morris for oysters, and then returned to Scalands.

In drawing up his list of complimentary copies, Gabriel asked his publisher to try and find the address of 'a Captn. Thompson living at Hampstead',[42] evidently in the hope of sending a copy of his *Poems* to Annie Miller, now Mrs Thompson. While this may have been a simple gesture of friendship, it also suggests that Annie, in her days as a model, had shown an interest in poetry. It was some seven years since she had seen Gabriel, and it is to be hoped that her address was discovered and she received the book.

Publication was an anxious occasion and perhaps wisely, in view of the contents of his volume, Gabriel was worried by the prospect of hostile reviews, particularly from one Robert Buchanan, who had earlier been himself critically reviewed by William Michael and had retaliated with an 'evidently personal onslaught'.[43] He was likely to be biased against the name of Rossetti. In order to forestall unfavourable notices, Gabriel made energetic and largely successful efforts to 'fix' all the major reviews in advance. As part of this campaign he had arranged for Morris to write about the book in the *Academy* and Morris had agreed. On the face of it, this was a curious, almost perverse, idea, but it illustrates well the desire of both men to defuse the burgeoning rumours and the possible inference that the love poems in the book were addressed to Jane; a friendly review by her husband must surely suggest that some other woman was intended. The fact that many of the poems *were* addressed to Jane was of course to remain their private secret, perhaps guessed by friends who knew the true state of her marriage, but admitted to none. The *Academy* review was, however, an unpleasant task. Morris simply reported to Jane that he had despatched it after reading it out to Brown 'who thought it good'.[44] To Aglaia Coronio he was more expressive. 'I have done my review just this moment – ugh!' he wrote.[45] On 10 May he went down to Sussex to escort his wife home, in further defence of her respectability.

Gabriel planned to spend the summer with Jane, and retained a house near Scalands for the purpose, but November found him still in Chelsea, his money wasted. 'Perhaps he could not manage to get the "hollow-chested" matron out to that neighbourhood,' speculated Bell Scott.[46] It may be that Morris had vetoed the plan, or Jane herself regarded it as too risky; she had no desire to forfeit her reputation. In the autumn she went with her daughters and Bessie to Torquay. Morris's letters to her there were affectionate and matter-of-fact, apart from one gnomic paragraph, evidently in response to a remark of Jane's. 'As for living, dear,' he wrote on 3 October, 'people like you speak of don't know either what life or death means . . . For me I don't think people really want to die of mental pain.'[47] Jane returned to London for only a short time before departing again to stay with her sister-in-law, leaving Jenny and May with their father at Queen Square. When the time came for Morris to fetch her, she decided to stay an extra week. This time he proposed to join her. 'If my vanity doesn't deceive me, I might make it pleasanter for you,' he wrote, adding, 'I should rather enjoy it than not.'[48] Jane's reply is not preserved.

Her preference for being out of London, however, coincided with Gabriel's continuing search for a country residence, and by the spring of 1871 it was understood that this was a joint project. The house-hunting led unerringly, as it seems with hindsight, to Kelmscott Manor in Oxfordshire. Kelmscott so fitted Morris's character and enthusiasms that the house has ever since been indelibly associated with his name – and not without reason, since it played a major role in both his life and his vision of a post-industrial and socialist utopia. It is forgotten that its first purpose was a holiday home for Jane, the girls and Gabriel. And much as Morris liked the house, it was Jane who elected to spend most time there, and who succeeded at the very end of her life in purchasing the property. Whether it was leased with the intention of providing a retreat to share with Gabriel without causing gossip is a nice point that cannot now be resolved; certainly a joint tenancy between Morris and Gabriel was the only way she and Gabriel could sleep under the same roof together without scandal.

Morris gave one explanation in a letter to Faulkner. 'I have been looking about for a house for the wife and kids,' he wrote, describing Kelmscott and adding, 'I am going down there again on Saturday with Rossetti and my wife: Rossetti because he thinks of sharing it with us if the thing seems likely.'[49] Gabriel presented the plan a little differently. 'Morris and I had been for some little time in search of a place to take jointly in the country,' he told his uncle, 'when this one was discovered in a house-agent's catalogue – the last place one would have expected to furnish such an out-of-the-world commodity.'[50] He at once arranged for Webb to design and supervise some alterations to the studio at Cheyne Walk, and moved himself to Kelmscott for the summer. Jane soon followed and Morris, after escorting them there, as Georgie's diary recorded, left almost at once for Iceland. It is hard to believe that the arrangement was not deliberate.

Divorce was out of the question for Jane, as it was only possible by proving that she had committed adultery and that Morris had not condoned her behaviour. There was no such thing as mutual divorce, and the respondent was denied access to the children, on the grounds of moral corruption and ritual punishment; as a divorcee Jane would have lost Jenny and May as well as her reputation as a respectable woman. In addition the scandal would have made remarriage to Gabriel difficult and dangerous, threatening his career and earning power. This is not to say that she considered this option: rather she adopted the best alternative.

Her behaviour, and her husband's, puzzled and disturbed many contemporaries, and later commentators found the arrangement at Kelmscott to be outside the agreed bounds of propriety, but could not, nevertheless, identify anything manifestly improper about it. Indications of unease are tucked into the correspondence of the time and as late as 1950 Sydney Cockerell and Bernard Shaw, who had both known the Morrises in their later years, were still debating the problem of Morris's *complaisance* or otherwise in the 1870s. 'I imagine Janey the Beautiful became completely dominated by the passionate, fascinating and determined Italian, and returned his devotion,' wrote Cockerell, doing his bit for the myth. 'It may be that high principles and not dishonourable ones compelled M. to accept the situation. It is all rather a puzzle . . .' He noted that Morris always wrote affectionately to his wife, even from Iceland, but that neither Jane nor her daughter had destroyed

Gabriel's love letters, 'well knowing what they were . . . Altogether a considerable drama.'[51] But he could not quite relinquish the view that *mari complaisant* was a shameful term.

It seems undeniable that Kelmscott was meant as a place where Jane and Gabriel could be together, and that Morris, reluctantly, accepted this. Their excitement at the forthcoming holiday is evident in Gabriel's letters during June; among other plans he ordered a complete set of Walter Scott's novels for Jane to read in the country. As for Morris, the repeated words from Iceland, 'Please dear Janey be happy'[52] suggest that he was well aware of what Kelmscott meant to her.

Whether he believed her relationship with Gabriel to be sexual is as difficult to answer as whether or not it was sexual. This is an issue that has aroused speculation for a long time, and I do not intend to contribute much to it, for it seems evident that Jane and Gabriel were lovers in all other respects. They were in love with each other and effectively lived together, and only the patriarchal belief that affection expressed through copulation is more signifi-cant than other forms makes us pay greater attention, in this case as in others, to sex than to love. On the one hand, there was every opportunity for a sexual relationship at Kelmscott and it may have been leased for that very purpose. On the other, Jane later told Wilfrid Blunt that she 'never quite gave herself to Gabriel' (Blunt evidently shared the same prurient curiosity as everyone else)[53] and in support of this one might cite Gabriel's hydrocele, a distressing although not dangerous swelling of the testicles which probably inhibited sexual activity. Furthermore, although they were together at Kelmscott, they were far from alone. Besides Jenny and May, then aged ten and nine, there were also the girls' nanny from Queen Square and Gabriel's two servants from Cheyne Walk, as well as what he described as two 'native' or local servants, which made a total of five employees, two adults and two children, bringing the full household up to nine persons. And Kelmscott Manor was not an excessively large house.

It was, however, extremely remote. All services and supplies had to be ordered from Lechlade or Farringdon and there was little local transport and no through traffic. Installed in her new domain at the end of the first week of July 1870 Jane set about furnishings and improvements. 'I am getting the fireplace set straight in the dining room, the one with the broken mantelshelf,' she wrote to

Philip Webb, back in London, asking him to send six dozen tiles from the firm's workshop in Queen Square: 'Will they look best of various patterns or all alike?' she wondered. 'They must be blue. The mantelshelf is stone I find, so I am making the masons scrape off the former drab paint. The next thing to be thought of is a grate . . .' She sent love from Jenny and May, who were 'a little out of temper with the weather, we have a deal of rain'. The following week she thanked Webb for his efforts, remarking, 'I will never pull another fireplace down as long as I live, I feel inclined to leave it till Topsy comes back, for there are no competent workmen in the place, however the masonry is nearly finished and they cannot make any great mistakes provided I stand by to show them which is the right way up of each tile . . .'[54]

Jane also inquired of Webb whether the spire was as old as the rest of Lechlade church and commented that the countryside 'is not so beautiful after one gets away from the river, though it is all delightful and home-like to me, and I love it . . .' This, it may be noted was as close as she seems to have come to acknowledging her local origins. When Gabriel complained that the landscape was flat and featureless, she was obliged to agree, but it still felt comfortable to her. Her mother, who had died that February in Oxford at the age of sixty-six, had been born at Alvescot, less than five miles away across field paths from Kelmscott, and Jane still had relatives living there as well as in her father's village of Stanton Harcourt to the south-east. But there is no evidence that she sought them out.

As well as Walter Scott, she was reading Goethe's *Elective Affinities*, which, 'with all due respect', she pronounced a most unsatisfactory book. 'What! is nothing real? Must everything that is delightful change and leave nothing behind? I can't believe it; one begins by liking his characters very much, then they change, and one can no longer look on them as real people. I still feel like little Margaret [Burne-Jones] at the play when she asked me if May was really sewing.'[55] Webb replied with his own views on Goethe, a suggestion that a visit to the Uffington White Horse would relieve the feeling of flatness, and an embroidery design for a cushion she had requested.[56] 'I had not expected anything half so elaborate or beautiful,' Jane replied. 'I shall work it carefully in fine wool on blue serge I think, taking care to get different shades of blue for the flowers.' She added that she had 'no news of Topsy yet, is it not rather odd?'[57] But in none of her letters did she mention Gabriel's presence, which is surely odder, since he and Webb were also corresponding over the studio alterations. In one of his letters to Webb, Gabriel added a jokey postscript: 'Let us hope Top is up to his navel in ice by this time and likes it.'[58]

Gabriel wrote quite openly of Jane's presence to his mother, since to have done otherwise would have fuelled speculation. 'This house and its surroundings are the "loveliest haunt of ancient peace" that can be well imagined,' he wrote. 'It has a quantity of farm buildings of the thatched squatted order, which look settled down into a purring state of comfort, but seem (as Janey said the other day) as if, were you to stroke them, they would move.'[59] He added that Jane was well and able to take walks of five or six miles across the fields and along the river, and that the girls were 'able to amuse themselves all day long without needing to be thought about by their elders' – a most satisfactory state of affairs. He and Jane thus spent the summer very pleasantly. A punt was acquired for outings on the river, and a pony and trap was considered. In the evenings, there was reading and embroidery. Gabriel wrote some new poems, painted a replica of *Beata Beatrix*, did chalk drawings of Jenny and May and a picture of Jane called *Water Willow*, showing the river, the punt, the church and the manor in the background.[60] It is one of the sweetest, softest, calmest and least mannered of his paintings of her, quite without the brooding intensity of other studies and subjects, and seems to reflect happy days at Kelmscott. One of the poems he wrote during this summer was a long and fanciful, not to say ludicrous, ballad, entitled 'The Beryl Stone', which concerns a medieval girl, her mother and a magic foretelling crystal. It contains little that relates to its author's life, but among the items Jane kept to the end of her life was a fair copy of this poem written out for her in a lined exercise book.[61]

On 10 September her husband returned from Iceland, bringing with him a pony named Mouse for his daughters to ride. He stayed only a night or two, taking the punt on the river for a day's fishing and prompting Gabriel to a cartoon illustrating the lines:

> Enter Skald, moored in a punt
> And jacks and tenches exeunt.

in reference to the fact that the Icelandic press had publicly greeted Morris as 'skald' or poet. After another short visit from Morris at the end of the month, Janey and Gabriel and the rest returned to London on 7 October and the Manor was shut up for the winter. The land around was liable to flooding, and the house itself was cold and damp.

It was the end of a happy summer. In town, the Kelmscott intimacy could not be maintained without scandal, and the social difficulties which Jane had avoided in the country but now faced were illustrated by Bell Scott's response when he learned that Jane would be dining with Gabriel on an evening when her husband entertained half a dozen male friends. 'I asked Gabriel the evening before if he was to be there and on his answering no, I said "Why then?"' he wrote to Alice Boyd. 'His reply was "Oh I have another engagement". This engagement was, actually, Janey at his own house for the night! . . . Is it not too daring, and altogether inexplicable?'[62] Inexplicable or not, it indicates that Jane's affair with Gabriel was well established. We may suppose that she was well and happy.

15

The careful management of the reviews of Gabriel's 1870 *Poems* was not ultimately successful, although the attack was delayed. When it came, however, it justified his worst fears, for it was an attack on his morality as well as his verse. It came, as expected, from the poet and critic Robert Buchanan and appeared in an article in the *Contemporary Review* for October 1871, just as Jane and Gabriel returned from Kelmscott. Encouraged by Brown and against the advice of William Michael, who rightly felt that this would only aggravate matters, Gabriel issued a reply in December, defending his work. Buchanan then hit back with an extended essay published as a 100-page pamphlet, which appeared in May 1872 and was itself the subject of reviews in the various cultural journals of the day, as well as a topic of discussion in literary and artistic circles. It was written and received as a personal assault, and its impact on Gabriel was extreme, triggering off a severe mental breakdown.

As a pamphlet, *The Fleshly School of Poetry* was in the best tradition of literary polemic. Because of its effect on Dante Gabriel Rossetti, the Pre-Raphaelite hero, it has been harshly judged and castigated as one of Mrs Grundy's contemptible, narrow-minded outbursts against Art, and its author reviled and despised as a poor critic and worse poet. In fact, Buchanan's essay is keen and vigorous, full of wit, irony and fine defamatory phrases; its detractors seem by contrast specious and mealy-mouthed. It was undoubtedly excessive, but so was the *Dunciad*; *The Fleshly School* was similarly unfair, but very entertaining. It was also accurate, and its argument was acute. Buchanan alleged that Rossetti and his 'school', by which he meant Swinburne and Morris, although this

was cleverly qualified so that the whole force of the attack was
levelled at Rossetti, wrote indecent, semi-pornographic verse
which merely supplemented 'the literature of Holywell Street',
where cruder but more honest filth was on sale. This poetic
infection – the Scrofulous School of Literature, or the 'Italian
Disease' – was disgusting in its subject matter and affected in its
style. 'Step where I may, the snake sensualism spits its venom
upon me,' wrote Buchanan; 'there are many other functions of the
flesh which it is not the custom to perform in public, but which
are quite as interesting as "the deed".' He was critical of the
studied archaism of the diction, saying that when the audience
reads of damozels and citherns, 'a suspicion is awakened that the
writer is laughing at us. We hover uncertainly between pic-
turesqueness and namby-pamby . . .'[1] Attacking Gabriel's claim
that his poems elevated the beloved's Soul more than her Body,
Buchanan simply produced a string of quotations from the book's
'House of Life' sonnet sequence, which he compared to a brothel,
and described as a 'very hotbed of nasty phrases', 'flooded with
sensualism'. His fine comic performance was punctuated with
ironic protests – 'I dare not quote another line', or 'there are ten
sonnets to come, but *must* I quote from them?' He made his points
by exaggeration: 'Mr Rossetti is never so great as on "kisses" and
"beds".' He hit shrewdly at 'Eden Bower' with the observation
that 'the reader feels a horrible sense of sliminess, as if he were
handling a yellow serpent or conger eel', and laughed at the
obsession (in 'Troy Town') with the breast-shaped chalice by
remarking that 'Paris, poor fellow, has a fair prospect of being
suckled by Helen.' And he ended by demolishing all pretensions
to high-minded purity:

> One would swear, to hear these Cupids of the new Fleshly
> Epoch, that English literature had been veritably getting blue
> mouldy with too much virtue, that the spirit of Imagination had
> lived in a nunnery, fed on pulse and cold water, since Chaucer's
> time . . . Perhaps, since so many centuries of Sexuality have
> done so little for poetry it might be advantageous to give
> Spirituality a trial . . .

There was much justice in the attack. Rossetti's verse, like
Swinburne's, was indeed sensual and concerned with sexual

attraction and connection, even if it was also preoccupied with Love and Idealism. Sex pervades Rossetti's poems. 'Nuptial Sleep' is about coition, not kissing; 'Vain Virtues' does indeed suggest the rape of virgins, as Buchanan alleged. And to a degree he was right when he asserted that for such subjects directness is preferable to soft pornography masquerading as high art.

So far, so professional. Gabriel was over-sensitive to criticism of his work and had rarely exhibited his painting in public in order to avoid unflattering notices, but he could not hope to claim absolute immunity for his poetry, and indeed his response to Buchanan's original article showed that he was prepared to enter a public defence. But Buchanan also indulged in personal insults, which were harder to bear and close to the mark. Gabriel was described as 'a painter and poet idolized by his own family and personal associates', who was 'too sensitive to exhibit his pictures and so modest that it takes him years to make up his mind to publish his poems', but who was quite ready to 'chronicle his amorous sensations' and 'wheel his nuptial couch into the public street'. This, it was implied, was very disrespectful to the deceased Mrs Rossetti. Worse still, since literary gossip would soon apply it to the poet's new love, the silent, sultry-looking Mrs Morris, were the allusions to those whom the 'fleshly' poets loved as 'females who bite, scratch, scream, bubble, munch, sweat, writhe, twist, wriggle, foam and in a general way slaver over their lovers'. These were 'the kind of women whom it seems the unhappy lot of these gentlemen to encounter', and 'must surely possess some extraordinary qualities to counteract their otherwise most offensive mode of conducting themselves'. The inference, of course, was that they were not ladies. This accompanied a general attack on London's bohemian class – 'men and women of indolent habits and aesthetic tastes' – which was identified as the 'seat of the cancer', with Gabriel at its centre. Furthermore, the Fleshly School's life and lyrics were not only full of debauchery; by organizing their coterie into a counter-attack on Buchanan, they proved themselves 'cowards, too spoilt with flattery to bear criticism'.

Some three weeks after the pamphlet appeared, Gabriel's mind gave way, collapsing under paranoid delusions of persecution and aural hallucinations, which made him hear voices conspiring against him: his enemies were muttering in ceilings and walls, and passers-by were laughing at him, even birds and animals had the voices of conspirators. He suffered from acute insomnia and agitation and was, as his brother wrote, 'past question, not entirely sane'.[2] He was sufficiently deranged, in fact, for his family and friends to consider sending him to a lunatic asylum, although owing to the stigma involved, which would have permanently blighted his reputation and earning power, this step was stoutly resisted as long as other hope prevailed.[3] His nervous collapse began at the beginning of June and he was soon removed from his own home to that of Thomas Hake, a retired medical man and aspiring author, in Roehampton. Here, on 8 June, there was a crisis when Gabriel saw some revellers in the street carrying poles which he interpreted as gibbets from which he was to be hanged by his enemies. He also heard a voice call out 'at him a term of gross and unbearable obloquy', which delicacy prevented William Michael from printing even thirty years after the event.[4] It is only possible to speculate what this dreadful word was, conjured up in the delusions of insanity. Gabriel's chief biographer[5] suggested that it was 'murderer' and related to guilt over Lizzie's death. This would fit with the associations of hanging, but I would tentatively suggest that the term Gabriel's voice flung at him was 'adulterer'. This would explain both William Michael's epithet 'gross' and his reticence: writing in the 1890s, when Jane was still alive, he knew that this would fuel speculation as to the exact nature of her relationship with his brother. And it relates more closely to the substance of Buchanan's attack, and to the insoluble emotional problems brought about by his love for Jane. Courtly love for an ideal lady was one thing; real passion for a married woman was another. In moral terms, his love for Janey was adulterous.

The contradictions in his life had become intolerable. His self-image was that of an idealistic artist and lover, but he was in danger of being exposed as a very 'fleshly' fellow. I do not doubt that Gabriel knew that his work – *Bocca Baciata*, *Venus Verticordia* and *The Blue Bower* as much as 'Eden Bower', 'Troy Town' and 'Nuptial Sleep' – was sensual, even indecent. He suppressed his most sexually explicit sonnet, 'On the French Liberation of Italy', and he knew his Aunt Charlotte would be shocked by the young prostitute in 'Jenny', despite his insistence on the poem's high-mindedness. At the same time, he did not admit any knowledge of lewdness; as a Romantic, Love was a deity in both art and life. It is indeed the tension between spiritualized

admiration and physical desire that forms the mainspring of
Rossetti's art, erotically charged yet aesthetically chaste; this is a
large part of its appeal. At a personal level, however, the
contradiction was more painful. It was felt by many of Rossetti's
contemporaries, striving to reconcile physical attraction, defined
as lust by many moralists, with worship of the beloved. To admit
desire for a woman was to degrade her, reduce her to the level of
whore, and thus in describing 'nuptial' ecstasy, as in the sonnets
Buchanan singled out as expressions of 'animalism', Gabriel had
polluted those whom he aimed only to honour. His writing
threatened to bring Lizzie and Janey down to Fanny's level. There
were other difficulties too. Not only was there the immediate
problem of how to live with the reputation of being the seducer of
another man's wife, if his affair with Janey was ever to be made
public; there was also the latent issue that he had betrayed Lizzie
both by opening her grave and by loving another. In some ways it
was not at all surprising that publication of the *Poems* precipitated
his collapse: the implications of what the volume contained were
too problematic to live with. And on the night of 8 June, after
seeing the 'gibbet' and hearing the voice, Gabriel tried to kill
himself with a large dose of laudanum. He survived, as Lizzie had
not, thus adding another twist of remorse to his soul.

Many of their friends believed that Jane was the cause of
Gabriel's breakdown, and tried to prevent him seeing her. She was
at Kelmscott, expecting him to join her for the summer, and
immediately returned to London. However, she did not at once
hurry to Cheyne Walk, nor did he demand her presence; in fact,
both seem to have wished to maintain a distance between them at
this time. On 6 June Gabriel asked Bell Scott who, with Brown
and William Michael, was taking an active role in coping with the
crisis, to go to Queen Square, because 'she had expected him and
was becoming anxious'. Scott found Janey 'on the sofa and not
discomposed by my intelligence'.[6] It may well be that she knew
the news already; in any case she was experienced in masking her
feelings. Her composure was welcome; it meant there was no
danger of her 'rushing out to Roehampton or Chelsea' nor of 'his
derangement being increased by thinking of her'.[7] His friends
were urgently searching for somewhere to send him as an
alternative to an asylum. When Jane did write to Gabriel, saying
she hoped to see him before he left London, the depth of his

paranoia was apparent when he confided to Scott that the letter was forged.

Jane's behaviour was designed, like that of his other friends, to minimize any scandal that might attach to Gabriel's breakdown if it became widely known, and she was seen to act 'correctly'. When she went to see him, on 14 June, she took her husband. Scott, believing that 'sweet Lucretia Borgia' was the cause of the collapse, remarked that Morris was 'more than amiable' in the circumstances, but in fact Morris was distressed, as an old friend, by Gabriel's crazed condition and offered to share in the task of looking after him. This offer was declined, however, and on 20 June Brown took Gabriel off to seclusion in Scotland, where his hallucinations continued and his sleeplessness was counteracted by large doses of whisky and chloral. Jane remained anxious and at the beginning of July wrote several times asking for news, and discussing future plans for his welfare with his 'minders'. 'You have been talking as to the possibility of his using the house at Kelmscott for a time,' she wrote on 15 July to Bell Scott, who had replaced Brown, 'but he has said to me so often that he could never go there again, that I doubt if he could be persuaded to think of it now.' She commented that Gabriel would not welcome Morris as a companion.[8] Dr Hake, who replaced Scott, also believed Jane to be a main cause of the trouble and did not give Gabriel her letters, although at the same time he did not return them, as he did those that arrived from Fanny and Alexa Wilding; he doubtless made a social distinction as to the amount of courtesy each deserved. Gabriel began to recover and when he wrote to Jane for the first time on 12 August, Hake added a note asking her to report to him any reference to the troublesome delusions and to be 'very guarded' in her replies. Actually, Hake feared that corresponding with Jane would itself increase the delusions and agitation, and almost failed to forward the letter. But in fact, as she reported both to him and to William Michael, Gabriel's letter was reasonably sane and cheerful. 'No one could have told he had been ill,' she wrote, adding, 'I have had many from his hand of a far more depressing kind.'[9] They then resumed their accustomed correspondence, although no letters have survived, and when the time came for Gabriel to leave Scotland, she arranged to be with him at Kelmscott. This arrangement materially aided his recovery; all depended, he wrote to William Michael in a passage later suppressed, 'primarily on my not being deprived of the prospect of the one necessary person'.[10] Jane's offer must, I believe, be judged an act of real love and generosity, for it is not easy to care for a disturbed and paranoid person, and mental affliction was not well understood or sympathized with. 'That Gabriel *was* mad was but too true,' she wrote many years later; 'no one knows better than myself.'[11] To give her some support, Hake's student son was detailed to accompany Gabriel to Kelmscott.

Jane and the girls were there already. At this point she seems to have written in confidence to Philip Webb following an occurrence that had given his 'soul a twist'. We don't know what she said, but he thanked her for clarifying things, agreed on the need for 'resource in despair' and assured her of his sympathy. Time had 'tossed all of us about', he wrote, and their roles were altered, but 'I see that you play yours well and truly under the changes'. He ended by stating that he had no wish 'to penetrate into sorrows which I can in no way relieve', and remained her true and loyal friend.[12] In the face of difficulty, Jane maintained her dignity and one can only guess at the distress she felt at her lover's loss of sanity.

Gabriel arrived at Kelmscott on 25 September. George Hake immediately took May out in the punt and Gabriel began writing profusely to all his friends, announcing his recovery and his delight at being back at the Manor. He asked William Michael to get Fanny to send down some green velvet from Chelsea for use as curtains. On 28 September Morris and Jenny arrived and, after Morris had returned to his responsibilities at Queen Square, it seemed all was well. 'I have renewed my tenancy and paid up arrears,' Gabriel wrote to his brother shortly, 'so I have as good a right to ask you down as anyone else. Janey joins warmly, and so would Top if here.'[13] This, as it happened, was not quite true. Not only did Morris find William Michael unbearably boring, but he had begun to enjoy being at Kelmscott himself, and did not like Gabriel being there all the time. In fact after a couple of weekend visits, one of which he was obliged to share with William Michael, Morris realized that it was a 'farce' for him to be in the same house as Gabriel. He felt ashamed of such 'pettinesses' in view of Gabriel's trouble, especially since Kelmscott had provided a solution to the problem of seclusion without scandal, but he felt that it was 'a specially dismal time' for himself, left alone at Queen

Square with only Bessie for company; he was seeing little of Georgie at this time.[14] In November Jane returned to London with the girls, who had spent a delightful autumn with George Hake always on hand for boating, riding and other excursions; Gabriel was left in Oxfordshire. It had been decided that the Morris family should move from Queen Square now the firm was expanding. Jane would have liked Kensington, but in the event Horrington House was taken at Turnham Green, further west; this was described by Jane as suitable for 'one person to live in, or perhaps two'.[15] Morris retained rooms at Queen Square, where the firm was still located, and expected to be there more often than with his family. In practice he seems to have been at Horrington House frequently, no doubt partly for the sake of seeing his daughters, who this winter began to attend Notting Hill School where Margaret Burne-Jones was a fellow pupil, and partly because Jane needed him in all sorts of practical ways. The move, in fact, seems to have been designed as part of a plan towards a separation which never took place. For Jane's situation was radically changed by Gabriel's breakdown. She was still in love with him but she could not rely on him. There was now no longer any real possibility that she could leave her husband for her lover, for to do so would have meant risking all. And it is clear that Gabriel did not expect her to.

He designed a monogram for her at Kelmscott, incorporating a tiny heartsease flower, and tried to arrange for stationery to be printed. There were endless difficulties – Jane objected to one silver-coloured sample as 'too like wedding stationery' – and the project appears to have been unsuccessful.[16] The only hint as to what the design may have been like is found in a monogram drawn in a tiny hand-bound commonplace book compiled by Jane in the 1880s, where her initials are enclosed within five petals.[17] The difficulty Gabriel had in completing such a relatively straightforward task may indicate that he had not fully recovered his equilibrium. He remained at Kelmscott all winter, while Jane settled into her new home.

The consequences of Gabriel's breakdown were alarming for Fanny. She was financially dependent on him, and any interruption in his earnings might leave her unsupported with no legitimate claim on his estate. As early as 1868, when he began to suffer from problems with his eyesight, Gabriel planned to make a legal gift of all his property to William Michael; then, should he be unable to paint, his creditors would have nothing to seize. He estimated that his assets were worth about two thousand pounds and stipulated that if this sum was realized, half should go to Fanny.[18] At the same time, contingency plans were made for her to emigrate to America.[19] The concern was understandable, for Fanny had her own household to maintain in Royal Avenue, a few blocks from Cheyne Walk, for which the rent, furniture and other domestic spending came directly from Gabriel's pocket. The Census of 1871 recorded her residence there, together with a twenty-five-year-old servant named Ellen Read and what appears to be the rest of the Read family: widowed Lydia, a laundress aged fifty-four, and her children Harry, Rose and William. Fanny entered herself on the enumerator's schedule as Sarah Hughes, married, aged thirty-five, born in Sussex. She had aged only eight years since the previous Census.

Gabriel got Howell to handle all the negotiations for the lease on Fanny's house and employed a lawyer to register it on the list of ratepayers.[20] His finances were in a chronic state of disarray, and although he was earning large sums from his painting he never seemed to have enough money to meet the bills and debts presented by tradesmen and creditors. Harry Treffry Dunn, who became his studio assitant in 1867, often found him in a depressed state about his household expenses and searched for an explanation. He decided that the cause was 'great waste and improvidence in the housekeeping'[21] which he checked by supervising accounts kept by the servants, who he believed were grossly exploiting their employer. Domestic workers in the nineteenth century were generally held to be dishonest, but there seem to have been additional reasons for the squandering of Gabriel's income. Whistler regarded his acquaintances at this date as parasites, 'dangling after him';[22] one of his closest friends was Howell, who was notorious for living off others, so this was probably an accurate assessment. It is also possible that a good deal of his 'extravagance' was incurred by or on behalf of Fanny, for Gabriel was maintaining two households. He must have paid the bills for all Royal Avenue groceries, coal and clothing. In September 1871 he sent £5 to cover the wages of a servant named Lucy.[23] If he was not responsible, it is hard to see how Fanny managed, for she had no inherited money, no income and a husband who was, it appears, more of a liability than an asset. She was by now too old and fat to return to the streets, or to continue modelling. One of the last figures for which she posed was that in an illustration to Christina Rossetti's poem 'If' commissioned in 1866 from Gabriel's irregular lodger Fred Sandys. The drawing shows a large buxom woman with loose hair, who looks a good deal like Fanny.[24] As William Michael later complained, the figure is not appropriate to the poem, for she has a solid appearance and a sulky rather than yearning expression. She is chewing a strand of hair in direct reference to *Delia*, and it is not surprising that the friendship between Sandys and Gabriel later foundered on the issue of chronic plagiarism. At the same time, it is worth noting that lodgers like Sandys also accounted for extra household expenditure. Fanny should therefore not be blamed for Gabriel's improvidence, although the evidence suggests that she too handled money in a relatively careless manner.

In Gabriel's absences from London, Fanny was appointed to look after domestic matters at Cheyne Walk, which would have been another source of friction since Dunn was responsible for his employer's professional affairs and for the studio. It was Fanny who looked after curtains and other soft furnishings, for example, and was asked to send velvet fabric to Kelmscott in the summer of 1871. A few weeks later, there was an obscure misunderstanding over a 'poor fawn' which, as far as I can discover, was the carcass of one of the many unfortunate animals inhabiting Gabriel's garden. Like most of the others, this died and Fanny arranged for it to be sent to Kelmscott. Dunn, believing or pretending to believe that it was a side of venison sent like some grouse by a patron from Scotland, and thinking its condition already high, buried it in the garden. Fanny took umbrage when she found out, and complained to Kelmscott. 'My dear Fanny,' wrote Gabriel in reply, 'your poor dear letter has almost made me cry . . . I cannot tell how grieved I feel to think that your affectionate remembrance of me in sending the poor fawn should only have brought you disappointment and vexation. I wish I was with you at this moment, poor kind Fan, to kiss you and tell you how much I feel about it . . . .'[25] Even if he was overdoing the balm, the expression of affection is touching. Unfortunately I cannot quite banish the suspicion that, safe at Kelmscott, he and Jane had a laugh or two over Fanny's indignant missive. She was not, of course, invited to the Manor.

With Gabriel's breakdown in the summer of 1872, the financial aspects of her relationship came to the fore, and his family and friends became aware of it, perhaps for the first time; hence Fanny's mercenary reputation. Her anxiety was, of course, well-founded. There was no public system of social welfare beyond that provided by the Poor Law, and if her source of support failed there was a real danger that she would be reduced to destitution and the ultimate humiliation of the workhouse. This was a future faced by many of a better social origin, and all successful figures in the nineteenth century were familiar with appeals on behalf of indigent acquaintances. Earlier in 1872, for example, a childhood friend of the Rossetti family, Elizabeth Rovedino, sent begging letters to both Gabriel and William Michael and might have continued to extract money from them had she not then tried to forge a cheque in Gabriel's name.[26] The middle classes were familiar with such appeals, and all professional men feared ill-health and destitution; in such cases subscriptions would be solicited to save them from utter disgrace. Ned Jones once said he would prefer the workhouse to 'sending round the hat' in this manner.[27] However when Fred Sandys' friends gathered at Cheyne Walk to discuss raising funds to send him to the colonies, he is said to have remarked that with that amount of money he could afford to stay in England.[28] A model had some claim on the artists for whom she had worked, as illustrated by the sad letter sent by Antonia Caiva, one of Ned's best professional models, when she wrote from hospital to ask him for assistance.[29] But generally private charity could not be relied on.

Fanny's worries were thus real ones. But it was not, I think, purely mercenary motives that took her to Cheyne Walk at the very beginning of Gabriel's collapse. When the paranoid delusions became acute at the beginning of June 1872, his friends were surprised to find that it was to 'the ancient Fanny' that he turned, rather than, as expected, to Jane.[30] Fanny 'has been in and out constantly,' wrote Bell Scott.[31] She was not considered as a companion, however, or perhaps did not offer herself, when Gabriel was despatched to Scotland. It is evident that her welfare was important to him for the second letter he wrote to Perthshire was to his brother, about Fanny's furniture; she was anxious lest

her husband Timothy Hughes, or his creditors, should seize any
of the movables at 36 Royal Avenue, to pay his debts. This fear
reminds us, incidentally, of another source for Fanny's sense of
insecurity, in that she could not possess any income or property in
her own right; everything she owned belonged in law to her
husband. In fact, the first Married Women's Property Act was
passed this same year, but Fanny may not have been aware of this.
Gabriel's solution was to sign an affidavit, stating that the
furniture belonged to him, and that he was transferring ownership
to his brother.[32] This was presumably to enable William Michael
to protect Fanny's belongings from seizure should Gabriel be
certified insane and a possession order be taken out by Hughes. It
was further suggested that in order to protect Fanny's tenancy of
36 Royal Avenue, the lease also be transferred to William Michael,
but the latter demurred at this. There was also some discussion of
buying the house for her.

At this point it emerged that in order to insure Fanny against
want, Gabriel had been contributing to a savings fund to purchase
a house for her. A house which could be rented out whole or as
lodgings was something many lower-middle-class people aspired
to in the nineteenth century; it offered a secure income that could
never fail. Fanny apparently estimated that £400–500 was required, and by the middle of 1872 Gabriel had already contributed
£100. This was the origin of the 'Elephant's Hole', later alluded to
as a fund that forever needed adding to; 'Elephant' was now
Fanny's main nickname. In order to discharge what he felt to be
his responsibilities to her before he became either totally insane or
bankrupt – both distinct possibilities – Gabriel now proposed
using £650 from the sale of his blue china collection to buy Fanny's
house.[33] This seemed reasonable to Brown and to William
Michael, who commented that it would 'in any event clear off all
Fanny claims',[34] and when Bell Scott disagreed, Brown wrote to
explain, 'You understand that to G. Fanny is the one responsibility
that presses on him at this moment.'[35] Gabriel himself told his
brother that he was more anxious to provide for Fanny than pay
any creditor and asked William Michael to call on her. He even
suggested that he might invite her to call on him at his office in the
government buildings at Somerset House – a suggestion that
William Michael may have regarded as confirming Gabriel's
derangement. In the first anxious days and weeks of his

breakdown, Fanny's needs were at the forefront of Gabriel's mind, and he was not so insane as to ignore her plight. To Fanny herself, he wrote, 'I am anxious that you should not begin spending that £100 you had laid by, & sooner than you should do that, I would send money at once . . .'[36]

Another of her worries was that she could not rely on Gabriel's family and friends to carry out his wishes should he become incapable and that, through personal dislike or moral disapproval, they would let her starve. Gabriel tried to reassure her, saying she should 'not suppose that either William or Brown are anything but true friends to you'. As for himself, he repeated his pledge: 'You are the only person whom it is my duty to provide for, and you may be sure that I should do my utmost as long as there was a breath in my body or a penny in my purse.'[37] This was unequivocal recognition of a duty that, customarily, was owed only to kin or a spouse: Gabriel was treating Fanny as he might his wife.

Her actual husband Timothy, whom Gabriel called her 'in-cubus', died in November 1872. Any hopes she may still have had of marrying Gabriel, however, were now ruled out, both by his breakdown and by his relationship with Jane. There is evidence that Fanny resented Jane, which is not surprising in view of the fact that although both women had come from a similar social background, Jane had both married well and had won the devotion of another man, whereas Fanny's situation was very insecure. At the very end of Gabriel's life, Fanny abused Jane to his young companion Hall Caine, making 'charges which I knew to have been lies'.[38] Whether her charges were true or false cannot be guessed, but Fanny clearly disliked Jane sufficiently to slander her. After his breakdown Gabriel went back to Kelmscott and Fanny had to be content with regular payments and friendly letters, rather like an ex-wife. The letters concerned her welfare: advice on obtaining the best prices for the pictures he had given her and contributions to the Elephant's Hole. At least ten cheques were sent during 1873.[39] They were sometimes accompanied by comic sketches that suggest Gabriel still felt a good deal of affection for 'good old Fan'. One showed an elephant stowing a pile of cheques into a wall-safe. Another was about a 'mislaid' Chinese jar, depicting an elephant digging with a spade, the text reading:

Hullow Elephant! Just you find that pot! Do you think I don't know you've wrapped your trunk round it and dug a hole for it in the garden? Just you find it, for I can't do without it.

P.S. I promise faithfully to return it when I have painted it. But you know in fact that you have no business with it, as I never gave it you, and now I want it badly for my picture. You shall have it back quite safe when done with which will be before long.[40]

She understood that she could not go to Kelmscott, but was upset when she discovered that Alexa Wilding, the model to whom Gabriel paid a retainer, had been there to pose in the summer of 1873; he replied to her message, 'I am very sorry indeed to disappoint you – indeed it gives me great pain to do so, as I should like to see you here, but the thing is quite impossible. Please don't ever press the matter again, as it is very distressing to me to refuse, but as long as I remain here it is out of the question.'[41]

On Gabriel's return to London in 1874, her relationship with him remained steady. He completed two portrait drawings of her done in coloured chalks,[42] perhaps as a token of his affection, or as a contribution to the Elephant's Hole. They are glamourized portraits, such as began to dominate his work, and they show her as a fine woman, looking no older than in the pictures done a decade and more earlier; they were his last pictures of Fanny.

Money, however, continued to flow. With one payment went a sketch showing a fat elephant, hands clasped over its middle and a playing card in its trunk, captioned 'Money to the House', and on 25 March 1875 an IOU for £300 was made out in favour of 'Mrs Sarah Hughes'.[43] After Gabriel's death it was revealed that in addition he had given her a total of £1,100 10s 6d, together with, as William Michael firmly believed, several gifts in cash and kind – some of them valuable paintings to which the Rossetti family felt she had no legal claim and had only acquired because Gabriel had never asked for them back. How much this figure was exaggerated owing to jealousy is hard to tell; certainly the family seems to have been shocked to discover just how much of Gabriel's wealth Fanny had shared. It is thought that Mrs Rossetti and Gabriel's sisters were kept in ignorance of her existence, but one letter from Christina suggests otherwise. Thanking her brother for sending a book about elephants, 'whose pathetic ending is truly painful and goes to one's heart', she wrote, 'Delicious is the prosperous elephant ladling out rice to medicants. I wish all Elephants were prosperous.'[44] Fanny made a belated effort to improve upon her education. 'I think you have improved decidedly in your spelling and handwriting,' Gabriel wrote encouragingly in 1875. 'I don't know whether you have been studying hard, but your letters have decidedly improved. I am glad to see an Elephant improving at its time of life.'[45] Fanny was now over forty and the compliment was well-deserved. The only surviving example of her handwriting is from a later date, so the improvement cannot be measured, but it is as fluent and legible as that of any of her contemporaries.

In the summer of 1873 Lucy Madox Brown, Emma's step-daughter, became engaged to William Michael Rossetti. He was forty-three and had been for a long time the chief provider and support of his widowed mother and sisters. Lucy was twenty-nine, 'sweet, gentle and sensible', according to her husband, 'the mainstay of her father's house' and an accomplished painter who had studied in her father's studio.[46] (Emma's daughter, Cathy, who had also studied there, had married Franz Hueffer, a young German-born music critic, in 1872, and her first child, the writer Ford Madox Ford, was born at the end of 1873.) Lucy Brown generously agreed to share her husband's home with his mother and sisters, and began married life in the Rossetti home in Euston Square following her marriage in March 1874. William Michael promised she should have her own room in which to paint, but like Georgie she found that her art was overpowered by the demands of marriage and motherhood: she had six children, including twins, in five years, and gave up painting altogether. There were other troubles too, for the Rossetti women dis-approved of Lucy's lack of religion, which she shared with her husband, and resented her 'enthronement as bride' in their house. Her arrival provoked her sister-in-law Maria to enter an Anglican convent, as she had long thought of doing. Gabriel wrote to tell Fanny that his sister was now 'what is called a Sister of Mercy – one of those old things whom you see going about in a sort of coal-scuttle and umbrella costume';[47] Lucy's response was to offer to paint Maria in her new habit.[48] Despite its disruptive impact on the Euston Square household (leading Mamma and Christina to move to live with aunts), the marriage of Lucy and William Michael brought the Brown and Rossetti families even closer together, while at the same time it seems to have exacerbated the ill-feeling between them and Morris.

This was important to Jane for since Gabriel's breakdown she had been obliged to depend more on her husband. On the eve of the wedding, Morris complained to Georgie's sister Louie that he didn't care for either bride or groom, and that neither of them cared for him, but that he lacked the courage not to attend.[49] In the summer of 1873, a year after Gabriel's breakdown, Jane had again stayed with Gabriel at Kelmscott, while Morris made a second trip to Iceland; there she sat for a large new composition showing *Proserpina*, married half the year to the king of the underworld. This less than flattering allusion to Morris was accompanied by a plan for a poem based on the story 'The Cup of Water', outlined in Chapter 6. Although Jane returned to London in September promising to return soon, in fact she did not do so, pleading ill-health. Gabriel was several times on the point of travelling to town to see her, he told Brown, 'but just as I was starting she telegraphed twice to me to stay here . . .' He added, 'She writes regularly, or I could not stay away.'[50] It is evident that the heat had gone from their affair. The next time Jane saw him was in February 1874, when Jenny and May had measles and she took them to Kelmscott to recuperate. *Prosperina* was finished and sold, and Gabriel spent most of the time drawing May for *Rosa Triplex*, a bedizened picture full of gaudy sentimentality. May returned Gabriel's affection and he aspired to adopt her, a plan which must further have irritated her father, who felt that his country retreat had served too long as convalescent home for his wife's lover. In April Morris wrote to Gabriel, withdrawing from the tenancy. He pleaded both poverty and business commitments, indicating that as Gabriel was living there more or less permanently he should pay the full cost.

The rent of £75 a year was not large and the effect of this withdrawal was not primarily financial. By relinquishing his share of the lease, Morris was preventing Jane from going to Kelmscott without him, for it was improper for a married woman to stay unchaperoned in another man's house. At first Gabriel decided to take up the lease,[51] and when Morris asked for his punt to be sent to London, Gabriel ordered a replacement. He told friends he would be giving up Cheyne Walk and settling in the country permanently. Jane went down for Whitsun week, just before the joint agreement expired, but this was the last occasion she was with him there. For, following a cheerful, crowded visit from the whole Brown clan in June, Gabriel suffered another mental collapse, involving among other things a verbal attack on some anglers and a resurgence of the conviction that every passer-by was conspiring to injure him; within a few weeks he was back at Cheyne Walk, whereupon Morris took over the tenancy of Kelmscott. In July the whole Morris family, accompanied by Phil Burne-Jones, went on holiday together for the first time in some years, visiting Belgium and France. In Bruges, Morris remarked ruefully that he occupied the very same hotel room he and Janey had shared on their honeymoon fourteen years earlier. While abroad, Jane bought Gabriel a pair of Flemish inkstands.[52]

In the autumn Morris drove in another wedge by embarking on the reconstruction of the firm, which he proposed to take into his sole control. This brought about a complete estrangement between him and the Browns, for Brown strongly objected to being bought out, and an unpleasant legal wrangle developed from which the partners never recovered. Ned supported Topsy, while Gabriel backed Brown, and there was a complete rift between families. It says much for the strength of social convention that the women, who had no personal share in the quarrel, did not smooth it over; regretfully but righteously they sided with their men.

It was a particularly anguished time for Emma, for in November 1874 her son Nolly suddenly sickened and died, at the age of twenty. This was a severe blow to Brown, too, and must have aggravated his sense of injustice over being frozen out of the firm which he had done so much to sustain. Nolly had been something of a prodigy and personal grief was compounded by a sense of lost artistic and literary potential. Jane's position was difficult, for she had links with both sides in the dispute. Gabriel in fact arranged for his share of the compensation paid by Morris to the other partners to be invested on Jane's behalf; the sum was thought to be around £1,000 and was apparently meant as a fund on which she could draw for anything she did not want to ask her husband to pay for. This may be interpreted as a final dig at Topsy or as Gabriel's last attempt to provide Janey with the security he had not been able to give her. Either way, it illustrates the dependency of married women.[53]

Gabriel's residual feelings towards his former friend were
expressed in his scribbled comic sketch entitled 'The Death of
Topsy' and written after the dissolution of the firm. In this Mrs
George Wardle, wife of the manager of Morris & Co, is depicted
as replaying her real-life role as murderess Madeline Smith by
giving Morris a poisoned cup of coffee. After his dramatic
death, a spirit medium remarks that Topsy is a very
low-class spirit, since his language is so foul and his conduct so
coarse.[54] But Morris was far from being a domestic tyrant and
there is much to admire in the decisiveness that he displayed, albeit
with some insensitivity. He took firm and unconditional responsibility for the welfare of Jane and her children, and at the same time
placed no demands on his wife, allowing her almost complete
freedom. He showed no further jealousy of Gabriel and Jane spent
much of the winter of 1875–6 with her lover in Bognor, until she
became aware that his paranoia was harmful to her daughters.[55] At
Bognor she sat for one of Gabriel's last major paintings of her, the
alarming and lurid *Astarte Syriaca*, a figure which is both one of the
last legendary women and a forerunner of the fearful females of
Expressionism.

Astarte Syriaca is not in any sense a portrait or even a
representation of Jane, although we recognize her features in it. Its
distortions seem to mark a distance between artist and model, and
it seems to me that the model's active contribution to the picture
was in fact very slight: most of its meaning comes from notions in
the artist's mind rather than from what he saw, or from any
collaboration with the sitter. This is consonant with what we
know of the painter's state of mind at this date, and with his
relationship with Jane. It is rather a representation of Woman, as
were many of Rossetti's late works such as *Silence*, *The Bower
Meadow*, *Pandora*, *Penelope*, *La Ghirlandata*, *Fiammetta*, *A Sea Spell*,
The Day Dream and *Mnemosyne*. In these, Woman is the sole
subject, removed from association with the everyday world and
elevated on to a mythic plane. (Burne-Jones's work also contains
many examples of this.) This is clearly different from the 'picture
tells a story' approach that dominated art in the earlier part of the
century and was by no means confined to Pre-Raphaelite work,
but was seen across the whole field of painting. Part of the reason
for this presentation of Woman is to be found in art history and
the ideas of *l'art pour l'art*, but formal and aesthetic questions are

only part of a picture's meaning, and the curious domination of painting by large, glamorous images of women in the late nineteenth century requires further inquiry. If confronted at all, the issue of why women were so chosen and so presented in late Victorian art is usually answered in quasi-Freudian terms. This vision of woman as a desperately alluring but somehow threatening siren is felt to reflect an unconscious fear of women, leading the painters to express their latent feelings in images that combine beauty with danger. It is the concept of the *femme fatale*, which added greatly to what is labelled *fin-de-siècle* or Decadence, when artists 'gazed, fascinated but repelled, at women of a curious frigidity, cold but sensual, erotic but invulnerable – Flaubert's Salammbô, Nerval's Aurelia . . . Their attitudes are piped with a fear of female malevolence, and characteristically they attempt to control this fear by boiling down the variety of individual experience into the image of a single symbolic figure . . .'[56] This ignores the fact that in this form of representation, women are rendered decorative, depersonalized; they become passive figures rather than characters in a story or drama. It was a line that led to the cult of the chorus girl and the Edwardian actress, and thence to the first movie stars, culminating in glossy pin-ups and calendar girls where within a pretentiously artistic context, women are reduced to an aesthetic arrangement of sexual parts, for male fantasies. It is hard to see late-Victorian 'high art' pictures of women as essentially different in content.

However, the relation between the representation of women in art and their actual position in society is more difficult to determine, although a study of the changing representations of women in nineteenth-century art would be a rewarding field. Several strands of analysis might be employed, tracing for example the stirrings of feminist revolt and the ways in which men responded, feeling threatened by this and other alterations in the world around them. Making women into grotesque decorative objects could be a way of putting them in their place, and of working off male aggression.

It is also true that many middle-class women did become more decorative as the century progressed, in the sense of having less hard manual work within the house and more money to spend on their clothes and appearance. Cosmetics and 'beauty products' were among the century's new industries, aimed largely at women. With servants and labour-saving domestic appliances, including piped water and electricity, women's role within the home became more managerial and, in the highest social echelons, almost entirely 'idle'. The function of Society women was almost wholly that of conspicuous consumption, displaying their husbands' economic status through their pursuit of luxury and adornment. In this context painting may be said to reflect a trend in exaggerated form. Upper-middle-class women were indeed becoming decorative objects, as their frustrated daughters complained when barred from higher education and professional careers.

But the representations of women were not simple reflections of their position but also a means of structuring and defining, even enforcing it. At an ideological level, women were required to be like the paintings – alluring and silent rather than active and equal – in a correspondence that ultimately defended the interests of men. There are only a few equivalent pictorial representations of male figures in Victorian art, although the complexities of nineteenth-century sexuality should not be forgotten and simple analyses are often crude. It can be said, however, that complex notions of female dependency and gender roles were articulated through art in ways we are only beginning to understand. In this process Rossetti's art played a key role.

At Bognor, at the time of *Astarte Syriaca*, Jane came to the decision to end her relationship with Gabriel. She later told Wilfrid Blunt that she had been very much in love with Gabriel, but 'when I found he was ruining himself with chloral and that I could do nothing to prevent it I left off going to him'.[57] On another occasion she dated the end of their love to 1875.[58] She left Bognor early in 1876, having apparently come to an arrangement with Gabriel about their correspondence, for on 30 April he drew up a memorandum of instructions in the event of his sudden death, specifying that certain sealed packets of letters should be burnt.[59] These must have been Jane's, and it appears the order was carried out, for few of her letters to Gabriel survive. It seems she, too, had a bonfire, for when finally revealed, her treasured collection of love letters contained only those dating from the early years of 1868–9, and those from 1877 and later.[60] The correspondence that would illuminate the most passionate and private period of their affair was thus destroyed.

16

In the summer of 1876 a severe blow struck the Morris family when fifteen-year-old Jenny, the elder daughter, suddenly developed epilepsy. For the past few years she had been attending one of the new-style girls' day schools where academic subjects rather than accomplishments were top of the curriculum, and she had proved herself an able, advanced pupil, who was confidently expected to be one of the rising generation of girls for whom the recently opened university colleges for women were founded. Epilepsy brought all that to an end. Popular superstition, combined with the fact that repeated fits, for which no medication was available, left the brain clouded and successively weaker, meant that she was henceforth treated as a mentally backward invalid, who could never be alone and who was allowed to do little or nothing for herself. From her letters, it is clear that Jenny did not lose her wits, but the bright, serious student vanished and the one concern of all around her was the frequency and severity of her attacks. The condition affected the whole family, for their responsibility for her welfare had no limit and yet whatever assistance they gave could never be of much help. Her father was very upset, especially as he associated her epilepsy with his own uncontrollable rages, fearing it was inherited, and there were those among his friends who thought him less than stoical. 'One of the sources of embarrassment in his more intimate letters,' wrote Morris's biographer, 'is the perpetual recurrence of Jenny's state of health from day to day.'[1] This is also true of Jane's correspondence, but her distress was less public: she preferred to bear her sorrows in silence, with all the 'resource in despair' at her command. Her self-possession was legendary and it was now badly needed. At the same time, it is my guess, reading the family letters that survive from this date onwards, that Jenny's illness brought her parents closer together than they had been for over a decade.

After epilepsy was diagnosed, Jane took both girls to the seaside and then, in August, to Kelmscott, where Morris joined them. The whole family, with Ned, Phil and Margaret, were together at Crom Price's tower near Broadway on 4 September, and then Jane accepted an invitation from Rosalind Howard to spend the winter on the Italian Riviera. Though it cannot have been believed to do much for epilepsy, this was undoubtedly felt to be healthful and beneficial in other ways, and perhaps even educational for May, who was taken from school at the same time as her sister and never completed her formal education. By early December they were installed at Oneglia.

Rosalind Howard was an eccentric, strong-willed aristocrat of 'dominating character and impetuous temperament'. She was five years younger than Jane, had married the heir to the earldom of Carlisle and had had eleven children in twenty years. As was the custom of her class, she was not much involved in their upbringing, but her personality was an inescapable influence. She was extremely opinionated and demanding, and as her daughter's memoir recorded, she could talk uninterrupted for hours.[2] Her annual Italian holidays 'sounded like fairy tales' to the younger children left behind, until they went too, and discovered the pains of 'far too much aching necks in galleries and churches – five hours a day and hours of reading aloud at night'. With her strict prejudices over sex, drink and privilege went genuine generosity over money, interesting conversation and a rebellious radical idealism, and one can only assume that Jane enjoyed her company, for she went again to Italy with the Howards the following winter.

While they were there, Morris wrote brief, practical letters and apologized for not making them longer. 'I am one and you are three,' was one explanation, but he was much occupied, both by managing the firm on which the family depended even more, since Jenny's illness precluded marriage, and by new, energetic political activities. One letter provides a glimpse of Jane's role at home, showing that she continued to handle the embroidery business after the move from Queen Square to Horrington House.

Her absence abroad caused Morris some trouble, for one of the needlewomen employed by the firm had written to say that:

> she only got 13/– for 8 days work at Bessy's & so was obliged to give up working there: of course she is: but she clearly didn't intend working there: am I to give her more than £2 for the table cover (less the floss silk) which she has just sent in. She says you gave her that for it and had done an eighth yourself. I suppose Bessy will be able to give her the chairback she asks for: she wants more silk too: why didn't she ask for all this before you went . . .?[3]

This winter Morris was also house-hunting, in a search which was to lead to the home later known as Kelmscott House in Hammersmith, and which seems to mark an effective marital reconciliation. From Italy, Jane objected to Hammersmith as too far from town; she still favoured the fashionable districts of Knightsbridge and Kensington, and would have liked, she remarked, to inhabit a 'bran-new house' except that they were too expensive. Morris, who had recently been active in the foundation of the Society for the Protection of Ancient Buildings, was not to be persuaded; and in any case they had not the money to spare. By contemporary middle-class standards, their housing requirements were relatively modest: a room for each of the girls, a sitting room and bedroom for Jane, one large or two small rooms for Morris to sleep and work in, plus the usual drawing room and dining room and servants' quarters. In April 1878, just before setting out to join the others in Italy, Morris wrote to say that he had taken the lease on the Hammersmith house, despite Jane's objections. He argued that there was plenty of room to accommodate three servants, and promised to purchase a pony and chaise, to minimize the house's isolation. Gabriel, with whom Jane continued to correspond, was still sniping at Topsy's lack of conjugal care and insisted that the house would not do, as the basement was dark and liable to flooding, 'which I really do not think a wise choice', he wrote to her, 'if *you* are a person to be at all considered in the matter'.[4]

But this was simply ill-humour. The year before, Gabriel had suffered another acute mental breakdown, through which his mother and sister had nursed him, and which left him melancholy and reclusive. Some feeling between him and Jane remained, but it was a shadow. On her return from Italy she put off seeing him, excusing herself on the grounds that she had lost weight as a result of an infection and hated 'to appear before you as a Guy after this long absence', signing herself 'Your affectionate Scarecrow'.[5] Gabriel was rather upset. But Jane had found new strength in a realism which was very different from the romantic fantasies of their earlier relationship. At the end of the year she wrote soberly, 'Dear Gabriel, it would be but a mockery if I were to wish you a happy Xmas. I can only say that I hope & trust you may not be suffering more than your last letter led me to expect. Always yours affectionately, Janey.'[6]

When they met, her attitude was one of 'gentle kindness'[7] and it is clear that in correspondence she did what she could to lift his spirits. 'I really did not know what to say to such a very sad letter,' she wrote apologizing for a belated reply, urging him to write more cheerfully. As a result, most of the letters that still exist from Gabriel to Jane consist of malicious tales about Charles Howell and suggested remedies for various ailments: Jane continued to suffer from a bad back. She welcomed any drawings or poems he wished to send since such offerings indicated an improvement in his state of mind and, perhaps, brought back happier memories.

The intense, brooding females of his last paintings have contributed to the image of Jane as a silent, morose woman, suffering silently on a sofa. Her health was clearly important. Visiting Rosalind at the Howards' ancestral home of Naworth in Cumbria in the summer of 1879, she wrote to tell Gabriel of some sea-baths where, she had heard, 'one is made into a kind of pie with the sea-weed, when it is supposed that one absorbs vast quantities of ozone'.[8] Rosalind was also a hypochondriac. 'What was it that made us all feel she had suffered terribly?' wrote her son-in-law, suggesting that perhaps 'self-pity gave rise to a rather mythical heart and lack of exercise',[9] and it is possible that Jane's ailments were of the same sort. When she heard that Marie Stillman, after various travels and a number of children, was again sitting to Gabriel, she bemoaned the fact that she herself could no longer do so. 'So much has Happiness done for one and Misery for the other!' she cried melodramatically.[10] But this was only one side of her existence, as her letters to Crom Price about holiday visits to Broadway Tower illustrate. 'We can bring down plenty of provisions from London so that we need only cook for amusement when we feel inclined,' she wrote in the summer of 1877; 'May's excitement is tremendous . . . she wants to sleep on the top of the Tower.'[11] On another occasion she and May stayed at the Tower by themselves, taking their own food and wine. 'We went out early this morning to enjoy the lark's song,' Jane wrote to their host, adding, 'we made friends with the poor old dog, admired the hills, got very cold, and came in and got up a good fire.' This time she brought a sofa with her because of a 'vivid recollection of the legless one of last year'. Crom's Tower was rather spartanly furnished.[12]

Gabriel died in 1882. In one of his later letters, he wrote that his feelings for her were 'as fresh and unchanged . . . as ever, though all else is withered and gone. This you would never believe, but if life and fate had willed to link us together you wd. have found true what you cannot think to be true when – alas! – untried.'[13] Jane received in his will those portraits of her she wished to keep and, as we have seen, she also preserved his letters and poems. These were inherited by May and bequeathed to the British Museum on condition they were not made public until fifty years after Jane's death. This was an index of the importance both women placed on them, for when opened, the letters were discovered to be not at all compromising. Jane was not given, nor did she make, opportunities for expressing her feelings, but at the time of the posthumous exhibition of Gabriel's work at the Burlington Gallery in 1884 she wrote from Lyme Regis to Theodore Watts (the solicitor who among other things had handled the money from the firm invested on her behalf by Gabriel) thanking him for sending some reviews. She continued:

I suppose one must regard them as praising the works. But how they would have enraged the painter himself.

Fancy his hearing it said that his finest work was done about 1866! He would have gone raving mad on the spot even though it had been but a remark of the pink pig's (Quilter). The swinish tastes of the said creature are not to be wondered at, but it is little surprise to me that Colvin and one or two others of the more decent art-critics should have taken something of the same view of works painted about that time. I agree heartily with those who consider the *early* work the best, but I think the same might be said of most men's works; there is a freshness, an

interest in everything, a wealth of invention that is seldom seen
except in the productions of the first few years of manhood, and
all this without questioning the sanity of a man. That Gabriel
was mad was but too true, no one knows better than myself, but
that his work after 1868 was worthless (as Gosse has the
impudence to assert) I deny.

    I don't know why I am writing all this to you, but I feel that I
want to talk to someone about him. I am not likely to be in
town for a very long time to have any actual talk with you.
Jenny is very ill still, I am almost in despair about her . . .[14]

The directness of this letter, with its plain use of the term 'mad',
combined with the reticence of the personal feeling expressed,
is a powerful and moving testimony to Jane's intellect and
personality.

Gabriel's madness was a recurrent problem to Fanny. Her
comfortable, companionable relationship with him, and the
regular donations to the Elephant's Hole, continued through the
1870s, disturbed only by occasional allegations of neglect. In
August 1873 Fanny seems to have believed that Alexa Wilding
was boasting about the presents she had been receiving from
Gabriel, and wrote to complain; Gabriel hastened to reassure
her.[15] The nature of their relationship may be judged from a
collection of short, undated notes, the equivalent of quick
telephone calls, from the years 1874–7. When in London, Gabriel
relied on Fanny for company. 'Dear Fan,' began one letter. 'It is
half past 7. I have put off the dinner to 8, hoping to see you. Do
come.' Another read: 'Why did you not come yesterday evening?
This is the third day that I am absolutely alone.' In these notes
Gabriel's signature, which was always 'R' to Fanny, came to stand
for 'Rhinoceros', in affectionate juxtaposition to her 'Elephant'.
Thus, apologetically: 'An old Rhinoceros was nasty last night &
his horn is wet with tears which he has shed on the subject. He
wants a good Elephant to come down as soon as possible & he will
give it something to amuse it.' Or, desperately: 'GOOD
ELEPHANT DO COME DOWN OLD RHINOCEROS IS
UNHAPPY DO COME TO OLD RHINOCEROS.'[16] It is clear
that more often than not Fanny obeyed these summonses and

Gabriel told Theodore Watts that her company was 'at times almost necessary' to him.[17] She was good-humoured and tolerant when many other friends felt awkward and embarrassed to be with Gabriel for long. His paranoia never left him and towards the end of this period, as the shaky handwriting of some of the later notes shows, he was moving towards another breakdown. At the beginning of 1877 George Hake left his service, 'owing to Rossetti's unprovoked attacks', which he, perhaps with unconscious male bias, interpreted as Fanny's fault. 'That woman,' he wrote to his father, 'has been planning the whole thing for the last month or two and has gained such an ascendancy over DGR that he is really not accountable for his action.' He alleged a plot to oust him, using a servant as 'a spy of Fanny's, every action and word having been retailed to her and thence to DGR . . .'[18]

Whether this was true or not, Gabriel was heading for another severe mental collapse, which came to a crisis in the summer of 1877. As a result Fanny felt there was a concerted effort to exclude her from his life. The details of his collapse are not clear, but in August Gabriel's family, which now included his sister-in-law Lucy and her father, who was his staunchest friend, decided that he must be sent away to recover. They had difficulty persuading him to go voluntarily and in the midst of arrangements for departure to Herne Bay, Fanny turned up unannounced, as William Michael complained to Lucy, 'much to the derangement of all rational projects for G's welfare'.[19] Once arrived in Kent, Gabriel was in too bad (or mad) a state to reply to Fanny's anxious letters; eventually he wrote sadly that he could 'only advise you to take the best step in life that you can for your own advantage, and quite to forget about me'. He told her that he did not expect to be able to work again and anticipated living quietly with his mother and sister. Altogether, he was deeply grieved, but felt it best if she ceased to rely on him in any way.[20] There is no doubt that Gabriel wrote this letter, but one wonders how much of it was dictated, or at least suggested. Fanny's presence in Gabriel's life at such times of crisis was a source of anxiety and irritation to his family, who feared, not without reason, that he might suddenly give away all his property and all his paintings in order to preserve her from want in her old age.

As a result, Fanny received what she felt to be 'cruel' treatment from her adversaries, whom she identified as the Rossettis and

Dunn. Unsure whether Gabriel would ever be fit enough to return to Cheyne Walk, they demanded Fanny's keys to the house, and forbade her to go there. She was extremely upset at this, and moreover she was behind with her rent at Royal Avenue, which only Gabriel would pay. In anger and distress she wrote a letter of protest and sent the keys in a packet to him at Herne Bay. He replied:

> . . . you seem to forget that you are writing to one who is at present a helpless cripple, with no means of judging as to future livelihood. If I recover the use of my hands, you will be my first care as always. If not, I shall myself be living on charity. At present I only live by exhausting a little borrowed money. Where the next is to come from I have not the least idea.
>
> What sum do you wish me to send you? Tell me, and I will see about it. I do not know what keys you are sending me nor have I opened the parcel. I am much too ill to be receiving angry reproaches, but I still hope to see you again before long and that you may then understand me better.[21]

Fanny's response to this, precipitated by panic, was to leave Royal Avenue, without leaving a forwarding address.

She turned to a new friend named John Bernhard Schott, a widower with two sons, who was the son of a bandsman and was later described in what seems an amalgam of prejudices as 'a misshapen German Jew'.[22] She had met him earlier in the year and he had proved useful to Gabriel, bringing possible clients to the house, inspecting new premises and collecting chloral prescriptions from various pharmacies around town.[23] With Schott's assistance, Fanny used her savings to acquire the tenancy of the Rose Tavern in Jermyn Street, off Piccadilly. She eventually wrote to Gabriel to let him know what she had done; he replied that her letter had greatly upset and worried him. 'To be uncertain of your whereabouts and well-being is greatly to add to my anxieties . . .' he wrote, adding:

> If you had told me that you meant to take such a step as leaving your house at once, I would much rather have sent you the money . . . If I return to Chelsea I shall be just as much in want of your help as before . . . I know what you say of your

willingness to give me all is perfectly true, for you have sometime proved it, but it will not do to desert me and leave me in utter solitude . . .[24]

Fanny replied, in her one surviving letter:

My dear R,
    You surely cannot be angry with me for doing what I have done after receiving such a letter from you telling me I must forget you and get my own living. You could not expect me to remain in the neighbourhood after what had taken place. Dunn frequently passed my place on the other side of the way and in the middle of the avenuye [*sic*] with a sneer on his face and I concluded that he was rejoicing in my downfall. Of course my intentions were to remain there until I saw you again. I have been living on my savings for some time but your letters led me to suppose you were tired of me. You shall never say that I forsook you although I felt it very much when another woman was put in my place when not wanted the keys taken from me and that is the way I was treated for taking your part. I hope I shall see you again and be with you as before but I never wish to meet any of your friends after the cruel way in which I have been treated.
    I must tell you my address is now 96 Jermyn St, which is the St James's St end and is an hotel. I keep three servants and an accountant and Mr Schott still interests himself for me. It im [*sic*] better than a lodging house where I should often be cheated out of rent and get people I did not like. I must impress on your mind that I have *none of your* pictures in any part of the house excepting my bedroom and private sitting room. I took this step thinking I should never be with you again and thought it a certainty.
    Trusting that you are getting right again I remain your
Aff Fanny.[25]

Despite the lack of punctuation and occasional misspellings, this letter conveys a sense of dignity and realism. John Schott was evidently a businesslike fellow who understood the irregularity of Fanny's position, and it may have been at his suggestion that, when he recovered, Gabriel signed a formal statement certifying that Fanny was the legal owner of all the pictures and furniture she had obtained from him over the years; he may also have found the 'accountant' to keep the books at the Rose Tavern. Certainly Fanny had cause to be grateful to Schott, and in November 1879, at the age of forty-five, she married him. This was not romance, and she did not desert Gabriel as a result, but continued to see and care for him. In return, Gabriel interested himself in Schott's concerns, notably in the education of his younger son Cecil, who was good at drawing. Cecil's work was shown to Bell Scott and to Fred Shields, and he eventually became the latter's studio assistant.[26]

Fanny remained Gabriel's most faithful friend until the end. In 1881, the faithful Dunn left Cheyne Walk: his wages were unpaid and his 'remonstrances' over the increasing doses of chloral taken by Gabriel were construed as 'censoriousness and coercion'.[27] He was replaced by the young Hall Caine, who was perhaps more innocent and indulgent. In September, they planned a holiday in the Lake District and Gabriel invited Fanny to accompany them. Caine was despatched to collect her from Jermyn Street, and they travelled north to the Vale of St John. Caine's knowledge of her character and role in Gabriel's life virtually all derived from this short acquaintance, and in retrospect he classified her as a baleful influence. She gossiped to him over breakfast, since Gabriel rose too late to join them, and on one occasion abused Gabriel's 'friends of the middle period', such as Morris, Swinburne and Ned, whom she believed did not like her, and made charges against Jane. Gabriel, coming into the room, merely laughed and said 'But who believes anything said by the Elephant?'[28] This may have been so, and Fanny's allegations may have been exaggerated, but evidently she still felt that Jane had threatened her own relationship with Gabriel in the mid-1860s.

There were happier moments in Cumbria, however; the ill-assorted trio climbed a local hill and Gabriel wrote to Schott: 'For a portion of the descent I found it convenient to adopt a broader natural basis than the feet, while Fanny lay down and almost burst with laughter.' She was, he continued, 'wonderfully active, climbs and takes leaps and looks wonderfully well'. A few days later she and Caine made another ascent, and Gabriel remarked 'she climbs as if she had done it all her life'.[29] It is a pleasant picture of two portly Londoners amusing themselves cheerfully on the Lakeland fells.

Caine however claimed to believe that Fanny went to Cumberland with a more sinister intent. 'One morning when Rossetti and I were out walking together,' he recalled, 'he asked me if I would make his will. He wanted to leave everything he possessed to F. I refused flatly.'[30] This refusal was followed by Fanny's abrupt return to London, and as a result it is alleged that she had gone to the Lake District with the sole intention of bullying Gabriel into making his will in her favour. This may have been so: she had some right to be regarded as his common-law widow. But it is equally likely that her presence reawakened Gabriel's concern for her welfare and security, and that he attempted, without much determination, to make a final gesture of support. But he also seems to have realized that his family and friends would resist any provision he tried to make for her.

After his return to London, it seems that it was decreed she should have no more direct contact with him. In November he sent a sad note to her, saying that 'such difficulties are now arising with my family that it will be impossible for me to see you here till I write again',[31] and it appears that they met again only once. According to Caine, Fanny called at Cheyne Walk to ask for £200. Gabriel was too ill to write out a cheque and Caine refused. Instead, he told Fanny to leave the house, and called a cab for her. When it arrived, 'she came out of the studio carrying a large chalk drawing. I made no objection. Simply held open the door and shut it behind her.'[32] This was the last time Fanny saw Gabriel. His will was made, leaving small bequests to friends, including Jane, and the residue to his brother. Fanny was not mentioned. She was deliberately kept from his deathbed at Birchington in Kent by his family and by Caine, despite his last request for news. 'Have you heard anything of Fanny?' Gabriel asked Caine, who replied 'Nothing at all.' 'Would you tell me if you had?' Gabriel inquired. Caine answered 'If you asked me, yes.' 'My poor mistress,' commented Gabriel sadly.[33] She was not told of his death in April 1882, nor invited to his funeral. She must have heard, since she wrote to William Michael, who carefully delayed his reply until the morning of the funeral, when it was too late for her to attend. The prospect of her meeting Mrs Rossetti and Christina at the graveside was no doubt a chief consideration, but it is sad to see her so firmly excluded. She was by this date approaching fifty years of age and had long since given up harlotry. But respectable society would never admit her to its ranks.

The 1880s were good years for Georgie. Her life was naturally overshadowed by the greater fame and achievement of her husband and that of her 'loving friend', but this should not obscure the fact that the years of Georgie's maturity saw a widening and strengthening of her activities. She always perceived her most important role in life as that of mother and aunt. Parenthood is often biographically neglected, and I want for a moment to look more closely at Georgie's experience in this respect, partly because of what it tells us about her, and partly because it was characteristic of the age and class to which she belonged. She was delighted with motherhood and perhaps found it a substitute for her lost pursuit of art; from the beginning she approached her task with care and thought. Before Phil was a year old, she was working out a method of childcare not then common. Her son, she wrote, had 'a happy disposition together with a passionate temper . . . and it is wonderful how already I can make his little heart understand which of the two I like best to see'. In accordance with good Victorian practice, the first task was to teach a child obedience, but Georgie aimed to do it with kindness.[34] When Phil was three and a half, his aunt Aggie wrote home of a typical instance of child's play by the whole family:

> Yesterday afternoon before dinner Ned had done his day's work, so ostensibly for Phil, but we enjoyed it, we had a romp in the dining room, to forget the cold and wet outside. We pretended to be strolling players who did the most ridiculously easy things and expected money for it. Georgie solemnly spun a top and made a string go under it while spinning. Ned played wildly on a violin with three strings while we danced: Phil sat on the table and put his hands thro' a hoop as an infant prodigy . . .[35]

This happy children's atmosphere was maintained when Phil's sister Margaret was born and when the family moved to the Grange in Fulham, where the Morris girls and all the Macdonald cousins were welcome visitors. Georgie's nephew, Rudyard

Kipling, recalled that there was a rocking horse in the nursery at the Grange, 'and a table that, tilted up on two chairs, made a toboggan slide of the best'; in addition, there was 'an incessant come and go of young people and grown-ups all willing to play with us – except an elderly person called "Browning" who took no proper interest in the skirmishes which happened to be raging at his entry'. At the centre, and 'best of all, immeasurably, was the Beloved Aunt herself', reading stories about pirates or the Arabian Nights, and allowing Ruddy to pump the organ in the studio as she played while Uncle Ned painted. Should 'Uncle Topsy' come in, 'full of business of picture frames or stained glass or general denunciations', it could be hard to keep pumping, but if the organ 'ran out in squeals', Aunt Georgie would be sorry, but never angry. Ruddy's sister Trix confirmed that Georgie was the perfect mother and mother-substitute; the emotional turmoils that swept through the older generation's lives in the late 1860s and early 1870s did not, it seems, touch the children.[36]

Yet despite her love for children, she failed to perceive that Ruddy was both unhappy and ill-treated in the 'house of desolation' at Southsea where he and Trix boarded while their parents were in India. Here he was beaten, bullied and terrorized until his sight became distorted and he suffered a nervous collapse into a form of infantile insanity, whereupon his mother was summoned. After his recovery, Georgie begged to know why Ruddy had told her nothing of his misery. He had been afraid, he said later, of losing his one glimpse of paradise, by being denied holidays at the Grange.

By comparison, Phil was well-treated and even rather spoiled. Early in the summer of 1874, a Secret Society met at the Grange, whose members were Jenny and May Morris, Phil and Margaret Jones, and whose activities were recorded and preserved. The importance attached to gender meant Phil, the only boy, was declared leader of the group, although Jenny was the oldest.[37] His sense of superiority and privilege were rudely shattered a few weeks later, however, when he was despatched to a public boarding school at the age of eleven. 'How we came finally to decide upon sending him from home to school does not matter,' his mother later wrote, probably concealing a tale of conflict.[38] There was no pressing reason to send Phil away. He was already attending one of the best day schools in the country and the public schools were notorious for their hierarchical bullying and juvenile homosexuality. It may have been felt that Phil was too soft, too spoilt, and that he would benefit from being separated from Ned, whose indulgence and egotism were not perhaps the best of influences. There was also Ned's growing consciousness of social position. From the start of his career he had, as he put it, 'stuck in the name "Burne" . . . in the natural yearning of mortal man not to be lost in the million of Joneses . . . solely from dread of annihilation',[39] and he could not but have been aware, as the century proceeded, that many forms of social advancement and privilege accompanied what later became known as 'the old-boy network' of men who had shared the same upper-middle-class education. Increasingly, it was a public-school background that defined the status of a 'gentleman'.

As early as 1872 Ned made inquiries about a school for Phil, focusing on Marlborough, Topsy's old school, and his chief concern is evident from the questions he put to Charley Faulkner at Oxford regarding the school's current reputation, or rather 'principally what sort of chaps they send to university'.[40] Morris himself had hated Marlborough: 'Nothing that has happened to me since,' he told Phil in a misguided attempt to cheer his first term, 'has given me quite as much pleasure as coming home for holidays.'[41] But he did not dissuade Ned from his plan, and indeed the two men went to the school on a visit of inspection. When the time came for Phil to depart, Georgie's stoicism failed her and she wept, leaving Ned to deliver his son to his fate, and to answer his miserable letters. 'Never mind,' began Ned's second reply bracingly, 'I know you will get happy soon . . .' It is clear that he wanted Phil to be toughened, to learn how to endure and fight. 'When you are a man it will be much the same,' he wrote, 'only backs of hairbrushes are not used, but things are more tormenting . . . I want you to know the world . . . that nothing afterwards may take you by surprise.'[42] As if to mitigate their cruelty, Phil's parents sent a watch and a box of paints as well as the customary hamper on his twelfth birthday at the beginning of October, but when Georgie visited the school at half term she did not report to his houseparents on the bullying he endured, no doubt knowing that in the closed world of a public school, a sneak is worse regarded than a coward. Ned belatedly promised to pay for boxing lessons in the holidays, so that Phil could learn to hit back. It was all very sad.

Equally sad was the way Phil's expensive education seems to have done him little good and perhaps harmed him for life by reinforcing snobbish values. He was not academically successful, but attended Oxford under Faulkner's special care, and his talent for witty illustration was hardly developed, owing to Ned's disdain for such a trivial form of art. His father's tendency to steal the limelight also had a blighting effect on Phil, who grew up to be an edgy, idle young man with ambitions of moving in high society. He joined a slightly fast aristocratic 'set' and aspired to entertain in style, on the basis of his father's hard-earned and carefully invested wealth. It was Phil for whom the Burne-Jones name was formally hyphenated, and he who begged Ned to accept the offered baronetcy in 1894. Georgie, with her strong low-church ethic, disapproved of fashionable society and of titles. But it is possible that it was partly her high sense of morality and scorn of worldly glamour that led Phil, in reaction, in the opposite direction. It must also have been a source of sorrow to her that her son, having been reared in a warm and loving family, evidently found it difficult to sustain deep relationships; though he boasted of many by-blows, he never married and though he had many friends, he does not seem to have been well-loved. This lends irony to his mother's words when he was a few months old, that 'if he is an odious child when he is old enough to be so, it will be my fault'.[43] One hopes she did not blame herself when Phil became a less than perfect adult. There were radical differences between mother and son, as Ned noted: 'Phil thinks nothing matters, and Georgie who thinks every little thing matters'.[44] The atmosphere in the house was sometimes tense.

To understand Georgie's later life, it is necessary to know more about what Ned deprecatingly called their 'matrimonial exist-ence'. Although the emotional upheavals generated by Mary died down in the later 1870s, there were still strains in the Joneses' relationship. These were not made public, and within the household the general tone was one of affectionate sparring. Tacitly, however, Ned acknowledged his debt to Georgie and made this as explicit as he knew how in several paintings of the 1880s. He began a family group in 1879, showing Georgie at her beloved piano, flanked by Phil and Margaret; it was a picture painted with much love, but it was never completed. Instead, Ned

moved to a portrait of Georgie herself, looking directly out from
the canvas, with the two children framed in a background
doorway, in a variation of one of his favourite compositions. The
picture gives Georgie an uncompromising, penetrating gaze of
great force and moral rigour, the sort that demanded the total
honesty and ethical seriousness which many remarked on in her
lifetime. 'The quiet in those wonderful eyes of clearest grey,'
wrote W. Graham Robertson effusively, 'was the centre of the
strange stillness' to be felt at the Grange.[45] The portrait also
expresses, in the words of her great-grandson, something of the
unhappiness of being the artist's long-suffering wife, which he
perhaps did not see when he was painting it.[46]

In contrast to the earlier, over-decorated portrait of Mary, Ned
gave Georgie only a few accessories: just her children, in the
distance, and in her hand Gerard's *Herbal* open at the page
showing heartsease pansy, with a flower of the same lying on it.
He worked at the picture intermittently for many years, unable to
bring it to a state that satisfied him. This was not uncommon with
his most serious paintings, and perhaps occurred, as commentators have pointed out, because it was an expression of how much
he owed his wife, who 'bore the burden of everything'.[47] Her
strength and tenacity sustained him and his art. This support,
ranging from her efficient household management to her active
judgements on artistic and personal matters, was Georgie's great
contribution to Ned's work, which was always prevented from
slipping into an indulgent fairy-tale world by a sense of
high-minded idealism: his aestheticism was informed by moral-
ism. Her contribution, like that of most painters' wives, is
generally ignored, but it is significant that Ned himself acknowledged it in his great painting of 1884, *King Cophetua and the Beggar
Maid*.

The subject, an old tale reworked by Tennyson in two simple
stanzas, was a popular Victorian fable, counterpointing the quest
for wealth and status that dominated the age. Its verses read:

> Her arms across her breast she laid;
> She was more fair than words can say:
> Bare-footed came the beggar maid
> Before the king Cophetua.
> In robe and crown the king stepped down,

To meet and greet her on the way;
'It is no wonder,' said the lords,
'She is more beautiful than day.'

As shines the moon in clouded skies,
She in her poor attire was seen:
One praised her ancles, one her eyes,
One her dark hair and lovesome mien.
So sweet a face, such angel grace,
In all that land had never been:
Cophetua swore a royal oath:
'This beggar maid shall be my queen!'

Although various women have been identified as the inspiration of
Burne-Jones's painting, its personal significance is attested by the
fact that the beggar maid's direct, challenging gaze is very similar
to that depicted in Georgie's portrait, while the head of the king
holds more than a hint of the artist.[48] Georgie herself admired the
picture, regarding it in some sense as a vindication of her view of
art as a moral activity and expressive of Ned's best qualities as a
painter; she interpreted it as his endorsement of the belief that
wealth and worldly pride are inferior to spiritual integrity.

Nevertheless, the beggar maid has an unapproachable, impersonal quality; she is dressed in stylized rags that express neither
poverty nor human frailty, and indeed suggest the armour of a
moral warrior. There are hints that Ned found Georgie's moral
rigour increasingly difficult to live with. He remarked that in his
dreams she was always 'unkind'.[49] Phil's conduct was a cause of
conflict, especially when he ran up debts and asked his father to
pay them. To Georgie, reared in nonconformist probity, 'a paid
bill is such a pleasure'.[50] And when he accepted the baronetcy,
Ned was ashamed and embarrassed to tell his wife, 'so profound is
her scorn'.[51] But she did not openly protest: as within her own
family, she had long adopted a policy of silence on topics where
agreement was not possible.

This silence was also her response to Ned's continuing
infatuations with other women. Now, Ned prudently kept his
romances within the bounds of English decorum; his declarations
were passionate but rhetorical. His most serious infatuation was
for Helen Gaskell, and in the summer of 1893, when he was rising

sixty, Ned apparently experienced some kind of crisis and suggested an elopement. Friends advised otherwise, and Mrs Gaskell joined her dull husband for his annual shooting party as usual. Ned was invited too, and the experience of consoling walks with the lady, while the rest of the men shot grouse, perhaps reminded him that fantasy was better not acted upon. Two years later, when Ned and Georgie both visited the Gaskells' country estate, he remarked to his hostess that he had nothing to say to his wife,[52] but it is clear that the final threat to Georgie's marriage was over. Ned's continuing emotional need for female adoration was conveyed in his last major painting, which occupied the final years of his life, showing *The Last Sleep of Arthur in Avalon*. In addition to its literary and artistic meanings and allusions, this is also a picture of an old man lying surrounded by eight women; his head is on the lap of one and his feet on that of another, and it is an unconscious but transparent reflection of the artist's lifelong demand for female attention.

Georgie never failed in her conjugal devotion and a large amount of her time was taken up with caring for Ned, reading aloud and doing his correspondence. Nor was she as entirely sober and earnest as her portraits suggest. The Burne-Jones household was known for its humour and delight in jokes, which characteristically focused on the Fat Women who figured in Ned's nightmares and the Wagnerian heroines who began to appear on the operatic stages in the closing decades of the century. Georgie was remembered for the stories she collected to amuse Ned; the punchline of one about an intoxicated cook was scribbled on her visiting card and inadvertently left at a smart household: it read 'Mrs Burne-Jones. It's not drink, it's worry.'[53] She also looked after Ned's health, and, as part of a strategy to persuade him to work less intensively, found and furnished a country cottage as a weekend retreat in the village of Rottingdean near Brighton in Sussex. Here too her own life and activities expanded. A pioneer in this as in other ways, she moved towards active engagement in public life as opportunities for women increased.

Bearing in mind the surprise with which Morris's friends greeted his conversion to political affairs – 'I was never so much astonished as when he turned socialist,' wrote Richard Dixon[54] – it is worth asking how far his close friendship with Georgie led him into active sympathy with her concern for private and public morality. An old friend of Ruskin's, she admired his writing on social policy and developed her own, emphatic ideas on the conduct of public affairs, which several of those who knew her well characterized as those of a long-standing, if idiosyncratic, socialist. Other things, of course, also nudged Morris towards politics, but Georgie's affection and shared interests were not the least important, and I would like to question the simple view that in this field Morris led and others followed.

17

The Pre-Raphaelite circle belonged, as did most of the metropolitan intelligentsia, to the Liberal rather than the Tory camp. Their general political outlook was supportive of the Liberal interest of the commercial and professional classes to which they belonged, and was combined with charitable feeling towards the poor. In their youth they had Radical sympathies – Hunt and Millais set out to observe, though not participate in, the great Chartist demonstration of 1848 – but they took no active part in later issues of the day. This lack of political activism is not surprising, for despite the widening of the franchise during the Victorian age, politics remained the 'professional' concern of certain social groups until quite late in the century; like most of the middle class the Pre-Raphaelite painters and their friends were more immediately concerned with their own affairs and advancement. Women, of course, were simply excluded from political involvement: they had no vote and were not encouraged to take part in public affairs, so that most aspects of politics were closed to them. Their consequent lack of interest in the events of the day partly explains the lack of reference in this book to events that are generally regarded as major features of nineteenth-century history. Even if they were aware of these events, the women evidently did not feel personally affected or engaged.

As the century progressed, however, the franchise was extended, enlarging the numbers of citizens with the right and the desire to take part in political affairs. Working-class agitation and labour organization grew to become important aspects of political life; alongside this was a middle-class tradition of dissent, critical of many aspects of British policy, whether Tory or Liberal. In the

Pre-Raphaelite group this developed from youthful radicalism: Madox Brown, William Michael Rossetti, Algernon Swinburne and Philip Webb all had strong republican sympathies, for example, and many of the others were critical and contemptuous of the monarch and the ruling class; the Queen became particularly unpopular and was referred to in disrespectful and scornful terms as 'the widow Guelph' and 'the Empress Brown'. More seriously, the development of British imperialism, combining violent subjugation with commercial exploitation, was viewed with profound distaste, as was the jingoistic patriotism drummed up at home to support foreign adventures.

These reasons led several of the Pre-Raphaelite circle in the mid-1870s to join energetically in the protest movement against British support for Turkey during what was seen as a shameful display of pragmatic rather than principled policy. The Turks had massacred a group of villagers in Bulgaria but despite this they were supported as important allies against the perceived Russian threat to British interests in the region. The victims were Christians and it was deemed doubly outrageous for Britain to disregard this. It was a complex issue but the moral elements seemed clear, and Morris, discovering a talent for political rhetoric, wrote letters and articles denouncing the government and appealing to the people of England to make their voices heard. He was elected to the campaign committee, known as the Eastern Question Association, and thus, late in life, began his political career.

To what extent he was drawn into this through his friendship with Georgie is an open question: we know virtually nothing about her political views before this time, for her gender and class made it more or less impossible for her to express those views. We know, however, that Ned was progressive; we may suppose that Georgie shared this position. In addition, they were close friends of Ruskin during the period when he was extending his writing from art criticism into social policy, publishing such works as *Unto This Last*, *Munera Pulveris* and *Fors Clavigera*. Ned later reminded his wife that he had liked Ruskin's political writing 'extremely'.[1] And the Joneses were also brought into contact with radical views through their acquaintance with exiles from the Paris Commune in the early 1870s. All of this was long before Topsy took the slightest interest in politics.[2]

On 18 September 1876, Georgie's diary recorded that Ned took his father to an Eastern Question protest meeting in Trafalgar Square. Three weeks later she went with them to a demonstration in Hyde Park, 'about the action of the Government with regard to the East'. As with so many similar demonstrations, it was disappointing. 'Few there and little enthusiasm,' she reported. 'Heavy rain fell.'[3] But support was growing. On 24 October the chief Liberal newspaper published a long letter of denunciation from Morris, and within a fortnight he and Ned had put together an impressive list of fellow protesters from among their friends and colleagues, including William Allingham, Robert Browning, Bell Scott, Charley Faulkner, Thomas Carlyle and even Gabriel Rossetti who, following his breakdown, could rarely be induced to take an interest in public affairs. For obvious reasons Georgie could not join the Eastern Question Association committee with Morris, but she attended the launching conference, held in St James's Hall on 8 December.[4] In subsequent weeks she was much involved in the agitation, and the fact that in May 1877 Morris sent her a proof copy of his manifesto, on the theme of *Unjust War*, addressed to 'The Working Men of England', suggests that she was involved in its drafting. Morris was absorbed by his new concerns, but I suspect that he largely depended on Georgie's support. Jane and the girls had been staying with Rosalind Howard in Italy for the winter, and he spent most of his free time at the Grange. Agitation continued throughout the year and resumed in the autumn; in January 1878 Georgie was among those who attended another major protest meeting, held in the Exeter Hall on the eve of the Parliamentary sitting. Morris wrote a song for the audience to sing, beginning 'Wake, London Lads, wake, bold and free!' He was also one of the main speakers. Georgie's letter to Rosalind Howard illustrates her feelings. 'It is such a blessing,' she wrote of Morris, 'to hear him put truth into straightforward words as no one else does at present, for he is free from the usual forms of public speaking and in awe of no man . . .'[5]

When the Eastern Question Association campaign collapsed Ned gave up political activity in disgust. He was, in fact, moving steadily if slowly to the right, as he later acknowledged, and although he was drafted in as a supporter of the Society for the Protection of Ancient Buildings, launched in June 1878, he did not support Morris's subsequent conversion to socialism. Years later, after Morris's death, Ned's studio assistant recorded the following exchange between Georgie and Ned on the subject of Morris's political activity, in relation to the biography then in preparation:

EBJ   I hope it won't be a keynote in the book.

GBJ   Well, but it was an important part of his life.

EBJ   It was a parenthesis in it, he was before all things a poet and an artist.

GBJ   But he talked much more to me about it than he did to you.

EBJ   As he well knew he must. I shall always deplore it.

GBJ   Well, you know Ned dear, we are not quite agreed on that.[6]

Her understatement here masked quite a serious lack of agreement. Ned became decreasingly radical in his views as he grew older. 'How am I to remain a Liberal?' he once asked plaintively. 'All my friends are Tories.'[7] He opposed female suffrage: 'I like women when they're good and kind and agreeable, objects in the landscape of experience – give life to it and pleasant to look at and think about,' he remarked. 'What do they want with votes?'[8] And he is reputed to have delivered a fierce attack on socialism at the first Arts and Crafts exhibition, standing on a piano decorated by Kate Faulkner.[9] Georgie, however, became a socialist.

This was a bold step since socialism was regarded as a godless, revolutionary, violent and even lunatic creed; nor was a married woman expected to espouse views markedly different from those of her husband. Although times were changing, it was still exceptional for women to take part in public life, and when they did campaign, it tended to be on moral and religious issues: the agitation against the double sexual standard of the Contagious Diseases Acts and Josephine Butler's participation in their repeal during the 1870s is a case in point. For these reasons, Georgie did not become a publicly active socialist in the same way as her comrade Morris, although it is said that she would have willingly founded a Fulham Branch of the Social Democratic Federation.[10] But she did not join any socialist organizations of the time. This showed wisdom as well as propriety, for the internecine strife of the socialist sects in the 1880s and 1890s was neither pleasant nor

constructive and eventually drove Morris himself out of active
politics. There were also ideological reasons which prevented
Georgie from joining, since her view of socialism was practical
rather than theoretical, organizational or bombastic, and owed
much to Ruskin's example. She believed in the conversion of
individuals and distributed improving tracts to servants and
villagers much in the manner of a Victorian lady philanthropist,
except that, in her case, the texts were by Ruskin and Morris. Her
granddaughter commented that Georgie 'honestly believed that
"The Seven Lamps of Architecture" on every working man's table
would go far to ameliorate the world'.[11] It does not seem that she
accepted Marx's analysis of economic behaviour, for it was
following what appears to have been a heated argument on the
question of capital and labour that Morris sent her the much-
quoted defence of his own position as an employer, evidently in
response to her Ruskinian view that all would be well if employers
acted benevolently towards their workforce. 'Dearest Georgie,' he
began, 'the question of sharing profits in order to shake off the
responsibility of exploitation is complicated . . .'

In the course of a long discussion on the inadequacy of
individual action, in which Georgie firmly believed, Morris
compared his own income of around £1,800 a year from the firm
plus the £120 earned by his books, to the £200+ paid to the skilled
colour-mixer, and agreed that both should have the same wages
for the sake of equality; then he went on to demonstrate that it
would be of little general benefit if 'a very small knot of working
people were somewhat better off amidst the great ocean of
economic slavery'. He stressed that the fact that his political
objective was to see the whole labouring class rise, not for a few
individuals to 'creep out of their class into the middle class', and
continued:

> Here then is a choice for a manufacturer ashamed of living on
> surplus value: shall he do his best to further a revolution as the
> basis of society (don't be afraid of a word, my friend) which will
> turn all people into workers, as it would give a chance to all
> workers to become refined and dignified in their life; or shall he
> ease his conscience by dropping a certain portion of his profits
> to bestow in charity on his handful of workers?

The tone of this shows that he was seriously addressing Georgie's views, and responding to her arguments as thoroughly as he would have done to those of a male friend, and it demonstrates that her views demanded a high level of reasoned and informed discussion. She had evidently made the vital connections between theory and personal practice, and forced Morris to defend himself; he had also to agree that in his own case, as well as the theoretical objections to profit-sharing, there were 'those other partners called my family', who 'ought to be able to live on £4 a week' but who could not. Jenny's condition required constant attendance, while Jane's health was dependent on certain comforts. These arguments probably reached Georgie, whose husband was now earning over £1,000 a year from his painting and designing, and who could not herself have run the Grange on £4 a week. At the same time, she genuinely believed that wealth was a snare rather than a blessing, and seems to have looked back fondly on the early, penniless days of her marriage, when Ned did not earn much more than a workman.

Morris concluded his letter by apologizing for his customary intemperance in conversation; his discussion with Georgie had evidently been a vigorous one:

> Whatever hope or life there is in me is staked on the success of the cause: I believe you object to the word but I know no other to express what I mean . . . I don't intend leaving my friends in the lurch: I shall offend you desperately some day I fear; meantime to think me quarrelsome is a misjudgement, for I commonly hold my tongue when my conscience (I don't like that ecclesiastical word) bids speak: so when at last I *do* speak it sounds quarrelsome, you know . . .[12]

This referred to his emotional over-commitment, which he acknowledged but could not change. She was concerned that he should continue to write, for, to Georgie, art was an integral part of socialism.

It was not until the late 1880s that she took up her first 'cause', that of extending art to the people. This was a genuine need, for while Ned, for example, often asserted that he wished his work to reach the widest public, in practice he produced very expensive paintings for a small, rich clientele, as was more or less inevitable in fine art at this period. It is clear that Georgie shared, and may have helped to shape, the views put forward by Morris in his writings and speeches on the position of art in society. 'I do not want art for a few, any more than education for a few, or freedom for a few,' he proclaimed in his most famous address on the decorative arts, which was reprinted as a pamphlet and may well have been one of those Georgie delivered to the less than grateful villagers of Rottingdean. Sharing Georgie's dislike of ostentation, Morris praised 'simplicity of life, begetting simplicity of taste, that is a love of sweet and lofty things', which would be the foundation of the new art. 'How can I ask working men passing up and down these hideous streets day by day to care about beauty?' he demanded, pointing out that the museums meant for the benefit of the public were of no use to the masses, being closed on Sundays, the only day when working people were free to visit them.[13]

These were the very issues that Georgie took up in her work with the South London Art Gallery. The gallery was the brainchild of William Rossiter, who was a follower of F. D. Maurice, founder of the Working Men's College where Ruskin, Gabriel and Ned had all taken classes, and who began a South London equivalent in 1868, specifically to cater for the cultural needs of artisans and 'actual workers'. There were lectures, a free reading library and an art exhibition, and in 1887 an appeal was launched for funds to build a permanent centre, with gallery, library and lecture room, for the free use of local residents. Rossiter described South London as 'a great dormitory of workmen . . . a great intellectual desert, with miles upon miles of flat, square, ugly homes, with scarce any beauty of architecture and with absolutely no public buildings'. He found the people, especially the young, initially hostile to bourgeois philanthropy. At a fund-raising function he told how in the early days, 'we got cabbage stumps shied at our heads and the children came and swore at us'. But with perseverance the gallery, opened in Camberwell in 1891, proved popular. 'Now children of all ages, from those who can scarcely walk, come in hundreds and really look at the pictures,' he boasted. The secretary pulled shy but inquisitive urchins in off the street, for the premises were meant for the least well-off members of society, and were open on Sunday afternoons, despite sabbatarian protests. If the Gallery were not open, those whom it was meant to serve 'would have nothing to look at but the outsides of rows of ugly buildings and the insides of public houses'.[14]

In launching his appeal, Rossiter asked the celebrated artists G. F. Watts and Edward Burne-Jones for their support, and was rewarded by the energetic services of their wives. Both Ned and Watts became members of the council but 'Mrs Watts and Mrs Burne-Jones have given such generous and untiring work for the gallery,' Rossiter explained, 'that even my grateful sense of its value can scarcely check my regret at the labour I have added to their lives.' By canvassing, mainly among their friends and acquaintances, the committee successfully raised ten thousand pounds to build the proposed gallery in Peckham Road. The story of the 'dear struggling gallery' was 'a romance', Georgie told George Eliot's widower in 1890, persuading him to donate some of her friend's works.[15] The same year Ned arranged a week's free showing of his *Briar Rose* series at the Toynbee Hall for the people of London's East End, following the show at Agnew's in Bond Street where an entrance fee was charged. His support for Georgie's work was halfhearted, however, and he claimed that her South London Art Gallery activities exhausted her strength and health. He joked about the 'miserable journey' to Camberwell, 'a seemingly needless neighbourhood', adding that, of course '*very* different views are held by one above', meaning Georgie.[16]

By 1895, a new crisis had arisen, partly because of the Gallery's growth in popularity. Two or three thousand visitors came every Sunday, and both Rossiter and his faithful secretary were ageing. Some of the designated beneficiaries of the free Gallery, mainly young men, came to regard it 'as a public recreation room where they might eat, smoke and amuse themselves as they pleased'; they had to be controlled by being asked to buy a penny catalogue of the works on show, and this went against the principle of free admission. In addition, the committee, whose members lived in every part of London except that where the Gallery was located, felt that they could no longer oversee its development, and proposed to hand it over to the newly-created local authority, so that it would become the responsibility of the Camberwell Public Libraries and Museums Commission. Georgie was a member of the three-person sub-committee that negotiated the difficult and complex transfer. She helped to safeguard the Gallery's original aims and objects by appointing the President of the Royal

Academy, her brother-in-law Edward Poynter, and other artistic
worthies to advise the local representatives, and by insisting that it
be maintained as a 'Free Picture Gallery for the inhabitants of
South London, open to the public on Sundays . . . for ever'.
Rossiter and his secretary retired with golden handshakes. When
all was finally settled, Ned confided to his assistant that 'there have
been times when I've cursed the place up hill and down dale, only
I've kept it to myself not to discourage her'.[17] Georgie possessed
neither conceit nor personal ambition, and would not have wished
her work in this field to be praised, but it seems to me it was in its
way as valuable as Morris's speeches. He talked of bringing art to
the people while she actually helped to do so. During the 1890s,
the South London Art Gallery welcomed over 100,000 visitors a
year; whatever one may think of the paternalism of the venture,
these visitors did belong to the 'great artisan class, whose work
beautifies the wealthier part of the metropolis', but who themselves lived 'with so little beauty either natural or derived from
art'.[18] Ruskin, whose name was frequently invoked for its local as
well as political associations, should have been proud to see the
determination and self-effacement with which his ideals were put
into practice by little Georgie, whose wood-engraving he had so
patronizingly discouraged all those years before. Her Gallery is
still there, in Camberwell, and is still open to the public on Sunday
afternoons.

Soon after the transfer of the Gallery to the local authority,
Georgie retired from its management and began to spend more
time at her holiday home in Rottingdean. Here she became a
parish councillor. This may seem to be a trivial step, politically
unimportant when compared with the immense economic and
social changes planned by Morris, Hyndman, Eleanor Marx and
Edward Aveling, in the Social Democratic Federation, Socialist
League and other similar organizations. But, in fact, it was the
start of increasing involvement by women in local democracy:
here too Georgie was a pioneer. Parish councils were new elected
bodies for which women could vote and stand. They were created
under the 1892 Local Government Act, which freed local
administration from direct control by landowner or church; in
some country districts this was regarded as almost equivalent to
revolution. In the 1880s and 1890s the rural areas of southern
England were often places of severe and intractable deprivation.

The labouring class endured poor housing, poor health, low wages and a low level of education; their children went into service at a young age. The pastoral vision of the happy swain seldom corresponded with reality, and poverty, inequality and lack of beauty were problems in a Sussex village as well as in the suburbs of South London. The causes of this were complex and the problem was not easily resolved but by standing for election to Rottingdean parish council in 1894 Georgie hoped to begin a process of improvement, bringing the village up to the standards she thought proper to a civilized community, demonstrating her belief in practical politics and progress. She showed courage, too, for the rural establishment of farmers and landowners did not welcome the challenge to their authority posed by the new councils and the secret ballot. Rural employers were accustomed to direct their labourers' votes as well as their own.

In her 'Open Letter to the Electors of Rottingdean' Georgie outlined the roles and duties of councillors and the secret-ballot method of voting. She listed the improvements that could be provided by the parish council, including allotments, public lighting, water supplies and rubbish collection, and urged villagers to vote for other benefits such as a public wash-house, where both baths and laundry facilities were supplied. This appealed most to the women, for the majority of dwellings had neither piped water nor bathroom. She also proposed to bring in a district nurse to look after the health of women, children and old people. The Rottingdean residents remembered Georgie as a person of great determination, who brought about unexpected alterations. 'Well, sir, did you ever?' said one elderly lady when asked by the vicar for her comments. 'What with the dust cart *and* the watering cart and *now* a District Nurse *as well*, I just don't know what the village is coming to!'[19] As is usual, one obstacle to improvement came from the ratepayers' resistance to provide the funds, and as a result Georgie herself advanced the necessary money to purchase a cottage for the district nurse. She and other councillors also undertook to repair the village fire-engine, to fix the railings round the village pond and to appoint an inspector at the local knacker's yard.

The subject of footpaths and access to the countryside provided one of the most contentious rural questions of the time, as landowners and farmers came up against the first wave of middle-class environmentalists determined to preserve common rights and footpaths for their own enjoyment of the rustic scene. Such was the opposition aroused by the changes made and promised by the new parish council that in the next election Georgie was defeated. The following year she returned to the fray, with a pamphlet entitled 'What We Have Done', and she regained her seat. It seems, however, that she was never able to get the public wash-house built.

By this time her closest friend and political sympathizer was dead, so she had no one to share her triumphs and trials. Morris grew weaker throughout 1896 and by the autumn was clearly failing. The last letter he wrote with his own hand was to Georgie at Rottingdean, saying simply, 'Come soon. I want a sight of your dear face.'[20] His biographer implies that at last they were able to express the tenderness they had felt towards each other for so long. With Ned, Georgie visited Topsy virtually every day during his last illness, and although she did not usurp Jane's role as widow, she was there when he died. This was her account of the last days:

It was only last Tuesday that I met Mr M going out in his basket chair to Ravenscourt Park [in Hammersmith]. He seemed better and said to me how delightful it was to feel all his ten fingers and ten toes again, and then just for one second I had the faintest glimmer of hope. But it passed directly and when I left him at noon again after the outing, he was quite deathly with fatigue and exhaustion. Then the next morning at 11 Mr Ellis came running over to say that a new haemorrhage had happened. He knew me when I went, but the next day he hardly did and not at all on Friday. But he died as easily as anyone possibly could, just as a baby who is satisfied drops off its mother's breast with a sigh – literally gave up his breath as though he had quite done with it.[21]

The last maternal image suggests something about Georgie's feeling. One immediate task was the production of an 'official' biography of the great Master-Craftsman, perhaps to forestall the kind of incomplete and unsatisfactory books that had appeared after Gabriel's death. The task was assigned to Jack Mackail, a young scholar who had married Georgie's daughter Margaret, and

Georgie was his chief source and collaborator; it is, one suspects, largely her view of Morris that shaped the two volumes.

In April 1898 she went to visit Red House for the first time in thirty years and recollect the 'green summer' time there. She was proud of her family and became a fond, if rather awesome, grandmother to Margaret's children Angela and Denis. One can indeed discern a fine matriarchal line of independent, loving women that stretched from Georgie's mother Hannah through to her daughter and granddaughter. Ned died in 1898, with Georgie by his side, after a heart attack in the middle of the night; her arrangements for the funeral were characteristically bold. These comments from neighbours were heard by Ned's assistant as he came round the corner of the Grange garden wall:

> 'Come to draw the funeral, sir? (*Calling out*) There *is* some flowers, Mrs ---, come and see! Beautiful flowers. But I *did* hear as his wish was to be that there was to be no flowers.' (*Exclamations of astonishment as Annie appears carrying flowers to put in hearse*) 'Servant hasn't got no mourning on! (*Neighbours aghast*) A blue dress!!' (*First woman*) 'There's a lovely wreath – how beautiful. Lilies of the valley! Look!'[22]

As the new century, and Georgie's sixtieth birthday approached, her reputation for unconventional views grew. In Rottingdean she was known as a formidable old lady whose determination was in inverse proportion to her size, and who 'was not afraid of voicing her opinions, however unpopular they might be'.[23] When a neighbour enclosed a grass verge with railings, Georgie angrily insisted, once a year, on asserting public access by solemnly marching up and down the contested turf, while her opponent played a garden hose over the hedge to discourage her. More seriously, she fell out with the whole village over the relief of Mafeking. With her progressive, anti-imperialist views she, like many others, took a 'pro-Boer' position on the Anglo-South African War, detesting the work of Cecil Rhodes and his followers, and she protested bitterly against fighting in defence of commercial interests. Violence was never acceptable to her, and she may have recalled the foreign policy she and Morris had originally criticized in the Eastern Question protests. She again defied the patriots:

When the news reached Rottingdean in the May of 1900 that
Mafeking had at last been relieved after a siege lasting 217 days,
the village went wild with excitement. A demonstration was
held on the green, but the mood of joyousness was turned to
anger when it was seen that Lady Burne-Jones was hanging a
large banner from an upstairs window . . . WE HAVE
KILLED AND TAKEN POSSESSION was her slogan, taken
from I Kings 21, verse 19.[24]

An ugly scene developed, with people threatening to burn and
stone the house. Georgie's nephew Rudyard Kipling, now a
famous author with imperialist sympathies, was summoned from
his own home on the other side of the green and asked to mediate
with his aunt. It appears she remained adamant and it was believed
in Rottingdean that this incident was the Kiplings' reason for
leaving the village soon afterwards. Georgie received support
from a long-lost quarter however, for when renewing acquaintance during work on her biography of Ned, she received a letter
from William Michael Rossetti congratulating her on her 'tenacity
and pluck in making an anti-jingo demonstration'.[25] Both retained
their radical sentiments to the end.

Memorials of Edward Burne-Jones, published in two volumes in
1904, was Georgie's most lasting work, and although she
characteristically effaced herself from its pages, it is partly her
autobiography too. The first volume chronicles the early, magical
years of her engagement and marriage, forming one of the chief
source-books of information on the second phase of Pre-
Raphaelite art. There is, as we have seen, only the barest mention
of Mary Zambaco, and the years of Ned's infatuation are virtually
missing from the record. In the second volume, Ned's place as
hero is shared with Topsy. *Memorials* was, naturally, a final work
of conjugal piety and has its limitations, but it was also a fine work
of biography and it made other accounts of Ned's life and work
unnecessary for many years.

Georgie died at the age of seventy-nine, in 1920, attended by her
faithful servant Annie, who recorded her passing:

My dear Lady gave me sweet counsel and how and where to
look for guidance . . . During the short illness my Lady talked a
good deal of a man that was good and pious and did see him at

times in her bedroom (who is·that man standing there?) . . . At 3 o'clock in the afternoon the Dearest Lady breathed her last.[26]

The obituary in the *Westminster Gazette* was slightly sharper:

it was hard to find a weakness in that small and lovely personality. To look into her clear eyes was to see to the very bottom of her candid soul, and if anyone proposed 'making a lie' of any part of life, it were good for them that they were removed from the presence of her whose strengths were perfected in weakness.[27]

There is not space to chronicle in detail the rest of Jane's life. She did not join in her husband's political activity, and although it is unfair to speculate on the reasons, it may be that as one who had successfully left her proletarian origins behind, she felt little inclination to promote working-class interests. Her daughter May did become an active socialist like her father, and among other activities was membership secretary of the Hammersmith branch of the Socialist League, which for some years met in the old coach house of Kelmscott House. On the occasions when Jane met the comrades she had little to say to them and her reputation for silence grew. Bernard Shaw, who paid court to May, claimed that the only remark of Jane's he recalled was one of satisfaction at having tricked him, a vegetarian, into eating some suet pudding.

During the 1880s, when in her forties, she had a curious affair with Wilfrid Blunt, maverick political figure and compulsive womanizer, who seems partly to have bewitched her, as he did many others, with his persuasive flattery. Blunt went to stay at Kelmscott Manor with the Morrises and described the excitement of traversing Morris's bedroom to reach Jane's bed. Jane certainly enjoyed Blunt's attentions, while he seems to have been partly motivated by a desire to emulate Rossetti, about whom he asked many questions. This was how he learned from Jane that their affair had not quite included sex – and that 'great rows' of chloral bottles at Bognor had signalled the end of her love. Blunt, incidentally, also tried to seduce Marie Stillman, another famous Pre-Raphaelite beauty. She was nearly fifty at the time and told him off, but he undid her glove and, reportedly, 'held her wonderful hand in mine' during a journey from Frascati to Rome, where the Stillmans were living.[28] Marie continued to paint throughout her life, and to correspond with Jane. She stayed at Kelmscott Manor on more than one occasion, and one of her last pictures was a watercolour view of the house from the garden.[29] Though Jane told Blunt she had 'never loved' her husband, her feelings towards Morris seem to have become affectionate in the last years of his life. She embroidered a coverlet for his bed at Kelmscott, and nursed him with care and devotion.[30] She was distressed by his final illness, although she was able to remark with wry humour that: 'He says that his patience is quite gone now! poor dear! he never had any!'[31] She was 'quite broken down' at the funeral, which was held at Kelmscott village, after a journey by train and carriage, with the plain oak coffin on a farmwagon decorated with foliage and vine leaves.[32] Ned made a percipient comment on Jane's dependence on her husband. 'She was always used to be managed for,' he said, 'and is only now learning what she's lost.'[33] To Blunt, who invited her and May to stay at his house in Egypt for a winter holiday, she allegedly said she was 'not unhappy, though it is a terrible thing'.[34] The holiday was not a success, since neither guest could ride and the sand was not suitable for walking, but it is a measure of Jane's affection for her host that she presented him with an oak table made for Red House, in memory of her husband, whose political and literary work Blunt admired.

Her own memorial to Morris was to use some of the money he left to build a pair of cottages at Kelmscott, as a practical contribution towards relieving the rural housing problem and promoting the use of the traditional building materials and style he so wished to preserve. Her old friend Philip Webb was the architect; now retired, he pointed out that both his first and his last houses had been designed for her. 'Even if you had not said so,' he added, 'I know you look on your work of the cottages as a *real* memorial in connection with the love of our "old man" for so many years.'[35] Shortly before her own death early in 1914, Jane managed to buy Kelmscott Manor.

Emma Brown died in 1890 and was buried in the new St Pancras Cemetery in Finchley, where her husband had purchased two grave plots, alongside her mother and her nephew. This was evidently a mistake, and three weeks later the coffin was exhumed and reinterred in the other Brown grave, where her two sons, Arthur Gabriel and Oliver, already lay, and where her husband was to join her in 1893. Her granddaughter Juliet, Cathy's daugher, remembered Emma as a very gentle elderly woman. When she fell ill she apologized for giving people trouble, and fed breadcrumbs to a visiting robin on the window sill. Then, at the end, 'once in the night, just before she died, when she'd forgotten all about the world already, she began to sing a song, but very gently, and my grandfather said her voice was just as sweet as when she was a girl and they used to sing it together'.[36]

Fanny's old age was perhaps not as comfortable, but she was saved from destitution. She and her second husband John Schott aroused William Michael Rossetti's anger when they tried to gain from Gabriel's posthumous fame by exhibiting Gabriel's pictures in Old Bond Street at what they called 'The Rossetti Gallery', but little more is known of her life. Schott himself died in 1891, leaving Fanny dependent on an allowance, which she shared with her stepson Fred; in 1898 the money was reduced to 14s, to cover Fanny's needs alone. By the turn of the century she was nearing seventy and her faculties had begun to fail, and in 1905 she was taken to Brighton, where she died.[37]

Not far from there, Annie Miller, wife of Captain Thompson, was living with her husband and daughters, in Shoreham-by-Sea. Little is known of her life after she left the artistic circle. She met Holman Hunt just once more, by accident, when she was, according to his account, out driving 'in a carriage with several children on Richmond Hill'. They greeted each other civilly and exchanged news. Hunt, in recounting the event, expressed the inimitable view that he had 'forgiven' Annie the 'offence' she had done him, feeling on mature reflection that it had 'in fact worked me good rather than harm'.[38] Annie's response was not recorded. Some time later she and Captain Thompson moved to Shoreham, a small Sussex fishing port, where her husband died in 1916. He was buried, according to the Shoreham cemetery grave records,

Maturity

under the name of Major R. J. Geo. Thompson. She herself lived on for nearly a decade, dying in 1925 at the age of ninety, thus being the last surviving Pre-Raphaelite Sister. Her success, in lifting herself from the squalor of her social origins, was attested in a letter recently received by Diana Holman-Hunt from a woman who had known her daughter, and who recalled Annie as lovely and ladylike, wearing 'exquisite' hand-made shoes and kid gloves.[39] She had come a long way from Cross Keys Yard.

Postscript

Feminist analyses have frequently catalogued the fate of women in the hands of history, biography, art criticism and the rest, demonstrating how masculine dominance is unconsciously maintained in our culture. Women, it is shown, characteristically suffer from invisibility, slander, disqualification, trivialization, exploitation . . .

As is obvious, the Pre-Raphaelite women were far from invisible. Indeed, in the stylized forms we recognize in Pre-Raphaelite art, they were and are seen everywhere: their faces are familiar in our homes and our galleries. Nor are they anonymous figures; we know their names and dates and something at least of their lives. They have, however, been rendered silent or mute; they are seen but not heard.

In the effort to retrieve the women's experiences, this book has illustrated how the actions and utterances of the Pre-Raphaelite painters have been thoroughly chronicled and discussed, in a process that in some cases began during their lifetime, so highly valued were these men by their contemporaries. By contrast, the words and deeds of the women – even those who were also painters – have been largely ignored or forgotten. Their actions were recorded only in so far as they related to the men's lives and careers; hence the difficulty of discovering what the women were doing when they were not in contact with the painters. Whole areas of their lives are lost to the record. In this sense, the women are absent, unseen.

One result of silencing the women in this way has been to open the way for misrepresentation. From the intense faces gazing from the canvases and from the available scraps of biographical information, a range of personalities has been constructed, claiming to describe Pre-Raphaelite women. These descriptions are often slanderous in effect if not in intention. The women are variously said to have been sickly, neurotic, sexually prom- iscuous, grasping, clinging, adulterous. The tone of this repre- sentation has, it is true, changed over time. The late Victorians, for example, divided women into madonnas and magdalens, beautiful angels or seductive sirens; those who fell into the latter category were kept hidden from view. The twentieth century, discovering concealed Victorian sexuality, brought these figures into the light, and imputed to all Pre-Raphaelite women a share in the easy, permissive bohemianism of the circle. Today, the resurgent interest in women's history, to which this book contributes, is nudging them towards a position as proto- feminists, stressing their oppression, imperfect achievements and demands for independence.

Even were it practicable, it is not necessary to demolish the mythic versions of Pre-Raphaelite Womanhood. But it is useful to identify them, to acknowledge which parts of the story serve a legendary as opposed to a historic function, and to understand why the myths, which say more about the society that recycles them than about the figures that inhabit them, remain so vigorous today. At the same time, it must be remembered that there is no objective, unmediated version of accurate, historical truth. All accounts are interpretations, ways of telling a tale.

History also disables women, defining the things they do as *ipso facto* of lesser interest and importance, through a process of disqualification by gender. They are shunted into special categor- ies, and find it hard to obtain equal treatment; attempts to do so are dismissed as special pleading, or they are marginalized as remarkable oddities. By this means, the Pre-Raphaelite women have been placed unequivocally in a minor role, which is difficult to contradict without in some sense distorting the evidence. It is undeniable that the art that matters was produced by the men. The women contributed to its production, but they were not the active, creative agents. Even a 'sympathetic' understanding of social and cultural forces comes to the same conclusion: because of their oppression, the women did not produce major works of art. Despite the work of feminist art historians, we are still some way from fully recognizing the way in which the production of post-Romantic art has been shaped in terms of male creative genius, and the concomitant suppression and diversion of women's creative energies. Without question, however, as the experiences of several of the Pre-Raphaelite women show, women were denied opportunities and then defined as inferior. This makes it hard to assess their abilities.

This difficulty has led, too, to trivialization, whereby things pertaining to women are relegated to a shallow, personal level that is not allowed depth and significance. Details of their emotional lives, domestic responsibilities, family relations and particularly their social activities, are regarded as too frivolous for serious attention and irrelevant to understanding the important aspects of their age. Accounts which treat of such matters are said to deal only in 'higher gossip' which is, naturally, less significant than, say, demographic patterns or socio-political events.

Biographical accounts of men, of course, concentrate less on the trivia of their private lives than on the importance of their work or public lives. It is useless to point out that women have generally been denied access to public life and achievement, for even when the injustice is conceded, the value judgement still stands: things domestic, like washing dishes, are unimportant and uninteresting when compared to things public, like artistic work.

This difficulty extends also to writing about women. The problem of being heard, or rather listened to, when discussing women's affairs – let alone the attempt to have them considered within the mainstream discourses of historical and critical studies – leads some writers to employ a heavy, academic style and vocabulary of the kind considered proper for intellectual work. It would be nice to think that this was not necessary and that women's lives can be seriously and creatively discussed in their own, unmystified language.

Lastly, there is the issue of exploitation. Sometimes with startling clarity, Pre-Raphaelite art shows how women were selected, shaped and presented in the production of paintings by and generally for men. The roles allotted to women were subsidiary: either they assisted in the making of art as models, the living objects to be employed, posed and depicted in a manner not so very different from the way a vase of flowers or a bowl of fruit is used in a still life; or as wives and other dependent womenfolk, who in traditional fashion looked after their husbands, ran household affairs, cared for children and invalids, and generally provided an emotional and practical support system for the painters' professional careers. In both situations they were exploited, because their contribution was seldom accorded its due share of the credit for the things their work helped to create. There is an added dimension in the Pre-Raphaelite painters' choice of working-class women as models and wives, which evokes a symbolic variant on capital's use of labour. Only if they married their employers did models obtain a commensurate share in the surplus value or wealth realized by the pictures for which they posed. If they did marry, they benefited in a material sense but never came into possession of the power conferred by reputation, earning power and male gender.

It is also worth pointing out that the exploitation of Pre-Raphaelite women still continues, as the art they helped to make is bought and sold, traded for profit, displayed and reproduced in auction rooms, galleries, bookshops and magazines around the world. I, at least, would like to acknowledge a debt to them in this regard.

The women of the Pre-Raphaelite circle – Lizzie, Emma, Annie, Fanny, Jane, Georgie and the other sisters who have featured in these pages – can therefore be seen as victims, of silencing, of slander, of double-bind disqualification, of disdain and of theft. But such a conclusion would, I think, do them less than justice. It would, too, be a little unfair to the men involved in their lives. It is always necessary to make a distinction between the workings of an ideology as a dominant set of ideas, internalized and re-created by both sexes, and the behaviour of any given individual. Within the Pre-Raphaelite circle the women found many encouraging, supportive, loving men, who were notable for their freedom from the overbearing chauvinism of their time. The women were offered opportunities denied to most members of their sex and class, and were in many ways liberated from what would have been far more oppressive positions, whether as working women or as idle wives in high bourgeois households. In the atmosphere of the artistic world they were freed from some restricting conventions imposed on their less fortunate sisters. They were able to pursue their own interests, develop friendships and participate in a wide range of activities. They were raised to a higher social level – even the genteel Georgie was elevated into

Lady Burne-Jones – and they shared in the material benefits so successfully earned by Pre-Raphaelite art. This was true even of the unmarried, disreputable Fanny. Furthermore, they were in some ways more fortunate than other middle-class wives, in so far as painting was still produced in a pre-industrial mode, with the workplace or studio located in the home and all members of the family participating in productive labour, as models, household managers, studio assistants and apprentices. This was particularly true of the Madox Brown family, where all three children were taught by their father without regard to gender. The style may have been a shade patriarchal but here, as in other ways, by the standards of their time the women were lucky.

However, more important, they were successful. They were not simply the passive recipients of benefits conferred on them by virtue of their connection with the artists. Nor were they merely 'discovered' by the men and moulded into Pre-Raphaelite shape. This book has shown how they were active, positive agents in the choice and definition of their own futures. They saw and took opportunities, they learnt and practised new skills, they asserted and implemented their right to decision-making and independence of action. They were, in short, very different from the soulful, static images of Pre-Raphaelite painting. Not all they did was easy: there were many hurdles to overcome and much to disguise lest it conflict too loudly with the ascribed view of women as weak, dependent beings. Nor was everything desired accomplished; Lizzie for example did not survive to enjoy the fruits of her effort. But among all the women whose lives I have traced, there was aspiration, ambition, determination and strength of character. In addition and by no means least, there was a sense of pleasure, of delight, of humour and irreverence, which adds to their achievements. It would be a mistake to overestimate these achievements – in many respects they can be seen to have suffered from the defeats and deficiencies imposed on their sex – but overall the story of the Pre-Raphaelite sisters is one of success. For me, its fascination lies in the sense of active struggle for identity and self-determination that shines from each phase of their lives.

Notes and References

The major primary sources used in this book are listed below in Sources and Select Bibliography, together with the abbreviations by which each is identified in the numbered Notes to each chapter, where other sources are given in full. The individuals frequently referred to are identified by their initials which are listed on p. 363.

There are so many secondary books and articles on Pre-Raphaelitism that it is neither possible nor helpful to list them all. An interim bibliography is provided in *Pre-Raphaelitism: A Biblio-critical Study* by W. A. Fredeman, 1965.

In general, references have been supplied for all direct quotations but for other textual material, references are given only when the information is new or disputed, or if it requires amplification in some way.

A good deal of Pre-Raphaelite correspondence is published in one form or another. In general the most accessible source is cited, for convenience.

Sources and Select Bibliography

Manuscript sources

BJ Papers Burne-Jones Papers, Manuscript Department, Fitzwilliam Museum, Cambridge.

BL Additional MSS and Ashley Collection, Manuscript Department, British Library, London.

Bodl. Bodleian Library, Oxford.

Rooke Notes A fair copy by G. Burne-Jones of MSS Notes by Thomas Rooke in Lance Thirkell Collection, London. (Large sections of this are published in *Burne-Jones Talking: His Conversations 1895–1898 preserved by his studio assistant Thomas Rooke*, (ed. Mary Lago), 1982.)

VH Papers Violet Hunt Papers, Ford Madox Ford Collection, Rare Books Division, Cornell University.

WM Gall. MSS material in the library of the William Morris Gallery, Walthamstow.

Select Bibliography

Allingham, William *A Diary* (ed. H. Allingham and D. Radford), 1907.

Angeli, Helen Rossetti *Dante Gabriel Rossetti: His Friends and Enemies*, 1949.

Baldwin, A.W. *The Macdonald Sisters*, 1960.

Baum, P.F. (ed.) *Dante Gabriel Rossetti's Letters to Fanny Cornforth*, 1940.

Boyce, George Price *Diaries of George Price Boyce* (ed. Virginia Surtees), 1980.

Brown, Ford Madox *Diary of Ford Madox Brown* (ed. Virginia Surtees), 1981.

Bryson, John (ed.) *Dante Gabriel Rossetti and Jane Morris: Their Correspondence*, 1976.

Burne-Jones, Georgiana *Memorials of Edward Burne-Jones*, 2 vols, 1904.

Cline, C.L. (ed.) *The Owl and the Rossettis: Correspondence between C.A. Howell and the Rossetti Family*, 1978.

Doughty, O. and Wahl, J.R. (eds.) *Letters of Dante Gabriel Rossetti*, 4 vols, 1965–7.

Faulkner, Peter *Wilfrid Scawen Blunt and the Morrises*, 1981.

Fitzgerald, Penelope *Edward Burne-Jones: A Biography*, 1975.

Fredeman, W.E. 'Prelude to the Last Decade: Dante Gabriel Rossetti in the Summer of 1872', *Bulletin of the John Rylands Library*, Vol 53, 1970–1.

Fredeman, W.E. (ed.) *The Pre-Raphaelite Brotherhood Journal, William Michael Rossetti's Diary of the Pre-Raphaelite Brotherhood, 1849–1853*, 1975.

Henderson, P. (ed.) *William Morris: Letters to His Family and Friends*, 1950.

Henderson, P. *William Morris: His Life, Work and Friends*, 1967.

Holman-Hunt, Diana *My Grandfather, His Wives and Loves*, 1969.

Holman Hunt, William *Pre-Raphaelitism and the Pre-Raphaelite Brotherhood*, 2 vols, 1905.

Hudson, Derek (ed.) *Munby: Man of Two Worlds. The Life and Diaries of Arthur J. Munby 1828–1910*, 1972.

Hueffer, F.M. *Ford Madox Brown*, 1896.

Mackail, J.W. *The Life of William Morris*, 2 vols, 1899.

Rose, Andrea *Pre-Raphaelite Portraits*, 1981.

Rossetti, Dante Gabriel *The Works of Dante Gabriel Rossetti* (ed. W. M. Rossetti), 1911.

Rossetti, William Michael *Some Reminiscences*, 1906.

Rossetti, William Michael (ed.) *Dante Gabriel Rossetti: His Family Letters with a Memoir*, 2 vols, 1895.

Rossetti, William Michael *Ruskin, Rossetti and Pre-Raphaelitism: Papers 1854–1862*, 1899.

Ruskin, John *Letters i* and *ii* in *The Works of John Ruskin* (ed. E.T. Cooke and A.D. Wedderburn) Vols 36 and 37, 1909.

Scott, William Bell *Autobiographical Notes* (ed. W. Minto) 2 vols, 1892.

Siddall, Elizabeth Eleanor *Poems and Drawings of Elizabeth Siddal* (ed. R.C. Lewis and M.S. Lasner), 1978.

Surtees, Virginia *The Paintings and Drawings of Dante Gabriel Rossetti: A Catalogue Raisonné*, 2 vols, 1971.

Tate Gallery, *The Pre-Raphaelites*, 1984.

Troxell, J.C. (ed.) *Three Rossettis: Unpublished Letters to and from Dante Gabriel, Christina, William*, 1937.

Notes

List of individuals referred to by initials in the notes

ACS   Algernon Charles Swinburne
AM   Annie Miller
BLS   Barbara Leigh Smith
CGR   Christina Georgina Rossetti
DGR   Dante Gabriel Rossetti
EBJ   Edward Burne-Jones
EES   Elizabeth Eleanor Siddall
EMB   Emma Madox Brown
FC   Fanny Cornforth
FGS   Frederic George Stephens
FMB   Ford Madox Brown
GBJ   Georgiana Burne-Jones
GBS   George Bernard Shaw
GPB   George Price Boyce
HC   Hall Caine
HRA   Helen Rossetti Angeli
JEM   John Everett Millais
JM   Jane Morris
JR   John Ruskin
MZ   Mary Zambaco
PRB   Pre-Raphaelite Brotherhood
PW   Philip Webb
SCC   Sydney Carlyle Cockerell
VH   Violet Hunt
WA   William Allingham
WBS   William Bell Scott
WHD   Walter Howell Deverell
WM   William Morris
WMR   William Michael Rossetti
WSB   Wilfred Scawen Blunt

References

Prelude (pp. 1–11)

1. Tate Gallery 268.
2. Siddall, pl. 4.

Chapter One (pp. 15–36)

1. Elizabeth Gaskell, *Mary Barton*, 1848, ch. 8.
2. W.M. Rossetti (1895) i, 171; W.M. Rossetti, 'Elizabeth Eleanor Siddall', *Burlington Magazine*, May 1903, 273.
3. W. Holman Hunt i, 198.

4. W.M. Rossetti (1895) i, 171.

5. W. Holman Hunt i, 199.

6. Contrary to general belief Violet Hunt's book on EES, *Wife of Rossetti*, 1932, is not wholly inaccurate and worthless. The style and opinions are wild but much of the material is based on interviews and research, some documentation for which survives in manuscript in Cornell University Library. Where appropriate such material is cited here, under VH Papers; usually such quotations are taken from VH's respondents. It should be noted that when HRA, the chief Rossetti family archivist, read *Wife of Rossetti*, she commented: 'I thought it would be much worse. She evidently has original sources' (HRA to SCC 9.10.1932, BL ADD 52750).

7. Allingham 144, entry for 9.11.1866. WA was one of EES's earliest friends and in recognition of this was presented by DGR with a posthumous portfolio of her work in 1867.

8. See 'PRB and Walter Deverell: Letters from DGR and others with a narrative and illustrations', written by Frances Deverell with preface and corrections by WMR, in Huntingdon Library, California. A useful account of WHD as artist is Mary Lutyens 'Walter Howell Deverell 1827–1845', *Pre-Raphaelite Papers*, ed. Leslie Parris, 1984, 76–96.

9. EES' introduction to the Pre-Raphaelite circle is usually placed as 'some time in 1849'. The precise date cannot now be established and perhaps does not matter greatly except in so far as it is used to fix the 'historic' meeting with DGR. The chief source of information was WMR, but he was not certain of the date. EES is not mentioned in the Pre-Raphaelite Brotherhood's *Journal*, kept by WMR and covering the early years of the movement, and although it was later alleged that mutilations to the *Journal* made in the mid-1850s by DGR were for the purpose of removing all references to EES, most of the excisions related to dates before EES was known to the PRB. The earliest ascertainable fact about EES in relation to the PRB was her sitting to WHD for Viola in *Twelfth Night*, but a reference to DGR helping with a difficult passage involving hair, see Fredeman (1975) 21, does not necessarily refer to EES; no model is mentioned and EES' long hair does not feature in the painting. The most likely date for her introduction to the PRB circle was the post-Christmas period early in 1850, when milliners were laid off. WHD was known to be working on *Twelfth Night* at this period.

10. See Notes by Mrs E.E. Higgins, 16.3.1930, VH Papers. Some time in 1900–10 local historian W.T. Freemantle showed that Siddalls were living in Derbyshire in C18, and supported the idea of a family crest and motto, as believed by the family, but later investigations did not confirm this – see letters to and from Miss E.E. Higgins, 3.4.1930 and 7.4.1930, VH Papers. The family tree given by VH was based on Freemantle's researches but is not reliable.

11. See Census 1861, enumeration book, where Mrs Siddall's age was given as 59.

12. Notes by Mrs E.E. Higgins 16.3.1930, VH Papers.

13. In Census 1841, Ann Siddall's age was given as 16, but the handwriting is not wholly clear. Charles jnr was not enumerated at home. In Census 1851, Ann was not at home and Charles jnr's age was given as 24. On his death the following year, he was said to be aged 23. It is hard to be more precise about

these ages, as compulsory registration of births was not introduced until 1837. In Census 1851 Charles jnr's birthplace was given as 'Yorkshire'.

14. Entry for 23.8.1830, Holborn St Andrew's Parish Baptism Register, Greater London Record Office (GLRO). The occupations of fathers of the six other infants baptized on the same day indicate the social class to which all belonged: tailor, glasscutter, paperstainer, tobacconist.

15. Details from Census 1841, 1851 and 1861, but not all family members were enumerated on each Census. Lydia Siddall was only at home in 1841, and Mary first appeared in 1861; it is not known where they were staying on other occasions.

16. Henry Mayhew, *London Life and the London Poor*, 1861, i, 9.

17. According to the Census 1841, nine-year-old Robert Evans, presumably Mrs Siddall's nephew, was listed in the household, which also included a young labourer and his wife, evidently lodgers. The whole dwelling thus accommodated four adults, eight children and a shop.

18. Information from Census 1851, contemporary street directories and C19 maps in GLRO.

19. Reports of trial and execution of James Greenacre, *Times*, April–May 1837.

20. Notes by W.T. Freemantle, 9.5.1923, and Miss E.E. Higgins, 7.3.1930, VH Papers.

21. Occupational Census figures cited in G. Stedman-Jones, *Outcast London*, 1971, App. 2, Tab. 11.

22. Hudson 19.

23. Ibid., 20.

24. Ibid., 19.

25. See WHD's study for *Twelfth Night*, Tate Gallery, cat. no. 116; WHD's engraving in *The Germ*, May 1850, depicting Viola and Olivia; and WHD's finished oil *Twelfth Night*, Tate Gallery cat. no. 23.

26. *The Critic* 1.7.1850.

27. See Brian and Judy Dobbs, *Dante Gabriel Rossetti: An Alien Victorian*, 1977, ch. 5.

28. Tate Gallery cat. no. 25.

29. Fredeman (1975) entry for 2.2.1850.

30. Tate Gallery cat. no. 164.

31. Fredeman (1975) entry for 13.3.1850.

32. W. Holman Hunt i, 199.

33. Doughty & Wahl, 92.

34. 'WHH and PRB' typescript, VH Papers.

35. Surtees no. 45.

36. See *Gretchen and Mephistopheles*, Surtees no. 34, and *La Belle Dame Sans Merci*, Surtees no. 32, both of which date from 1848, before EES entered the PRB circle.

37. W.M. Rossetti, *Burlington Magazine*, op. cit., 274.

38. W.M. Rossetti, *Dante Gabriel Rossetti: Paintings and Designs*, 1889, 22.

39. W. Holman Hunt i, 199.

40. Ibid., 238.

41. Ibid., facing 234.

42. Tate Gallery cat. no. 36.

43. *Times*, 13.5.1851.

44. W. Holman Hunt i, 256.

45. *Summary of 1851 Census*, 1854, 137.

46. Surtees nos. 62 etc. The series of drawings is reproduced and discussed in A.I. Grieve, *The Art of Dante Gabriel Rossetti*, Vol. 3, 1978, 56–9.

47. W. Holman Hunt i, 34. This is over-emphatic, but DGR did tend to glamourize his sitters.

48. Surtees no. 118. This is often said to have been begun in 1851 but stylistically and emotionally it belongs to 1860 and I am convinced that the inscription is part of the subject rather than simply the date of execution.

49. W.M. Rossetti (1906) 200. The information was supplied to WMR many years after the event by James Siddall, brother to EES.

50. JEM to WHH 9.1.1852, quoted Tate Gallery, 98.

51. Quoted from Arthur Hughes by J.G. Millais, *John Everett Millais: Life and Letters*, 1899, i. 144. Hughes was a close associate of JEM at this date.

52. W. Holman Hunt i, 307.

53. See Frances Borzello, *The Artist's Model*, 1982.

54. Fredeman (1975) entry for 7.12.1850.

55. Boyce 5 and 7.

56. Tate Gallery Collection no. 4536.

57. J.G. Millais, op. cit., i, 149.

58. See also Oswald Doughty, *Dante Gabriel Rossetti: A Victorian Romantic*, 1949.

59. Surtees no. 50.

60. Doughty & Wahl, 122.

61. Mary Howitt, *An Autobiography*, 1889, ii, 87–8. The Howitts took over the lease from Edward Bateman, who allowed DGR to use the cottage.

62. Scott, i, 316. WBS's memory was notoriously unreliable but as DGR was only at the Hermitage for a few weeks in 1852 this recollection is unlikely to be misplaced.

63. Doughty & Wahl, 109.

64. Ibid., 115.

65. Surtees no. 58; the subject had been designed earlier, when Dante's visitors were all shown as male (see Tate Gallery cat. nos. 162 and 198) so the introduction of a female visitor was evidently made with EES in mind, despite DGR's elaborate alternative justification, see Doughty & Wahl, 197–8.

66. JEM to WHH 4.11.1852, quoted D. Holman-Hunt, 92.

67. Doughty & Wahl, 127.

Chapter Two (pp. 37–54)

1. See death certificate and gravestone in St Pancras Cemetery London where date of death was given as 11 October 1890 and age as 55 years; also biographical records which give EMB's dates as 1834–90.

2. Including John Thomas Gandy, born 1846, Emily Gandy, born 1852 and Henry Gandy, born 1856. For further details of Brown and Hill families, see W.D. Paden, 'The Ancestry and Families of Ford Madox Brown', *Bulletin of John*

Rylands Library, Vol. 50, 1967–8, 131–5.

3. Juliet Soskice, *Chapters from Childhood*, 1921, 42.

4. Hueffer 39.

5. Soskice, op.cit., 42.

6. W.M. Rossetti (1906), 136.

7. Hueffer 60.

8. W.M. Rossetti (1906), 136.

9. Tate Gallery cat. no. 16.

10. Tate Gallery cat. no. 7.

11. Birmingham Art Gallery Collection no. 789'06.

12. See Brown, entries for 7–8.12.1848 and 13–15.1.1849; it is also possible that some of the sessions with unidentified models refer to EMB.

13. Brown 58.

14. Ibid., 66.

15. See Hueffer, 59.

16. Ibid. FMB went to Paris and the Lake District in 1848, not to Stratford.

17. Exhaustive searches in the Birth Records of the Office of Population, Census and Statistics (OPCS) London, have failed to reveal a birth registration certificate, but it is possible that the birth was registered, either under a different name or at a much later date.

18. Tate Gallery cat. no. 38.

19. Brown 76.

20. Tate Gallery cat. no. 39.

21. Brown 74.

22. Tate Gallery cat. no. 82.

23. Ibid., 149–50.

24. Brown 194.

25. Tate Gallery cat. no. 156; originally known as *Oure Ladye of Saturdaye Night*, this shows a young mother giving her child its weekly bath and was perhaps derived from FMB's observation of his first wife and daughter Lucy.

26. Brown xiii.

27. See Paden, op. cit., citing St Pancras Baptism Register for 1852.

28. Brown 78.

29. FMB to EMB n.d. in Ford Madox Ford Collection, Cornell University Library.

30. Brown xiv.

31. Tate Gallery cat. nos. 62, 178, 179.

32. Brown 80.

33. Ibid.

34. DGR to EMB 9.4.1853, Doughty & Wahl 130.

35. Surtees no. 272.

36. W.M. Rossetti (1906), 136.

37. There is a tradition, that seems to be based on a misunderstanding by a later acquaintance, that EMB and EES were already friends through their mothers. VH pursued this line of inquiry in depth and without results.

38. Brown 185.

39. After her death, DGR had all EES' work photographed and reproduced in a limited number of portfolios, distributed to close friends. Two of the portfolios

are extant in Fitzwilliam Museum Cambridge and Ashmolean Museum Oxford. Nothing obviously relating to Wordsworth's poem is included.

40. Surtees no. 440.

41. Surtees no. 695.

42. Surtees no. 668, where the title is given as *A Parable of Love* and the date as c.1850. But the subject matter and the fact that the lovers are shown 'in their own intense world, the world of art' (Grieve, 3, 60) surely places this work as post-1852, when EES first took up drawing, and probably locates it in the 1853–4 period when she was painting her self-portrait under DGR's instruction.

43. Doughty & Wahl, 146.

44. Surtees no. 462; from DGR's many portraits of EES in this mode has been derived the long-standing myth of her beauty, to which an account of her personality has been added. That by John Gere is representative: to EES he attributed 'the fatal gift of extreme beauty . . . morbid and withdrawn . . . the moon to his sun, merely reflecting his light . . .' etc etc, (J. Gere, *Dante Gabriel Rossetti: Painter and Poet*, 1973, 14 and 48).

45. See Tate Gallery 266 and 183.

46. Tate Gallery cat. no. 200. EES' version is believed to have been begun in August 1853.

47. Tate Gallery cat. no. 198.

48. Tate Gallery 266.

49. See also Tate Gallery cat. no. 54.

50. Doughty & Wahl, 121–3.

51. Ibid., 167.

52. Ibid., 183.

53. Ibid.

54. Ibid., 184.

55. Ibid., 192.

56. Ibid., 191.

57. See Stephanie Grilli, 'Pre-Raphaelitism and Phrenology', *Pre-Raphaelite Papers*, ch. 3.

58. W.M. Rossetti (ed.) *The Family Letters of Christina Georgina Rossetti*, 1908, 24.

59. BLS to Bessie Parkes, c.1854, Troxell Collection, Princeton University Library.

60. Doughty & Wahl, 190.

61. Ibid., 258, where DGR wrote of carving initials on 'a blocked up door' on East Hill and again on 'a stone at the Old Roar'.

62. See Violet Hunt, op. cit., 133 and Hester Burton, *Barbara Bodichon*, 1949, 54, where an account of this nature seems to have been handed down within the Leigh-Smith family. VH claimed to have her version from Henrietta Blackadder, housekeeper at Scalands.

63. See Siddall for the texts of all EES verse, originally printed piecemeal by WMR (see below, ch.6, n.99).

64. Neither poem was written in or around 1854 when the alleged events took place, but some years later, when EES began writing verse. The connection between 'The Portrait' and *How They Met Themselves* is even clearer if both are regarded as belonging to 1858–60.

65. See Doughty & Wahl, 191, 200, 108; also EES Portfolio.

66. See also Siddall, pl. 14.

67. Doughty & Wahl, 258.

68. Ibid., letter no. 170, which is misplaced, as it refers to two visits to Scalands, only one of which had taken place by 12.5.1854, the date assigned to the letter by the editors. It must in fact have been written later in the month, or possibly in June.

69. Ibid., 208–9.

70. Siddall, pl.6.

71. Ibid., pl.7.

72. Surtees no. 69.

73. Surtees no. 78.

74. Doughty & Wahl, 209.

Chapter Three (pp. 55–78)

1. WHH to DGR 21.3.1855, Troxell, 40.

2. Tate Gallery cat. no. 157 and no. 104 for references to WHD's treatment of *Margaret in Prison*.

3. Tate Gallery cat. no. 32.

4. W. Holman Hunt ii, 429; Grieve, op. cit., 54–5.

5. See Tate Gallery cat. nos. 38 and 45.

6. W. Holman Hunt ii, 430.

7. WHH to FGS 15.2.1861, Bodl. MS Don.e.66.

8. See Tate Gallery cat. no. 39. One of WHH's aims was to depict real as opposed to Dresden shepherdesses, and it is clear that the temptations of the flesh were much in his mind as part of the subject of the painting.

9. Information on WHH's personal life as a young man was successfully controlled and censored by his widow Edith Hunt, who also helped compile his autobiography. Details of WHH's relationship with Emma Watkins and AM were first researched and published in D. Holman-Hunt, with assistance from genealogist Bridget Lakin. Before this was issued, AM was an extremely shadowy figure who made only brief appearances in the histories of Pre-Raphaelitism.

10. Tate Gallery 1984 cat. no. 39. Emma Watkins was again employed in July–August 1852, when the Shepherdess's head was retouched.

11. W. Holman Hunt ii, 430.

12. Reproduced in Violet Hunt, facing 190.

13. WHH to FGS 15.2.1861, Bodl. MS.Don.e.66.

14. For detailed discussion of this see Tate Gallery cat. no. 58. While in progress, the painting was referred to by WHH as 'the Woodbine Villa picture' (WHH to FGS 23.9.1853, Bodl. MS.Don.e.66).

15. Brown 172.

16. Tate Gallery cat. no. 84.

17. There is however a certain similarity between the way in which WHH painted both the hair of the goat and that of the artist in his later self-portrait. In other respects the picture which most resembles that of the scapegoat is the

portrait of WHH's patron Thomas Combe.

18. WHH Journal 1854, John Rylands Library Manchester, quoted in Judith Bronkhurst, 'Holman Hunt's visit to the Dead Sea 1854', *Pre-Raphaelite Papers*, 152–3.

19. Census 1851 shows Sarah Bradshaw, age 34, former governess, resident at 5 Prospect Place, Cheyne Walk, together with Mrs Harriet Bradshaw, age 42, who was landlady or housekeeper of the lodgings occupied there by WHH and a number of other people.

20. D. Holman-Hunt 97.

21. Brown 181.

22. JEM to WHH 10.4.1854, quoted Mary Lutyens, *Millais and the Ruskins*, 1967, 150n; and M. Halliday to WHH, Apr–May 1854, quoted D. Holman-Hunt, 132.

23. For *Waiting*, see Tate Gallery cat. no. 29; *Girl in the Pink Bonnet* is reproduced in black and white in D. Holman-Hunt. The identification is disputed by art historians, Mary Lutyens claiming that the model for *Waiting* is AM and Malcolm Warner stating that she is not (see D. Holman-Hunt 132, and Tate Gallery cat. no. 59).

24. FGS to WHH May–Jun 1854, quoted D. Holman-Hunt 133.

25. Surtees no. 57.

26. There are problems over the dating and alterations to *Hesterna Rosa*, see Grieve, op. cit., 54–6; there also appear to be two identical original versions.

27. FGS to WHH Mar 1855, quoted D. Holman-Hunt 154.

28. Brown 136.

29. FGS to WHH 14.11.1855, quoted D. Holman-Hunt 154.

30. Ibid.

31. See D. Holman-Hunt 247.

32. Ibid., 154.

33. FGS to WHH 14.11.1855, see above n.29.

34. Ibid. FGS wrote to WHH saying, 'before receiving your letter which says you had written to Annie Miller recommending matrimony . . .' (14.11.1855, quoted D. Holman-Hunt 154).

35. W.M. Rossetti, *Burlington Magazine*, op. cit., 277.

36. Brown 101.

37. Ibid., 106.

38. See Doughty & Wahl, 230; Surtees no. 67.

39. Doughty & Wahl, 233.

40. That this was not purely a modern phenomenon is shown by the following observation in the *Morning Chronicle*, 18.1.1850: 'It really seems in many places to be taken as a matter of course that a young woman will be found with child before she is married. Many are married as soon as they become pregnant . . . in an immense number of cases young people come to a distinct understanding with each other to cohabit illicitly, until the woman becomes pregnant; the man promising to "make an honest woman of her" as soon as that takes place. This they find much more convenient than marrying at once . . .'

41. Tate Gallery cat. nos. 73 and 97.

42. See Lyn Nead, 'On the Brink', *Art History*, June 1982; and 'Representations on Sexuality and the Female Nude', *Art History*, Sept 1983.

43. Doughty & Wahl, 214.

44. A rough sketch of a male and female figure in EES' Portfolio may possibly represent a version of *La Belle Dame Sans Merci*.

45. Tate Gallery cat. no. 217, where it is noted that this 'design may have been made initially in connection with a plan to involve Elizabeth Siddall in the illustrated edition of Tennyson's poems published by Moxon'.

46. Doughty & Wahl, 245; the price included all the drawings.

47. This drawing eventually found its way back to the rightful owner and was printed in the collection of *Letters of DGR to WA* published in 1897 (ed. G.B. Hill).

48. See G. Greer, *The Obstacle Race*, 1979 and R. Parker and G. Pollock, *Old Mistresses: Women, Art and Ideology*, 1981.

49. JR to Ellen Heaton c.1855, *Sublime and Instructive*, ed. V. Surtees, 1972, 157–8; this letter cannot date from February 1855 as suggested, since JR did not see EES' work until March.

50. Doughty & Wahl, 249.

51. *Sublime and Instructive*, 182.

52. Doughty & Wahl, 249.

53. Ruskin i. 203.

54. Ibid., i, 204.

55. Brown 133.

56. Doughty & Wahl, 222; this letter has been misplaced. The first meeting between EES and Mrs Rossetti took place in April 1855.

57. Ibid.; the name Barnsbury must be mistranscribed. EES' niece recorded: 'It was my mother who was first seen by my father hanging up candles in Aunt Lucy's shop and fell in love with her. The shop was situated in the Roman Road, Barnsbury, opposite Pentonville Prison' – Notes by Mrs E.E. Higgins, 16.3.1931, VH Papers.

58. Brown 126.

59. Ruskin i, 195.

Chapter Four (pp. 79–97)

1. *Summary of 1851 Census*, in fact late marriage age was common throughout Europe up until the end of C19, and the perception that it was more marked in the British middle class may be based more on fear of social instability than on demographic evidence.

2. *Englishwoman's Domestic Magazine*, March 1865.

3. S.W. Partridge, *Upward and Onward: A Thought Book for the Threshold of Active Life*, 1857.

4. Published 1854–62.

5. WHH to JEM 1852, quoted W. Holman Hunt i, 284.

6. WHH to WMR 12.8.1855, quoted Bronkhurst, op. cit., 123.

7. JEM to Charles Collins 3.7.1855, quoted Mary Lutyens, op. cit., 261.

8. Effie Millais' diary, quoted Mary Lutyens, 263.

9. JEM to WHH Jan 1856, quoted D. Holman-Hunt, 168.

10. See Mary Lutyens, *Effie in Venice*, 1965, as well as *Millais and the Ruskins*,

op. cit.

11. Petition text printed in Hester Burton, *Barbara Bodichon*, 1949, 70–1.

12. The family version of BLS's life story is contained in Hester Burton's book; information on her relationship with John Chapman is in G.S. Haight, *George Eliot and John Chapman*, 1967, 87–92.

13. Joseph Knight, *Life of Dante Gabriel Rossetti*, 1887, 71–3. Knight acknowledged assistance from FMB and WMR and seems to have taken most of his information (? including this assertion) from FMB.

14. W.M. Rossetti (1899) 79–80.

15. Ruskin i, 207.

16. See Ruth Brandon, *The Spiritualists*, 1983.

17. Ruskin i, 207.

18. Ibid., 206.

19. Henry Acland to DGR 25.4.1866, remarking, 'I often think of you – I look at the photograph *she* gave me of some sheep, now so faded that you can scarce see the outlines of the flock.'

20. Doughty & Wahl, 262.

21. Ruskin i, 216–17.

22. W. Holman Hunt i, 326–7.

23. See E.M. Bell, *Josephine Butler*, 1962, 34–7.

24. Ruskin i, 217.

25. Ibid., 206.

26. Doughty & Wahl, 262.

27. Ibid., 261.

28. W.M. Rossetti (1899), 96.

29. It is possible that the sketch is that entitled *Design for a Capital*, in EES Portfolio.

30. Brown 113.

31. Ibid., 124.

32. Ibid., 129.

33. Ibid., 133.

34. Ibid., 134.

35. Ibid., 142.

36. Soskice, op. cit., 43.

37. Brown 149.

38. Ibid., 154.

39. Doughty & Wahl, 271.

40. Ruskin i, 226.

41. Scott ii, 30.

42. Surtees no. 75.

43. JR to Ellen Heaton, 30.12.1855, quoted *Sublime and Instructive*, 181.

44. W.M. Rossetti (1899) 110–13.

45. Doughty & Wahl, 288–9.

Chapter Five (pp. 98–116)

1. WMR was engaged to Henrietta Rintoul, daughter of the *Spectator*'s

owner-editor, for whom WMR wrote art criticism and reviews. The marriage never took place. With regard to the Rossetti family, it is my belief that Mrs Frances Lavinia Rossetti was ambitious for all her children and unconsciously hindered them from making marriages to persons she felt unworthy, such as EES, Miss Rintoul and, perhaps, the young men to whom Christina was engaged, whose religious deficiencies were also a bar to wedlock. Both her daughters were lifelong spinsters; the elder, Maria, at one time aspired to marry JR, who would perhaps have been thought worthy, but who did not make an offer.

2. FGS to WHH autumn 1855, quoted D. Holman-Hunt, 154.

3. FMB to WHH Sept 1855, ibid., 153.

4. JEM to WHH early 1855, ibid., 168.

5. *Household Words* 3.12.1856.

6. JEM to WHH May 1856, quoted Nuel Pharr Davis, *The Life of Wilkie Collins* 1956, 164–5. JEM's view that Caroline should be abandoned because she was disreputable (it was believed she had been the mistress of another man before meeting Wilkie Collins, and she had a young daughter whose parentage was never properly explained, although Caroline may well have been married to the child's father) was not creditable but it underlines the PRB's sense of moral rectitude. Caroline Graves was later famous for having inspired the opening sequence of Wilkie Collins' novel *The Woman in White*, 1859–60. Collins subsequently established another relationship with Martha Rudd, by whom he had a clandestine family; he maintained his relationship with Caroline but refused to marry her even when free to do so.

7. Thomas Woolner to WBS 4.10.1854, quoted *The George Eliot Letters*, ed. G.S. Haight, 1954–78, ii, 175–6.

8. Brown 189.

9. W. Holman Hunt i, 83.

10. Surtees no. 81.

11. WHH to FGS mid-1859, Bodl. MS Don.e.66; here the incident is dated as occurring shortly before AM was 'sent to school'.

12. Hudson 146.

13. WHH to FGS 15.2.1861, Bodl. MS Don.e.66.

14. Brown 181.

15. Ibid., 184.

16. Ruskin i, 232.

17. Several versions of the drawing of this subject are reproduced in EES' Portfolio. The finished watercolour is in the Fitzwilliam Museum.

18. Some writers have assumed that EES lived in Weymouth Street during most of the 1850s, but it is clear that before receiving the allowance from JR she could not afford her own apartment. She is not likely to have retained the rooms when she was away from London, so it is probable that Weymouth Street was her residence only from May–November 1856.

19. Lucy Madox Brown born 19.8.1843.

20. Brown 174.

21. Ibid., 175.

22. Ibid., 178.

23. Ibid., 183.

24. Ibid., 184–7.

25. Tate Gallery collection no. 3471.

26. Brown 191.

27. Ibid., 195.

28. WHH to FGS 1856, Bodl. MS. Don.e.66.

29. FGS to WHH 9.12.1856, quoted D. Holman-Hunt 177.

30. WHH to FGS 10.12.1856, Bodl. MS. Don.e.66.

31. FGS to WHH 9.12.1856, quoted D. Holman-Hunt 177.

32. WHH to FGS Dec 1856, Bodl. MS. Don.e.66.

33. See Brown xii and 183 n.55.

34. Ibid., 164–5. Ruth Herbert was the professional name of Mrs Crabbe, who was separated from her husband and earned her living as an actress. A study of her life and work would make an interesting comparison to the women discussed here.

35. Doughty & Wahl, 316.

36. Brown 194; the artists' colony idea is also mentioned in W. Holman Hunt ii, 142.

37. Doughty & Wahl, 320.

38. Ibid., 321.

39. Brown 195–6.

40. Ibid., 196–7.

41. Doughty & Wahl, 323; Arthur Gabriel Madox Brown was eventually christened on 14.7.1857, shortly before his death.

42. W. Holman Hunt i, 97–8; WHH's claim to total recall need not be taken literally here, and the exact tone of DGR's defence of EES is hard to judge, although he is known to have retained his admiration for her work despite the fluctuations in their relationship.

43. 'Exhibition at Russell Place', *Spectator*, 6.6.1857.

44. Ruskin i, 262.

45. Tate Gallery cat. no. 222.

46. WMR attributed the work to 1854 but there is no reason to dispute EES' own dating. The earlier references presumably relate to sketches and drawings done c.1854, probably in relation to the Moxon Tennyson; they are included in EES' Portfolio. For a full discussion of *Lady Clare*, see Tate Gallery, 283.

Chapter Six (pp. 117–35)

1. The information on EES' stay in Sheffield derives from sources in VH Papers, notably a letter dated 9.5.1923 from W.T. Freemantle and notes on his lecture on EES to the Sheffield Literary and Philosophical Society, 5.3.1912. One former student at the Sheffield School of Art in the 1850s, Charles Green, recalled EES' enrolment and her participation in the trip to Manchester. VH was correct in saying that Charles Howell also went on an excursion to the Art Treasures exhibition, but not that EES met him there.

2. Margaret Fleming, 'Where Janey Used to Live', *William Morris Society Journal (WMSJ)* Winter 1981, 67 ff.

3. See J.W. Mackail's Notebooks in William Morris Gallery, Walthamstow.

These were used by Mackail to record material gathered for the two-volume official biography of WM issued in 1899. The story of JM's 'discovery' exists in many variants; Mackail's version was taken down from EBJ and as that of an eyewitness is used here. It is unlikely that WM was present when JM was first seen, as he was a reluctant theatregoer.

4. G. Birkbeck Hill, ed., *Letters of Dante Gabriel Rossetti to William Allingham 1854–1870*, 1897, 144.

5. Val Prinsep, 'Chapter from a Painter's Reminiscences', *Magazine of Art*, 1902, 170.

6. Ibid., 170.

7. Mackail Notebooks, WM Gall.

8. Burne-Jones i, 231.

9. Hilary Morgan points out, however, that the heroine of Charles Kingsley's *Two Years Ago*, published February 1857, is described in very similar terms to JM and it may be that the Oxford set, who read and admired Kingsley's work, were responding to rather than setting a trend.

10. See Rose, introduction.

11. See Margaret Fleming, *WMSJ*, op. cit.

12. Mackail Notebooks, WM Gall.

13. J.W. Mackail to SCC 19.9.1898, BL ADD 52734.

14. PW to JM 27.8.1898, 19.10.1898, 31.10.1898, BL ADD 45342.

15. Henderson (1950), 231.

16. Mackail Notebooks (comments by EBJ) WM Gall.

17. Surtees no. 93c.

18. Surtees no. 94.

19. Surtees no. 95.

20. Surtees no. 95a.

21. Surtees no. 363.

22. Surtees no. 97.

23. See Penelope Fitzgerald, introduction to WM, *Novel on Blue Paper*, 1982, xi.

24. Mackail i, 111.

25. See SCC to GBS 17.4.1950, BL ADD 50531.

26. Margaret Fleming, *WMSJ*, op. cit.

27. WSB Notebook entry for 10.3.1903, quoted Elizabeth Longford, *A Pilgrimage of Passion*, 1979, 323.

28. Tate Gallery cat. no. 94.

29. 'La Belle Iseult is what the dear father always called the picture, and I think we ought to stick to that' – JM to May Morris, July 1910, BL ADD 45346.

30. Doughty & Wahl, 325. This was presumably the subject WM was occupied with when GBJ saw him painting in the Maclarens' garden in Summertown in June 1857. It was not finished but the design reappeared as a stained-glass window for Bradford in 1862.

31. Surtees no. 597.

32. The issue of WM's appearance is a difficult one. Miss Price, sister to EBJ's lifelong friend, wrote in her diary in August 1855, 'Morris *is* very handsome' (Mackail i. 80) and GBJ, although she paid WM little personal attention in the early days, later wrote of him at this time, 'He was very handsome, of an unusual

type' (Burne-Jones i, 111). These judgements should be set against those by
Prinsep and DGR.

33. Prinsep 168.

34. ACS to Edwin Hatch 17.2.1858, *Swinburne Letters*, ed. C.Y. Lang, 1959, i,
18.

35. Mackail Notebooks, WM Gall.

36. Doughty & Wahl, 329.

37. See R. Glynn Grylls, *Portrait of Rossetti*, 1964, pl. 10. The account does not
relate to EES or DGR.

38. Surtees no. 98.

39. Surtees no. 106.

40. Surtees no. 99.

41. Tate Gallery Collection no. 3202.

42. Doughty & Wahl, 333.

43. 'WHD and the PRB', Huntingdon, op. cit.

44. Hall Caine, *My Story*, 1928, 81. The information is garbled, however, and
serves only to show that some notion of a separation between EES and DGR was
current at a later date. Other evidence for an estrangement between EES and
DGR at this date is correspondence from EES' brother James Siddall to WMR
many years later, stating that at the end of the 1850s James Siddall 'saw much of
my sister', which may indicate that she returned home, and voicing the opinion
that as EES 'was given to fits of melancholy . . . there would be nothing
extraordinary in a man like Rossetti . . . withdrawing himself for the moment'
(quoted Grylls 87 and 94). James Siddall believed these momentary withdrawals
took place after the marrige, but it may well be that his sister's melancholy was
the result rather than the cause of separation from the man she loved. It is possible
that DGR returned to Matlock to see EES later in the year, telling his family he
was going to take the waters, as suggested in CGR's letter to WMR 18.8.1858,
saying DGR had 'utterly disappeared from these quarters. His water cure was
prescribed by himself, such treatment having formerly relieved him' (*The Family
Letters of Christina Rossetti* 25). Note also, however, that WMR hinted at a
separation in 1858 and 'the whole of 1859' in W.M. Rossetti, *Burlington
Magazine*, op. cit., 284.

45. 'The Cloud Before the Storm', in *DGR: List of Manuscripts*, ed. P.F. Baum,
1931, 62.

46. Surtees no. 108.

47. Tate Gallery 276.

48. Doughty & Wahl, 201.

49. The dating of EES's poems seems problematic, but may be very simple.
WMR, who first published them, did not know when they were written. The
Rossetti family first saw them in about 1865, after EES's death, when DGR was
advising CGR on the compilation of her second volume of verse; in gratitude for
his aid she suggested including EES' poems at the end of her book. Having read
them she changed her mind, commenting that although beautiful, they were too
hopelessly sad for publication. WMR published the poems in 1899 (8 poems) and
1906 (6 poems), ascribing dates to them which seem to be based on guesswork.
Had EES been writing verse during the early years of her relationship with DGR,
one would expect to find references to this in, for example, his letters; he

encouraged and praised her other artistic efforts. The only poem that in my view may date from the early period is 'True Love', a lament in ballad metre reminiscent of the traditional and modern ballads she, DGR and WA admired; it has affinities with works by both DGR and WA. But in the absence of solid evidence as to dates, the poems are best placed after the break in her relationship with DGR. Most express loss, sadness and bitterness and can logically be read as a verbal record of personal emotion. In terms of time, the two years from 1858 to 1860, when there is no record of EES, could account for the majority of the verses. Some, according to WMR, were written after her marriage in 1860 and there is no particular reason to dispute this. I have made no effort to date the poems more specifically.

50. Quoted in L.M. Packer, *Christina Rossetti*, 1963, 194.

Chapter Seven (pp. 139–59)

1. Information on FC is contained in Baum, based on Samuel Bancroft's correspondence with her and her stepson during the last years of FC's life. This gives her birthplace as Steyning, erroneously located by Bancroft in Surrey, and her birthdate as 3 January 1824, apparently derived from the parish register. Her real name was said to be Sarah Cox. In addition to this there is a small packet of correspondence relating to FC collected by T.J. Wise, which contains pencilled notes on blank pages torn from a 1924 pocket diary, stating that FC was 'Sarah Cox, daughter of a provincial blacksmith, born in 1828 . . . her professional name was "Fanny Cornforth" she came to DGR in 1854' (BL Ashley 3854). The Census records show a Sarah Cox, blacksmith's daughter, living in Steyning and born around 1824–5, who appears to fit the information known about FC but who was still living in Steyning in 1861 when FC was indisputably in London. Reliance should not therefore be placed on the scraps of information provided by Bancroft or Wise. An alternative version of FC's ancestry, involving a whole northern genealogy of Hyltons and Cornforths, was provided by VH, stating that she was born Sarah Cox in Darlington. There is no confirmation that FC was born there, or that she was related to any Cornforths in that locality or indeed elsewhere. I incline to the view that she was born in or near Steyning, and 'borrowed' certain attributes from the Cox family when inquiries were made about her background. It is probably impossible to obtain conclusive information.

2. Hudson 19.

3. Ibid., 40–1.

4. Ibid., 214.

5. W.M. Rossetti (1895) i, 202–3.

6. HC to GBS 24.9.1928, BL ADD 50531.

7. This may have been the South Bank pleasure gardens with concert hall, circus ring, rifle ranges, supper rooms etc., which was forcibly closed in July 1859, the site being used for building land.

8. The nut story is the version told by men; it comes in HC to GBS 24.9.1928, BL ADD 50531 and derives either from DGR or WBS, who included it in variant form in his *Autobiographical Notes*, locating the encounter in the

Strand, a street where clients and prostitutes met.

9. Brown 200; the entry is dated 27 January 1858 but covers the events of the whole previous week. This is always taken as the first extant reference to FC, but is somewhat puzzling. To which painters did FMB refer with 'Fanny, their model'? Both EBJ and WM, the tenants of the Red Lion Square studio at this date, were mostly in Oxford until February 1858, except for the Christmas period, and DGR was at Matlock until May 1858, with a similar visit to London at Christmas. FMB's reference appears to suggest that during this short break some or all of the painters were at work in Red Lion Square. If so, what work was FC posing for? FC stated that the first subject she sat to DGR was for the head of the figure in *Found*; was this done c.January 1858? It should be noted that FC, reminiscing about her meeting with the painters, placed the first encounter in the summer of 1856. This seems incorrect as to year, but I am inclined to credit her with accurate recollection as to season. It may be that the meeting in fact took place in or around May–June 1858, when DGR returned from Matlock, evidently fancy-free. FMB's habitual mistakes with names may be taken into account here, or his diary entry may relate to another, unidentified Fanny. It seems impossible to reach a definitive conclusion.

10. Baum 4.

11. Surtees nos. 64M and 64Q; see also Grieve, op. cit., part 2 for full discussion.

12. Boyce 25.

13. Brown 200.

14. Burne-Jones i, 171.

15. Rooke Notes 488.

16. Prinsep, op. cit., 282.

17. This police tally, taken on 20.5.1857, was published in William Acton, *Prostitution*, 1857.

18. See the section on prostitution by Bracebridge Heminge in Mayhew, op. cit., iv, 213.

19. See Judith Walkowitz, *Prostitution and Victorian Society*, 1980, 16–26.

20. Frances Finnegan, *Poverty and Prostitution: A Study of Victorian Prostitutes in York*, 1979. This is based on prostitutes known to the police or admitted to the penitentiary and the author points out that no information is available on 'higher-grade' or more discreet prostitutes. In York in 1842, the majority of prostitutes known to the police were aged between 18 and 25; very few seem to have been still operating on the streets after the age of 30, unless they had simply become more adept at avoiding arrest. The available evidence suggests that until later in the century prostitution was not a profession as such, but a casual, intermittent activity; ironically, partly due to the reformers' efforts, professionalization later accompanied criminalization.

21. Mayhew iv, 213.

22. Ibid., 214.

23. Finnegan 81.

24. Now in Carlisle City Art Gallery and identified subsequent to the publication of Surtees. This cannot have been drawn in 1858, as suggested in G.P. Boyce, 86 n.30, as GPB did not meet FC until the very end of that year and only really got to know her during 1859.

25. Burne-Jones i, 55.

26. Ibid., 56.

27. Baldwin 43.

28. Ibid., 16–17.

29. Ibid., 78.

30. Burne-Jones i, 105.

31. Baldwin 32.

32. Ibid., 36.

33. Burne-Jones i, 142.

34. Baldwin 52, quoting Louie Macdonald.

35. Burne-Jones i, 105; the actual words were 'I am confident that the mystery which shrouds men and women from each other in youth was sacred to each one of them'.

36. Ibid., 135.

37. Ibid., 142.

38. Ibid., 169.

39. Ibid., 155.

40. Ibid., 176.

41. Brown 201.

42. Burne-Jones i, 179.

43. Ibid.

44. George du Maurier Feb–Mar 1862, quoted in *The Young George du Maurier* (ed. D. du Maurier) 1951, 113 and 119. At Little Holland House, du Maurier wrote, 'instead of dressing for dinner, you undress . . . somehow in the very delightful atmosphere of this house I seem to perceive a slight element of looseness'.

45. Burne-Jones i, 186.

46. Ibid., 186.

47. Joanna Boyce was born 7.12.1832 and pursued art as a profession, as did her brother GPB. In 1857 at the age of 25, she married a fellow artist and miniaturist Henry Wells in Rome. She had two daughters and continued to paint: her abilities were highly admired. DGR described her as 'a wonderfully gifted woman' (quoted V. Surtees, *Reflections of a Friendship*, 1979, 169). She died on 15 July 1861. See also below, ch. 10.

48. Boyce 25.

49. Tate Gallery cat. no. 98.

50. Tate Gallery Collection no. 3232.

51. Boyce 25.

52. Ibid., 26.

53. Ibid., 87; on 2.3.1859 DGR did two drawings of a woman at Serle St, Lincolns Inn, which are identified as being of FC, but they do not much resemble her and there is no supporting evidence. In my view the head in the drawings at Serle St is more like that of Ruth Herbert than FC.

54. Boyce 26–7.

55. Ibid., 85 and 87.

56. For example, in *The Bower Garden*, Surtees no. 114, and possibly also *Golden Water*, Surtees no. 107.

57. Surtees no. 114.

58. DGR to GPB ?5.9.1859, quoted Surtees, 69. The cockney inflection and grammar indicate that the meaning is, 'Those [flowers] behind [are] marigolds.'

59. Tate Gallery 286.

60. There is no evidence that 'Jenny' was written earlier. DGR always claimed to have had the idea of a particular piece of work for months or years before actually starting on it, and he had been thinking about the 'Fallen Woman' theme since at least 1850, but the poem 'Jenny' dates from 1858–9. A finished text was shown to JR in 1859–60 in the hope that he would place it in the *Cornhill*. He declined on the grounds of its indecent subject matter. It is not known if the text was the same as that finally printed in 1870.

61. Surtees no. 283.

62. *DGR Letters to WA*, op. cit., 67.

63. ACS to WBS 16.12.1859, *Swinburne Letters*, op. cit., i, 27.

64. WHH to Thomas Combe 12.2.1860, Bodl. MS Eng.lett.c.296.

Chapter Eight (pp. 160–76)

1. Tate Gallery cat. no. 85.

2. WHH to FGS 11.9.1857, Bodl.MS Don.e.66.

3. WHH to FGS c.1857, ibid.

4. WHH to FGS c.1857, ibid.

5. WHH to Thomas Combe n.d. Bodl, MS Eng Lett c.296, f.83.

6. Boyce 20–1.

7. Brown 201.

8. W. Holman Hunt ii, 115.

9. FGS to WHH 18.6.1858, quoted D. Holman-Hunt 196–7.

10. FGS to WHH June 1858, ibid., 198–9.

11. WHH to FGS 8.9.1859, Bodl.MS Don.e.66.

12. WHH to Thomas Combe 26.2.1859, Bodl.MS Eng lett.c.296.

13. Information from Judith Bronkhurst.

14. Thanks to Judith Bronkhurst and Hilary Morgan for suggestions and discussions on this. The dating of *Il Dolce Far Niente* is obscure and it may well be the case that AM did not sit for it at all; at the same time the subject seems to contain at least some reference to her alleged 'idleness'. It may also, however, represent WHH's pictorial 'reply' to DGR's sensuous beauties like *Bocca Baciata*, by showing a virtuous beauty, in a domestic setting. If so, it cannot have been begun before the beginning of 1860, by which time WHH had finally parted from AM.

15. WHH to FGS n.d., Bodl.MS Don.e.66 f.162. A Hogarth Club meeting took place in Martineau's studio at Tor Villas on 1.4.1859 – see Boyce 27. Other references in WHH's letter point to a date around mid-1859.

16. WHH to FGS n.d., Bodl.MS Don.e.66 f.156.

17. WHH to FGS n.d., Bodl.MS Don.e.66; extensive research for DHH revealed no apparent messages, indicating that WHH was almost certainly deluded about this.

18. WHH to FGS 23.8.1859, Bodl.MS Don.e.66.

19. Ibid.

20. WHH to FGS 7.?9.1859, Bodl.MS Don.e.66.
21. Boyce 28.
22. Ibid; the pencil study is identified as Surtees no. 355.
23. Surtees nos. 354–8.
24. Violet Hunt 192.
25. Boyce 29.
26. Mrs Sarah Ellis, *Wives of England*, 1843, 43.
27. Mackail i, 137.
28. Boyce 24.
29. Surtees no. 364.
30. Burne-Jones i, 168–9.
31. Boyce 27.
32. Ibid., 28.
33. Mackail Notebooks, WM Gall.
34. Burne-Jones i, 202.
35. Mrs Ellis 68–9.
36. On this, see Patricia Branca, *Silent Sisterhood: Middle Class Women in the Victorian Home*, 1975.
37. Baldwin 208.
38. See Baldwin 13, and Fred Macdonald *As a Tale that is Told*, 1919.
39. Baldwin 208.
40. Rooke Notes, 17.
41. Burne-Jones i, 204.
42. EBJ 1860, quoted Grylls, op. cit., 201.

Chapter Nine (pp. 177–94)

1. Scott ii, 58–9.
2. 'Thank God for Gabriel!' P.P. Marshall is supposed to have exclaimed after EES' death. Lucy Madox Brown 'heard the words and understood' – see HRA, *Pre-Raphaelite Twilight*, 1954, 80.
3. Letter from Miss E.E. Higgins 8.4.1930, VH Papers.
4. Ellen Macintyre, on inquest record 12.2.1862, reprinted Violet Hunt, 332.
5. Doughty & Wahl, 363.
6. Ibid.
7. HC to GBS 24.9.1928, BL ADD 50531.
8. 'HH and PRB', VH Papers. This is of course VH's account of WHH's interpretation of events, long afterwards, but it is interesting that she did not use it in her book since it did not accord with her view of a protracted struggle between EES and FC for possession of DGR.
9. Doughty & Wahl, 364.
10. Ibid., 365.
11. This poem was incomplete. It was given the title 'Speechless' by WMR who also assigned it to the early date 1854. By suggesting it relates to DGR's reappearance, I am not stating that it was therefore written in 1860, merely that it may reflect EES' feelings towards the event, and was written c.1860–1.
12. Doughty & Wahl, 367.

13. DGR to GBJ Jun 1860, BJ Papers.
14. Doughty & Wahl, 368.
15. Surtees no. 118.
16. Surtees no. 121.
17. Scott ii, 59.
18. Ibid., 60.
19. Doughty & Wahl, 370.
20. Burne-Jones i, 207–8.
21. Note by WMR in EES' Portfolio, Ashmolean Museum.
22. Doughty and Wahl, 371.
23. Ibid., 373.
24. Surtees no. 120.
25. Tate Gallery cat. no. 191.
26. Walters Art Gallery, Baltimore, no. 39.419.
27. W.M. Rossetti (1899), 246.
28. See Doughty & Wahl, 375.
29. W.M. Rossetti (1899), 246.
30. Ibid., 254.
31. Ibid., 246.
32. Boyce 30.
33. See Boyce 87 and 81.
34. Surtees nos. 128 and 128A.
35. Surtees no. 142.
36. Victoria and Albert Museum.
37. Tate Gallery cat. no. 230.
38. Tate Gallery collection no. 3872. TG Notes relate this to the von Bork pictures, suggest FC as model and refer to a 'lost' picture of 1861 by EBJ entitled *The Castle of Heavy Sorrow*. TG no. 3872 is known in the photographic catalogue as *Medusa*, but it seems to possess a more Germanic than Greek atmosphere. The model certainly looks as if FC.
39. Study reproduced in Troxell, facing 4, where it was incorrectly identified as a portrait of EES by DGR. It is in fact a study of FC by EBJ; for the history of EBJ's treatment of the Tannhauser theme, see Tate Gallery 229–30.
40. Tate Gallery cat. no. 231.
41. Burne-Jones i, 205.
42. Now in V & A Museum.
43. Burne-Jones i, 217.
44. Scott ii, 60.
45. Mackail i, 140.
46. Surtees no. 116.
47. Surtees no. 117, and see Tate Gallery cat. no. 104.
48. Burne-Jones i. 208.
49. Troxell 8–9, where letter is conjecturally dated 'October 1861?' as it is known that EES was then staying at Red House. However the reference to the 'picture going at a low price' seems to link it with the letter from EES at Brighton, in WMR (1899) 246.
50. See Anthea Callen, *Angel in the Studio: Women in the Arts and Crafts Movement*, 1979.

51. PW to JM 22.12.1905, BL ADD 45343.

52. WM, 'Story of the Unknown Church', *Oxford and Cambridge Magazine*, 1856; typically, the man does the figure work and the woman the flowers and foliage, but it is interesting that a male–female partnership is presented.

53. JM to May Morris c.1910, BL ADD 45341. See also Design Council, *William Morris and Kelmscott*, 1981, 141 item Tl dated 1857, and Tate Gallery, 1984, 287.

54. JM to May Morris c.1910, BL ADD 45341.

55. Ibid.

56. Of the twelve, projected Red House figure embroideries, JM herself stated that seven were completed, but only six are now known – *Penelope* and *St Catherine* (complete) at Kelmscott Manor; *Isoude Blanchemains* (unfinished, sometimes called Guenevere) at Kelmscott; *Flamma Troiae, Hippolyte* and *Woman with a Sword* (complete) in Castle Howard Collection. In addition two cartoons for what appear to be Venus and Diana are sometimes identified as designs for this series, although this seems unlikely, as goddesses are not appropriate to a frieze of illustrious women. There are other designs, of Saints Cecilia and Dorothea, which may have had some connection with the series. But it seems impossible to determine more precisely the contents of the scheme, which probably altered over time and was anyway abandoned before completion. The three figures now in the Castle Howard Collection were exhibited in 1888 as the work of Bessie Burden. For further discussion, see O. Fairclough and E. Leary, *Textiles by William Morris and Morris & Co 1861–1940*, 1981, 22–23, and E. Leary, 'The Red House Figure Embroideries', *Apollo*, April 1981.

57. Burne-Jones i, 269.

58. Now the V&A Museum.

59. Burne-Jones i, 211.

60. Ibid., i, 212.

61. Ibid., i, 213.

Chapter Ten (pp. 195–208)

1. Mackail i, 161.

2. See A.S. Wohl, *The Victorian Family*, 1978.

3. See J.A. Banks, *Prosperity and Parenthood*, 1954, ch. 3 for costs of household assistance.

4. Elizabeth and Thomas Reynolds were both single, therefore not married to each other.

5. ACS was advised not to return to the University rather than officially expelled.

6. The question of JM's feelings towards her parents is problematic. Her daughter May, for example, grew up not knowing much about her Burden grandparents, according to later correspondence (see BL ADD 52740), while WM seems to have had little or no contact with his in-laws. Despite the similarity of names, I am not persuaded that Mrs Maizey, the charming countrywoman in WM *Novel on Blue Paper*, written 1873, was based on Ann Burden née Maizey, although it is not impossible that certain features were taken from her.

7. Doughty & Wahl, 392; the wallpaper design sketch is reproduced in *DGR Letters to WA*, facing 257, but there is no evidence that the paper was ever printed or hung.

8. See Bryson 78.

9. Doughty & Wahl, 387.

10. WMR, *Burlington Magazine*, op. cit.

11. W.M. Rossetti (1895) 173.

12. Burne-Jones i, 220.

13. Ibid., i. 220.

14. Ibid., i. 219.

15. Doughty & Wahl, 384.

16. WMR Note on EES' Portfolio, Ashmolean.

17. M. Harrison and B. Waters, *Burne-Jones*, 1979, 29.

18. GBJ's name was associated within the family with *Gammer Grethel's Fairy Stories* (Baldwin 35) and the design may be identifiable from this, a translation of Grimm issued 1849.

19. Burne-Jones i, 217–8.

20. This entry is puzzling. Occupations were not normally given to married women by the Census enumerators, and 'painter's wife' would have been redundant; the information was already entered under the 'relationship to head of household' column. I have been unable to find out anything about Emily Sarjent.

21. Burne-Jones i, 218.

22. See ch.3 n. 48.

23. See W. Holman Hunt ii, 253, and Tate Gallery 212–3.

24. Mary Howitt, op. cit., ii, 117. Anna Mary Howitt abandoned painting in the spring of 1856, the year after *Castaway* was exhibited.

25. Brown 138; the entry was entitled *A Study*.

26. Tate Gallery Collection no. 3314, dated 1861.

27. Doughty & Wahl, 396.

28. Rooke Notes 180.

29. Rooke Notes 19.

30. Mrs Ellis 105–7.

31. Doughty & Wahl, 396.

32. Burne-Jones i, 222.

33. Doughty & Wahl, 397.

34. Boyce 33.

35. Doughty & Wahl, 398.

36. Doughty & Wahl, 402.

37. Burne-Jones i, 222.

38. Ibid., 228–9.

39. Ibid., 230.

40. See Boyce 94; Brown 94.

41. Burne-Jones i, 231.

42. Ibid., 230.

43. Rooke Notes 5.

44. Ruskin i, 393–4.

45. Burne-Jones i, 233.

46. In John Ruskin, *Sesame and Lilies*, first issued 1865.

47. For a useful discussion of this, and other Victorian relationships, see Phyllis Rose, *Parallel Lives*, 1984.

48. The works were Keats' 'In a Drear-Nighted December', set to Beethoven's Piano Sonata op. 10 no. 2, and DGR's 'Song of the Bower', set to an unidentified waltz (Baldwin 73).

49. Burne-Jones i, 236.

Chapter Eleven (pp. 209–30)

1. Burne-Jones i, 262, where the episode is outlined with excessive delicacy. The woman's name was Norma and she appears to have sat to DGR, see Surtees no. 551, c. 1860.

2. Hall Caine, *Recollections of Rossetti*, 1928, 38.

3. Doughty & Wahl, 403.

4. Ibid., 408; this piece of work is so far unidentified.

5. WM Gallery Walthamstow; the paper is watermarked 1861 and cannot therefore belong to the 1857–8 courtship phase as hitherto believed, and the title is therefore probably a misjudgement. The subject is now thought to relate to themes connected with the Red House decorations such as the story of Troy. At this date WM was also reworking Greek myths in verse, such as the *Life and Death of Jason*, published 1867.

6. Troxell 8, where the date is given as June 1861, a slight error as Joanna Boyce Wells died on 15 July.

7. See above, ch. 7. FC was the first model for *Thoughts of the Past*, which was finished and hung in 1859, although the Tate Gallery Notes also refer to the name of another model (see Tate Gallery 174). The head bears signs of repainting, however, which may make it possible for EES to have sat in 1860–1; as Virginia Surtees comments: 'If the head is taken from Fanny Cornforth she is misrepresented, the artist having invested her with the wholly uncharacteristic appearance of a victim to consumption' (Boyce 85). EES' emaciated condition could have presented this appearance more effectively.

8. Lydia's daughter was born in March 1862 and named Elizabeth Eleanor Wheeler.

9. See W. Graham Robertson, *Time Was*, 1931, 208.

10. ACS to WMR 4.12.1895, BL Ashley 1427*.

11. ACS to WMR 24.12.1895, BL Ashley 1427*.

12. Burne-Jones i, 216.

13. Tate Gallery Collection no. 4348, entitled simply *Study of a Girl*. This identification is necessarily tentative; the drawing was executed in the period when EBJ was studying and practising art intensively and also seeing a good deal of DGR and EES socially. It does not have the look of a life-class model.

14. Surtees nos. 168, 168A and 168B.

15. Thanks to Barbara Elliott for this observation.

16. See Tate Gallery cat. no. 131.

17. Bessie Parkes's recollection was quoted by her daughter, Marie Belloc Lowndes, *I Too Have Lived in Arcadia*, 1941, 256. The second pregnancy was also believed by Emily Seddon, GBJ's fellow art student, who married solicitor

Virtue Tebbs (see 'HH and PRB', VH Papers). Neither is conclusive, and both may have confused their memories of EES in the months preceding her death. No mention of pregnancy was made at the inquest, where it would, if known, help to dispel suspicions of suicide.

18. Burne-Jones i, 237.

19. 'Fanny lived at Wapping, the heroine of the nut-stall in the Strand. But Ford [Madox Ford] says that the moment he found his wife was dead he raced off to fetch her sister Kate [sic] also a fille publique in the Commercial Road, and thus the legend arose' – note in VH hand in VH Papers. This contains so many errors and confusions that it confirms the falsity of the rumour. DGR was not likely to tell people he had been at the Working Men's College if he had not, for this was easily verifiable. EBJ was teaching there, and a few weeks earlier DGR had set out similarly, leaving EES at home, to visit the College (see Doughty & Wahl, 427).

20. See V. Berridge and G. Edwards, *Opium and the People: Opiate Use in 19th Century England*, 1981, 59. Other information on opium addiction in C19 is also taken from this source.

21. ACS to his mother, *Swinburne Letters*, i, 49–50.

22. Inquest proceedings, City of London and Borough of Southwark Coroners' Court, 12.2.1862, signed William Payne, Coroner; reprinted Violet Hunt 329–332.

23. Berridge and Edwards, Table 3, 275.

24. Hall Caine, *Recollections of Rossetti*, 198. In his earlier book (1882) HC mentioned no such incident.

25. This phrase features in VH Papers in notes based on conversations with Emily Seddon Tebbs, but sounds more like an imaginative suggestion than a concrete remembrance.

26. HRA in *Times Literary Supplement*, 27.10.1933.

27. Angeli 197.

28. Hall Caine, *My Story*, 1908, 201.

29. Ibid., 202.

30. See D. Holman-Hunt 211; had AM been in mourning she would not have sat to GPB in April.

31. WHH to FGS n.d., Bodl. MS Don.e.66.

32. FGS to WHH 12.11.1860, quoted D. Holman-Hunt 218–20.

33. WHH to FGS 15.11.1860, Bodl. MS Don.e.66.

34. WHH to FGS 25.1.1861, Bodl. MS Don.e.66.

35. WHH to FGS 15.2.1861, Bodl. MS Don.e.66.

36. Boyce 35.

37. Surtees no. 163.

38. Surtees no. 165.

39. DGR to FGS 12.3.1866, quoted D. Holman-Hunt 247.

40. Julia Jackson married (1) Herbert Duckworth and (2) Leslie Stephen. She became the mother of Vanessa and Virginia Stephen and the model for Mrs Ramsay in *To the Lighthouse*. Her portrait was drawn by her cousin Val Prinsep and by EBJ. WHH visited Julia's home in Hendon in November 1861 to paint from a calf procured for him by Mrs Jackson; see *The Orientalists Delacroix to Matisse* (ed. M.A. Stevens) 1984, 193.

41. WHH to FGS 20.7.1864, Bodl.MS. Don.e.66.
42. WHH to FGS 1866, ibid.
43. FGS to WHH 13.2.1866, quoted D. Holman-Hunt, 246.
44. JEM to WHH c.1866, quoted D. Holman-Hunt, 248.
45. See D. Holman-Hunt 246.
46. Edward Clodd, *Memories*, 1916, 200.

Chapter Twelve (pp. 233–53)

1. HC to GBS 24.9.1928, BL ADD 50531.
2. Baum 10.
3. Surtees no. 288.
4. Boyce 36.
5. Ibid., 36; Surtees no. 289.
6. Surtees nos. 290–2.
7. Surtees no. 287.
8. ACS to WMR 4.12.1895, BL Ashley 1427★. It was in 1866 that WHH heard or thought he heard ACS say that 'procuring abortions was an everyday amusement' to DGR. When told, FMB and EBJ felt it necessary to warn DGR against ACS' 'exaggerated and inconsiderate way of talking', but when DGR raised the matter with him, ACS denied it vehemently and demanded that the rumour be quashed. WHH then withdrew the allegation, leaving FMB in some embarrassment, complaining that it was an 'inexplicable' misunderstanding (see DHH 286–91 for relevant correspondence). The truth probably cannot now be reconstructed, but it may be noted that whatever ACS said or did not say, the others all believed him capable of this kind of slanderous assertion, which they knew to be untrue but might reach listeners who were unacquainted with ACS' hyperbolic style. DGR was not greatly upset by the incident, calling it 'foolish scandal and tattle', which suggests it had very little basis in truth, if any.
9. Doughty & Wahl, 492.
10. Ibid., 485.
11. Ibid.
12. Ibid., 498.
13. Surtees no. 164.
14. Surtees no. 174.
15. Surtees no. 205.
16. Surtees no. 182.
17. H.C. Marillier, *Dante Gabriel Rossetti: An Illustrated Memorial of His Life and Art*, 1899, 133.
18. Ruskin i, 491; Angeli 92 (full text); this seems to be the basis for HC's account of JR exclaiming, 'I don't object to Rossetti having sixteen mistresses, but I won't have Fanny' (HC to GBS 21. 9.1928, BL ADD 50531).
19. For WBS see Fredeman, 1970–1.
20. See H.R. Angeli, *Pre-Raphaelite Twilight: The Story of Charles Augustus Howell*, op. cit.
21. Boyce 35.
22. Ibid., 45.

23. See P.J. Keating, *The Working Classes in Victorian Fiction*, 1971.

24. Allingham 164.

25. Cline, letter no. 7.

26. Allingham 100.

27. Ibid., 101.

28. Baum, facing 18; original obtained by Bancroft from FC in ?1890s.

29. Doughty & Wahl, 526.

30. Ibid., 707.

31. Boyce 41–2.

32. Baldwin 100

33. See for example entry in Mackail Notebooks based on information from Arthur Hughes.

34. Brown 206.

35. Ibid., 207.

36. Ibid., 209.

37. Baldwin 100.

38. Speculation on this subject was fuelled for many years by the non-availability of the surviving letters between JM and DGR, which were held for 50 years by the British Museum before their release in 1964 – see Grylls, 235–40.

39. J.A. Banks, *Prosperity and Parenthood*, 1954. The reasons for a decrease in family size are less easy to account for.

40. Mackail i, 161.

41. Baldwin 89.

42. Robert Burden died in February 1865 at the age of 55, certified as suffering for four years from disease of liver and heart; death was notified by an illiterate neighbour, companion or layer-out, not by his wife or daughter. Ann Burden may have resided with her son William, who separated from his wife; she died on 2.2.1871 of bronchitis, at 65 Holywell Street. In the summer of 1867 the Morrises and Joneses holidayed together in Oxford, which would have enabled JM to visit her mother. Bessie Burden joined her brother-in-law's household in 1865 and was maintained by him, an arrangement that continued until her death in 1924 when she was found to have '£1,000 in the teapot!' according to her niece May (BL ADD 52740).

43. Ruskin i, 346–7.

44. Surtees no. 105.

45. Surtees no. 370.

46. BL ADD 45336 is a notebook belonging to WM containing a list of pairs of legendary lovers, alongside sketches for stained glass, a draft advert for the firm and what looks to be a rough drawing of an Illustrious Women frieze; the notebook dates from the early 1860s.

47. For the artistic and technical aspects of this project, see Joseph Dunlap, *The Book that Never Was*, 1971, and Harrison and Waters op. cit., 81. Finance was also a constraining factor; in 1865 WM's income dropped substantially, and he was obliged to make economies.

48. Mackail i, 210.

49. Surtees no. 177.

50. Some interpretations offer an opposite view, identifying the fair girl as the one tempting the youth away from the dark girl, who represents the past. But the

symbolism of the wine glasses as well as the known features of DGR's emotional biography indicate an alternative interpretation. Again, this should not be read as the intentional meaning of the picture, which was not meant as autobiography.

51. Surtees no. 179.

52. Marillier 139.

53. Surtees no. 180.

54. See Boyce 98, although her virtue seems to have been in doubt only because of her lowly occupation.

55. Ibid., 57.

56. H.T. Dunn, *Recollections of Rossetti*, 1984, 45–6.

57. Cline, letter no. 5, wrongly dated 28.5.1865, as JM did not move to Queen Square until November 1865 and even the firm took possession only in June. Living in town made it possible for JM to attend the theatre, opera and concerts, which she enjoyed and WM did not.

58. Henderson (1950), 61.

59. Surtees no. 200, where the figure of Yseult is said to be based on JM, although there is no documentary evidence that she sat or the figure was taken from life. The design had previously been used for stained glass, in the Tristram and Yseult series made by Morris & Co for Walter Dunlop in 1862; its emotional significance is that DGR returned to this subject in 1867, when his feelings for JM were being restirred. From 1857, JM had been associated with Yseult.

60. Surtees no. 372.

61. Bryson 1. It is very difficult to sort out the chronology of painting in 1867, but it is generally believed that the first of DGR's pictures of JM in this year was *La Pia*, although it would seem more likely to have been *The Blue Silk Dress*; 'a very easy pose' does not seem appropriate to *La Pia*, while the subject, with its depiction of a wife imprisoned by a boorish husband, would have seemed daring and unkind. WM's presence during the early Cheyne Walk sittings places the picture under execution within the conventions of portraiture. But the whole issue is very obscure, and it may well be that DGR simply did a number of studies of JM sitting in various poses which during the year evolved into different paintings, including *The Blue Silk Dress*, *La Pia*, *Mariana* and *Reverie*.

62. Surtees no. 206.

63. Surtees no. 213.

64. Tate Gallery 35.

65. Either from Aglaia Coronio, see Doughty & Wahl, 658, or as a studio prop from Arthur Hughes.

66. Doughty & Wahl, 659. On 14.7.1868 WMR recorded in his diary that JM was sitting to DGR.

67. Bryson 2.

68. Bryson 4.

69. Boyce 47.

70. Allingham 181–2.

Chapter Thirteen (pp. 254–77)

1. Doughty & Wahl, 664.

2. Cline letter 79.

3. Cline letter 80.

4. Cline letter 86.

5. Cline letter 87.

6. See S. Weintraub, *Four Rossettis*, 1978, 147–52 for a summary of the seances conducted by DGR, WMR, FC and others with the aim of receiving communications from EES and other deceased persons. FC, it may be noted, declined to receive a communication from her mother when offered such contact by a medium.

7. Doughty & Wahl, 669.

8. Ibid., 675.

9. According to GBJ, who must have been so told by WM; otherwise the poem appears to invoke the Kentish countryside around Red House.

10. Doughty & Wahl, 686.

11. Burne-Jones ii, 5.

12. Doughty & Wahl, 688–9.

13. Ibid., 751.

14. DGR to WMR 15.10.1869, quoted Fredeman (1970–1) 108.

15. Doughty & Wahl, 752.

16. Ibid., 761.

17. ACS to DGR 28.10.1869, BL Ashley A 3870.

18. Doughty & Wahl, 702.

19. Surtees no. 374.

20. Doughty & Wahl, 708.

21. See notes to Ch. 4 of Mary Hartmann, *Victorian Murderesses*, 1977.

22. Bryson 11.

23. Mark Girouard, *The Return to Camelot*, 1981, 204.

24. W.S. Blunt, Fitzwilliam Museum MS 42–1975, 47, quoted Girouard 206 where this point is expanded.

25. Surtees no. 605.

26. Bryson 15.

27. See BL ADD 45353, also DGR's MS notebook *Sonnets and Songs*, presented to and kept by JM (Bodl.MS).

28. Annotated proofs in BL ADD 45353.

29. Henderson (1967) 103.

30. In Fitzwilliam Museum.

31. See Roderick Marshall, *William Morris and His Earthly Paradises*, 1979, 134.

32. JR to Pauline Trevelyan 20.7.1862, in *Reflections of a Friendship*, 188–9.

33. GBJ to JR 20.6.1862, BJ Papers.

34. GBJ to JR 30.8.1862, BJ Papers.

35. GBJ to JR 14.9.1862, BJ Papers.

36. Tate Gallery cat. no. 236.

37. Burne-Jones i, 277.

38. EBJ to WA December 1864, BJ Papers.

39. Burne-Jones i, 307.

40. Ibid., i, 298.

41. EBJ A/C book, BJ Papers.

42. JR to Ellen Heaton, November 1862, *Sublime and Instructive*, 245.

43. Soskice 43.
44. Allingham 140–3.
45. Burne-Jones i, 294.
46. Cline 9.
47. Burne-Jones i, 303.
48. Letter dated October 1860, in *The Young George du Maurier*, 20.
49. Ibid., 31.
50. See Fitzgerald 114.
51. The British Library catalogue contains the following titles by Demetrius Alexandre Zambaco: *Des affections nerveuses syphilitiques*, 1862; *L'Hérédité de la lèpre*, 1906; *Voyages chex les lèpreux*, 1891; and *Les Eunuques d'aujourd'hui et ceux de jadis*, 1911. The last is a 254pp. BL casebook.
52. See Bryson 20.
53. Burne-Jones i, 309.
54. Ibid., i, 305.
55. Ibid., i, 309.
56. EBJ to DGR 1869, quoted Fitzgerald, 125.
57. Tate Gallery cat. no. 244.
58. Doughty & Wahl, 708.
59. See Burne-Jones ii, 10; also Arts Council, *Edward Burne-Jones*, 1975, 45–6. The verse comes from WM, *A Book of Verse*, written and presented to GBJ in 1870, see below, ch. 14 n. 12.
60. This is not to read biography from art: the differences in *Summer* and *Winter* are iconographic rather than personal. But there is an unmistakable correspondence between EBJ's representations of female form here and his private life.
61. Doughty & Wahl, 685.
62. Ibid., 685.
63. W.M. Rossetti (1899) 494, and Burne-Jones i, 229, for two slightly different versions.
64. GBJ to Rosalind Howard 1869, quoted Fitzgerald, 121.
65. GBJ to Louie Baldwin 5.1.1869, Lance Thirkell collection.
66. GBJ to Louie Baldwin 7.1.1869, Lance Thirkell collection.
67. GBJ to Rosalind Howard 1869, quoted Fitzgerald, 121.
68. EBJ to Crom Price August 1869, quoted Lorraine Price, *WMSJ*, Winter 1983–4, 35.
69. Bryson 12.
70. WM to PW 22.7.1869, BL ADD 45342.
71. WM to PW 31.7.1869, BL ADD 45342.
72. GBJ to May Morris 6.9.1910, BL ADD 52734.
73. BL ADD 45298A.

Chapter Fourteen (pp. 278–98)

1. Brown 209.
2. First published in *William Morris, Artist, Writer, Socialist*, ed. May Morris, 1936, i, 538.

3. Henderson (1950), 30.

4. Fitzgerald 124.

5. EBJ to DGR 1869, quoted Fitzgerald, 125.

6. Bryson 36.

7. CAI 1, Ionides Collection, V & A Museum; Surtees no 540. This is not thought to be the portrait commissioned by EBJ in 1870, now said to be lost, but was probably similar to it.

8. CAI 12, Ionides Coll. V & A.

9. Fitzgerald 124; Bryson 36.

10. Fitzgerald 127.

11. See Arts Council, *Edward Burne-Jones*, 46.

12. Original in V & A; facsimile published 1980.

13. Fitzgerald 129.

14. EBJ A/C book, BJ Papers (entry for 24.10.1870).

15. originally *Venus Hymenea*; and see entry for 10.5.1871, GBJ Diary, BJ Papers.

16. EBJ List of Paintings, BJ Papers.

17. Luke Ionides, *Memories*, 1925, 46.

18. Angeli, *Pre-Raphaelite Twilight*, 166.

19. *The Whistler Journal*, ed. E.R. and E.J. Pennell, 1921, 62–3.

20. Cline, letter 438.

21. Rooke Notes 61.

22. Fitzgerald 147.

23. Henderson (1950), 47.

24. Ibid., 50.

25. See Fitzgerald 52; also Mackail Notebooks, where an entry under 1873 reads 'To Italy with EBJ 2 April & returned on 17th. *M.Z. also.*' There is no evidence that MZ went with EBJ and WM to Italy.

26. EBJ to H.M. Gaskell January 1893, quoted Fitzgerald 150.

27. Rooke Notes 90.

28. EBJ to H.M. Gaskell January 1893, quoted Fitzgerald 127.

29. Burne-Jones ii, 347.

30. Rooke Notes 34.

31. GBJ Diary typescript, BJ Papers; this was used in preparation of GBJ *Memorials*, written 1903–4. NB: Lewes' = Marian Evans and G.H. Lewes; Denmark Hill = Ruskin's home; Faulkner, Magnusson and Evans were WM's companions on the trip to Iceland.

32. WM to PW 27.8.1869, BL ADD 45342.

33. PW to WM 1.9.1869, BL ADD 45342.

34. DGR to WMR 15.10.1869, quoted Fredeman 1970–1, 108.

35. Bryson 25.

36. WBS to Alice Boyd 9.11.1869, quoted Fredeman 1970–1, 100. Mrs Street was the wife of G.E. Street, to whom WM had been briefly articled as an architectural student/pupil.

37. WBS to Alice Boyd 26.11.1869, quoted Fredeman 1970–1, 101–2.

38. Bryson 33.

39. Ibid., 33.

40. Ibid., 34.

41. Doughty & Wahl, 848.
42. Ibid., 862.
43. Ibid., 796.
44. WM to JM 25.4.1870, BL ADD 45338.
45. Henderson (1950), 34.
46. WBS to Alice Boyd 28.9.1870, quoted Fredeman 1970–1; 103.
47. WM to JM 3.10.1870, BL ADD 45338.
48. WM to JM 5.12.1870, BL ADD 45338.
49. WM to C.J. Faulkner 17.5.1870, WM Gallery.
50. Doughty & Wahl, 993.
51. SCC to GBS 17.4.1950, BL ADD 50531.
52. WM to JM 16.7.1870, BL ADD 45338.
53. WSB Notebook 11.8.1892, quoted Faulkner, 30.
54. JM to PW 1871, John Brandon-Jones 'The Importance of Philip Webb', *William Morris and Kelmscott*, 1981, 91.
55. JM to PW 1871, quoted Brandon-Jones, 92.
56. PW to JM 1871, BL ADD 45343.
57. JM to PW 1871, quoted Brandon-Jones, 91–2. My ordering of letters differs slightly here, but not materially.
58. Doughty & Wahl, 949.
59. Ibid., 951.
60. Surtees no. 226.
61. BL ADD 45352.
62. WBS to Alice Boyd, quoted Fredeman 1970–1, 104.

Chapter Fifteen (pp. 299–318)

1. All references taken from the 1872 pamphlet.
2. W.M. Rossetti (1895), 308.
3. For a full account of the events of 1872, see Fredeman 1970–1.
4. W.M. Rossetti (1895) i, 313.
5. Doughty, *A Victorian Romantic*, op. cit., 520.
6. WBS to Alice Boyd 17.6.1872, quoted Fredeman 1970–1, 282.
7. WBS to Alice Boyd, ibid.
8. JM to WBS 15.7.1872, quoted Fredeman 1970–1, 301.
9. JM to WMR 15.7.1872, quoted Grylls 155.
10. Doughty & Wahl, 1062.
11. JM to Theodore Watts-Dunton 1884, BL ADD 45353.
12. PW to JM 7.9.1872 and 12.9.1872, BL ADD 45342; the events alluded to cannot have been DGR's presence at Kelmscott as PW arrived there, as Henderson (1967) 132 states, because at this date DGR was still in Scotland.
13. Doughty & Wahl, 1084.
14. Henderson (1950), 47–51.
15. Quoted Henderson (1967), 137.
16. See Cline, letters 180–97.
17. BL ADD 45351.
18. WMR *Diary* 18.9.1868, quoted Angeli 222.

19. Ibid.

20. Doughty & Wahl, 1000, but women were ineligible to vote in parliamentary elections, so this must mean simply that FC was registered as the householder and ratepayer.

21. Dunn, op. cit., 31.

22. See *The Whistler Journal*, op. cit., 34 and 62.

23. Baum 34.

24. Tate Gallery cat. no. 241.

25. Baum 33.

26. Doughty & Wahl, 1066–1090.

27. Rooke Notes 262.

28. W. Graham Robertson, op. cit., 91–2.

29. Fitzgerald 82–3.

30. W.M. Rossetti *Diary*, entry for 3.6.1872.

31. WBS to Alice Boyd 17.6.1872, quoted Fredeman 1970–1, 281.

32. Doughty & Wahl, 1049.

33. Ibid., 1051.

34. FMB to WBS 8.7.1872, quoted Fredeman 1970–1, 294.

35. Ibid.

36. Baum 39.

37. Ibid.

38. HC to GBS 24.9.1928, BL ADD 50531. But HC did not know much about the relationship between JM and DGR and was disposed to think FC's allegations were false, whereas her knowledge was probably greater than his, although she was undoubtedly hostile.

39. Baum 42–62; the total for 1873 may have been anything between £100 and £200, which probably covered FC's living expenses as well as additions to her savings.

40. Ibid., 48–9.

41. Ibid., 60.

42. Surtees nos. 308 and 309.

43. Baum 121–2.

44. Troxell 161.

45. Baum 71.

46. W.M. Rossetti (1906) ii, 420.

47. Baum 59.

48. See Weintraub, op. cit., 205. Lucy's portrait of Maria in nun's coif is reproduced in G. Battiscombe, *Christina Rossetti*, 1981, 154.

49. Henderson (1950), 62.

50. Doughty & Wahl, 1227.

51. Ibid., 1271.

52. Bryson 79.

53. For details see Angeli 116; also Dobbs, op. cit., 204.

54. BL Ashley, 1412.

55. WSB Notebook 13.5.1890, quoted Faulkner, 25.

56. Rose 5.

57. WSB Notebook 5.5.1892, quoted Faulkner, 30.

58. WSB Notebook 13.5.1890, quoted Faulkner, 24.

59. BL Ashley 1413.

60. The actual gap is from March 1870 to November 1877; between these dates only a fragment survives, relating to painting.

Chapter Sixteen (pp. 319–37)

1. J.W. Mackail to SCC 16.6.1897, BL ADD 52734.
2. Dorothy Henley, *Rosalind Howard Countess of Carlisle*, 1958.
3. WM to JM 14.12.1877, BL ADD 45338.
4. Bryson 64.
5. Bryson 68.
6. Bryson 84.
7. Bryson 97.
8. Bryson 115.
9. Dorothy Henley, foreword by Gilbert Murray.
10. Bryson 115.
11. Lorraine Price 33.
12. Ibid., 34.
13. Bryson 66.
14. JM to Theodore Watts-Dunton 1884, BL ADD 45353.
15. Doughty & Wahl, 1205.
16. All letters undated, in Baum, 98–109.
17. DGR to Theodore Watts-Dunton, Doughty & Wahl, 1500.
18. George Hake to Thomas Hake 13.1.1877, BL ADD 49467.
19. WMR to Lucy M. Rossetti 17.8.1877, quoted Grylls 173.
20. Baum 90.
21. Ibid., 92–5.
22. HC to GBS 24.9.1928, BL ADD 50531.
23. See Baum, 83–5.
24. Ibid., 92.
25. FC to DGR 24.9.1877, BL Ashley 3854.
26. See Baum, 111–2; and Grylls 174.
27. Gale Pedrick, *Life with Rossetti*, 1964, 210.
28. HC to GBS 24.9.1928, BL AD 50531.
29. Baum 113.
30. HC to GBS 24.9.1928, BL ADD 50531.
31. Baum 114.
32. HC to GBS 24.9.1928, BL ADD 50531.
33. Ibid.
34. GBJ to JR 30.8.1862 and 23.9.1862, BJ Papers.
35. Baldwin 90.
36. Rudyard Kipling, *Something of Myself*, 1937, 11–13. The importance of Aunt Georgie to the Kipling children was confirmed by Ruddy's sister Trix to Lance Thirkell.
37. BL ADD 45346.
38. Burne-Jones ii, 47.
39. EBJ to FGS June 1885, quoted Fitzgerald, 206.

40. WM to C.J. Faulkner on behalf of EBJ 18.11.1872, WM Gallery.
41. WM to Phil Burne-Jones 1874, BL ADD 52708.
42. EBJ to Phil Burne-Jones 29.9.1874, BJ Papers.
43. GBJ to JR 30.6.1862, BJ Papers.
44. Sara Anderson, Notes on EBJ, BL ADD 52703.
45. Graham Robertson 75.
46. Personal communication from Lance Thirkell.
47. Fitzgerald 181.
48. Fitzgerald 200. This is not incompatible with interpretations relating the picture to other individuals such as the painter's daughter Margaret, or his close friend Frances Graham: autobiography is not the subject nor dominant meaning of the picture.
49. Fitzgerald 155.
50. Rooke Notes 134.
51. Quoted Fitzgerald 251.
52. Quoted Fitzgerald 259.
53. Graham Robertson 80.
54. Mackail Notebooks, WM Gall.

Chapter Seventeen (PP. 338–54)

1. Rooke Notes 199.
2. See E.P. Thompson, *William Morris: Romantic to Revolutionary*, 1976, 192–202.
3. GBJ Diary 18.9.1876, BJ Papers.
4. See Thompson 211 for details.
5. GBJ to Rosalind Howard January 1878, quoted Fitzgerald 177.
6. Rooke Notes 199.
7. Sara Anderson, Notes on EBJ, BL ADD 52703.
8. Rooke Notes 316.
9. Sara Anderson, Notes on EBJ, BL ADD 52703.
10. Estimates of GBJ's adherence to socialism varied widely. In view of her antipathy to self-promotion and violence it seems unlikely that she would have wished to join the SDF, led by H.D. Hyndman and avowedly revolutionary in nature; temperamentally she believed in changing hearts and minds rather than bringing about political change through organization.
11. Angela Thirkell, *Three Houses*, 1932, 79.
12. WM to GBJ 1.6.1864, Henderson (1950) 196–200.
13. WM, *The Lesser Arts*, 1878; reprinted in *Hopes and Fears for Art*, 1882.
14. Documents on South London Art Gallery (SLAG) in Southwark Local Studies Library, London.
15. GBJ to J.W. Cross 4–11.10.1890, SLAG Documents, Southwark Local Studies Library.
16. Rooke Notes 35.
17. Rooke Notes 348.
18. W. Rossiter speech in SLAG Documents, Southwark.
19. S.M. Moens and H.E. Blyth, *A History of Rottingdean*, 1952.

20. WM to GBJ 1.9.1896, quoted Henderson (1967), 362.

21. Rooke Notes 194.

22. Rooke Notes 416.

23. Moens and Blyth 117.

24. Moens and Blyth 118.

25. WMR to GBJ 4.6.1904, BJ Papers.

26. Baldwin 159.

27. Baldwin 156–7.

28. Longford, *A Pilgrimage of Passion*, 279–81.

29. See John Christian, 'Marie Spartali', *Antique Collector*, 3/84, 42–7.

30. See, for example, JM to WSB June 1896 from Folkestone, Fitzwilliam MSS 443–7, 1976.

31. Arthur Hughes to Alice Boyd 5.10.1896, quoted in W.A. Fredeman, 'A Pre-Raphaelite Gazette', *Bulletin of John Rylands Library*, Vol. 50 1967–8, 64.

.32. Ibid., 66.

33. Rooke Notes 327.

34. WSB Notebook 5.10.1896, quoted Faulkner, 39.

35. PW to JM 7.12.1902, BL ADD 45343.

36. Soskice 43.

37. Attempts to locate FC's death certificate under any of her several names have so far been unsuccessful.

38. Clodd 201.

39. See D. Holman-Hunt, 'Stunners', *Harpers*, March 1984, 154. Both AM and her husband are buried in Shoreham Cemetery, grave no. B.19.7; there are entries in the burial book but no headstone.

Index